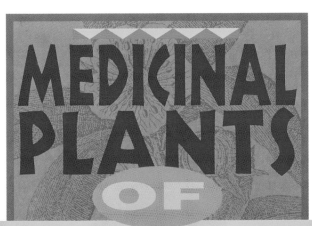

MEDICINAL PLANTS OF

SOUTH AFRICA

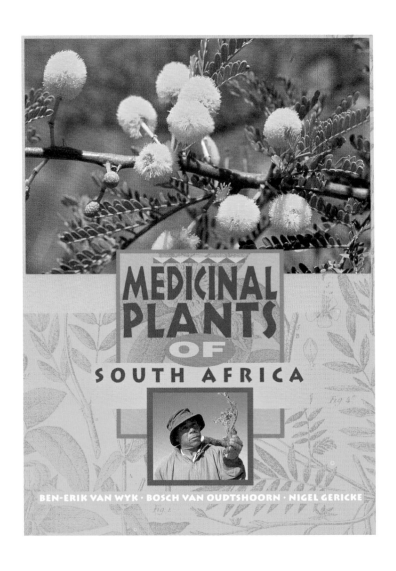

MEDICINAL
PLANTS
OF
SOUTH AFRICA

BEN-ERIK VAN WYK · BOSCH VAN OUDTSHOORN · NIGEL GERICKE

BRIZA

IMPORTANT WARNING

This book contains general information about medicinal plants and their uses. It is intended as a scientific overview and not as a medical handbook for self-treatment. Many of the medicinal plants described in this book are highly toxic and may cause severe allergic reactions or serious poisoning. Neither the authors nor the publishers can be held responsible for claims arising from the mistaken identity of plants or their inappropriate use. Do not attempt self-diagnosis or self-treatment. Always consult a medical professional or qualified practitioner.

Published by
Briza Publications
CK 90/11690/23

P.O. Box 56569
Arcadia
0007
Pretoria
South Africa

First edition 1997

Text © Ben-Erik van Wyk, Bosch van
Oudtshoorn and Nigel Gericke
Photographs © various photographers
Cover design by Andrew Breebaart
Language edited by Janine Smit
Typesetting by Ilse van Oudtshoorn,
Briza Publications
Reproduction by Unifoto, Cape Town
Printed and bound by Tien Wah Press,
Singapore

ISBN 1 875093 09 5

Cover photographs:
Top front – *Acacia karroo* by Ben-Erik van Wyk
Bottom front – Cape "bossiedokter " (see page 11) by Nigel Gericke
Back cover – *Boophane disticha* by Geoff Nichols
Spine – *Siphonochilus aethiopicus* by Ben-Erik van Wyk
Contents – *Ricinus communis* seeds by Nigel Gericke

CONTENTS

ACKNOWLEDGEMENTS

Ben-Erik van Wyk would like to thank to following persons and institutions:

• The contributing authors, Bosch van Oudtshoorn and Nigel Gericke, for their professional and inspiring collaboration.

• The National Botanical Institute, for providing some distributional data. The use of the library and the friendly assistance of the librarian, herbarium curator and other staff are much appreciated.

• The Durban Parks Department, and particularly Richard Simmonds, for his help with fieldwork and for the opportunity to take photographs at the Silver Glen Medicinal Plant Nursery.

• Geoff Nichols, for providing colour slides and for valuable advice. Other persons who contributed slides are Piet van Wyk, Frits van Oudtshoorn, Jo Onderstall, Pieter Winter, Pieter Zietsman, Alice Biemond, Morné Brits, Tony de Castro, Clive Bromilow, Duncan Butchart, Trevor Coleman, John Manning, Wally Menne, Vernie Naidoo, Rolf Oberprieler, Johann Pretorius, Braam van Wyk and Sasa Malan. This photographic material has made an invaluable contribution to the book.

• Tony de Castro, Gael Campbell, Alvaro Viljoen, Nozuko Makhuvha, Dinewa Moshe and other senior students of the Department of Botany, Rand Afrikaans University, and especially to my wife, Mariana van Wyk, for encouragement and logistic support.

• Briza Publications, especially Frits van Oudtshoorn for his support and Ilse van Oudtshoorn for the layout.

B-E van Wyk

PHOTOGRAPHIC CONTRIBUTIONS

All photographs are listed below according to photographer, page number, and alphabetically from top to bottom and left to right.

Ben-Erik van Wyk: 9abdf 13bcefgh 15e 17abce 19acd 21abcde 23abcd 25abc 29abd 31ad 33abc 35abce 37bc 39a 41abde 43ab 45ac 47a 49abd 51abcd 53abcd 55abcd 57abd 59ab 61ad 63abc 65ad 67ab 69abc 71c 75bc 77ab 79abc 81ac 83abc 85abc 87ab 89abc 91abc 93bc 95bcd 97abcd 99c 101abc 103abc 105abc 107abd 109ac 111abcd 113bcd 115bd 117abc 119abc 121c 123bcd 125cd 127ad 129d 131ac 133ab 135abd 137abd 139abd 141bc 143ac 145acd 147d 149abcd 151abcd 153bd 155cd 157acd 159c 163bcd 165ac 167a 169ac 171abc 173ab 175a 177abcd 179b 181abc 183ac 185abd 187bcd 189abc 191ab 193abc 195abc 197abd 199b 201abcd 203abcd 205a 207bc 209ac 211d 213abc 215abd 217cd 219abc 221abc 225d 227abcd 229bc 231bc 233ab 235b 237bcd 239abcd 241bcd 243abcd 245b 247abc 249c 251bd 253abc 255abcd 257abc 259c 261bcd 263acd 265abc 267abcde 269abcd 271ab 277ac 279abe 281abc 285abcd 287abcd **Nigel Gericke**: 9c 11b 13ai 15bf 17d 19bef 35d 39d 43c 45bd 47bcd 61b 65bc 67c 71abde 73b 81bd 85d 87c 93a 99b 103d 105d 107c 109bd 119d 123a 125b 131b 133c 135c 139c 145b 147b 161d 163ae 167c 169bd 171d 173cd 175bc 179c 183b 185c 187a 191c 199c 207a 217ab 235d 263be 271cd 273d 275abcd 279cd **Piet van Wyk**: 27abc 31bc 37a 73ac 75a 99a 115ac 125a 127bc 129abc 147ac 153ac 159b 161abc 197c 205bcd 209b 211abc 215c 223bcd 235ac 237a 245ac 251ac 261a 283abcd **Geoff Nichols**: 11a 29c 39bc 57c 61c 121b 159a 179a 241a 249ab 273c 277b **Frits van Oudtshoorn**: 95a 143b 157b 167b 223a 233c 273ab **Jo Onderstall**: 113a 165b 225bc **Pieter Winter**: 15cd 41c **Pieter Zietsman**: 259ab **Alice Biemond**: 9e **Morné Brits & Tony de Castro**: 15a **Clive Bromilow**: 155a **Duncan Butchart**: 225a **Trevor Coleman**: 141a **John Manning**: 137c **Wally Menne**: 121a **Vernie Naidoo**: 11c **Rolf Oberprieler**: 49c **Johann Pretorius**: 231a **Braam van Wyk & Sasa Malan**: 155b

INTRODUCTION

Medicinal plants are an important aspect of the daily lives of many people and an important part of the South African cultural heritage. This book is a **photographic guide to the most commonly used and best known South African plant medicines**, including their botany, main traditional uses and active ingredients.

Southern Africa has well over 30 000 species of higher plants. The Cape Floral Kingdom alone has nearly 9 000 species and is the most diverse temperate flora on earth, rivalling the tropical rainforests in terms of species richness. With South Africa's remarkable biodiversity and cultural diversity, it is not surprising to find that approximately 3 000 species of plants are used as medicines, and of these, some 350 species are the most commonly used and traded medicinal plants. Since it is not practically possible to illustrate and describe all the indigenous medicinal plants in a photographic guide, a selection of 132 plants has been included on the basis that they are presently the best known and most fully understood herbal medicines. However, several other, mostly related plants, are also mentioned and occasionally illustrated. The selection includes representatives of plants used by all cultural groups, including a small number of introduced species that have been incorporated into the traditional *materia medica*.

The descriptions given in the introductory pages are necessarily brief generalisations, and the magical, ritual, spiritual and symbolic aspects of the use of indigenous medicinal plants have not been included. It is our intention to afford the reader with an appreciation of the contribution indigenous plants make to Primary Health Care in its broadest sense, throughout South Africa. Wherever possible, the scientific rationale behind the remedies is discussed or speculations are made regarding their biological activities. Wherever possible, reference to published and unpublished information is cited. Where no references are cited, the information is drawn from the authors' own observations and experiences.

In preparing this work, it became abundantly clear that there is a lack of detailed documentation on the use of medicinal plants in South Africa. This is an urgent priority in view of the fragility of oral-tradition knowledge, and the rapid pace of urbanisation and acculturation in this country.

It is our sincere belief that with official support, formal documentation, research and systematisation, the beneficial practises of Africa's indigenous systems of medicine will one day claim their rightful place among the great healing traditions of the world.

IMPORTANCE OF MEDICINAL PLANTS

Plants were once a primary source of all the medicines in the world and they still continue to provide mankind with new remedies. Natural products and their derivatives represent more than 50% of all drugs in clinical use in the world[1]. Higher plants contribute no less than 25% to the total[1]. Well-known examples of plant-derived medicines include quinine, morphine, codeine, aspirin, atropine, reserpine and cocaine. Recently, important new anticancer drugs such as taxol (see *Taxus* below) and vincristine (see *Catharanthus roseus*) have been developed. In South Africa, a large part of the day-to-day medicine is still derived from plants and large volumes of plants or their extracts are sold in the informal and commercial sectors of the economy. South Africa's contribution to world medicine includes Cape aloes (*Aloe ferox*), buchu (*Agathosma betulina*) and devil's claw (*Harpagophytum procumbens*), but local equivalents exist for many of the famous remedies used elsewhere. There is a growing interest in natural and traditional medicines as a source of new commercial products. Medicinal plants are something of the future, not of the past! To illustrate the global importance and historical role of plant-derived medicines, some well-known examples are discussed and shown here.

Quinine (*Cinchona* spp.). Quinine is an alkaloid obtained from the bark of the quinine tree (*Cinchona pubescens*) and several other species, all restricted to the Andes, from Bolivia to Columbia. They are still cultivated in many parts of the world (South America, India, Java and tropical Africa). For more than 300 years, these plants provided the only effective remedy for malaria.

Atropa belladonna. Atropine and various other tropane alkaloids are extracted from the deadly nightshade and various other plants (see *Datura stramonium*). These medicines were originally used as heart tonics but are still commonly used in modern medicine. Extracted alkaloids are used in eyedrops and in skin patches to treat motion sickness, and are injected to treat Parkinsonism.

Papaver somniferum. Opium is the air-dried latex obtained by cutting the unripe fruit capsules of the opium poppy. The most important alkaloid is morphine, which is mostly converted to codeine. The world consumption of opium alkaloids for medicinal purposes is nearly 200 metric tons per annum. Morphine is a powerful analgesic, used to treat intense pain. Codeine is more widely used, as a headache remedy and an ingredient of cough syrup.

***Taxus* spp.** Taxol is a highly effective drug against breast cancer, recently also approved for the treatment of ovarian cancer. It is a diterpenoid originally extracted from the bark of the Pacific yew (*Taxus brevifolius*). Because of the shortage of supply and low solubility, semisynthetic derivatives are now produced from the leaves of *Taxus baccata* and others. The discovery of taxol has shown once again the importance of plants in providing new target molecules for drug development.

Aloe vera. An historically important medicinal plant of North African origin, still forming the basis of a large industry. Curaçao aloes are laxative bitters produced from the yellow leaf exudate and contain anthrones as active ingredients. The South African equivalent, Cape aloes (see *Aloe ferox*), is still important, both internationally and locally. Aloe bitters should not be confused with aloe gel, which is produced from the inner leaf pulp. The gel is nowadays the main focus of attention and the healing properties are ascribed to glycoproteins (see *Aloe ferox* and *Bulbine natalensis*).

Quassia amara. The bitter amara is of historic interest. The wood contains bitter terpenoids known as quassinoids, formerly much used as a bitter tonic to improve appetite and to treat minor stomach ailments. The name "amara" came into use for some local bitter plants used as substitutes, such as "amarabossie" (see *Geranium incanum*) and "groenamarabossie" (see *Vernonia oligocephala*).

1. **Kinghorn, A.D. & Balandrin, M.F. 1993.** Human medicinal agents from plants. *ACS Symposium Series 534*, American Chemical Society, Washington.

Quinine tree (*Cinchona pubescens*)

Deadly nightshade (*Atropa belladonna*)

Opium poppy (*Papaver somniferum*)

Yew tree (*Taxus baccata*)

Curaçao aloe or Barbados aloe (*Aloe vera*)

Bitter amara (*Quassia amara*)

CULTURAL ASPECTS OF HEALING

South Africa is blessed with a rich cultural diversity which is reflected in the formal and informal systems of medicine that are presently practised in different parts of the country. The informal oral-tradition medical systems of the Khoi-San peoples, the Nguni and the Sotho-speaking peoples have not yet been systematised, and are passed on by word of mouth from one generation to the next. These medical systems and their herbal, animal and mineral *materia medica* have ancient origins which may date back to palaeolithic times. The formal systems of medicine, which are well documented and systematised, were introduced to the country over the last three hundred years by European and other settlers, and are exemplified by today's modern Western medicine, also called Western biomedicine or allopathic medicine. Ayurvedic medicine from India, Traditional Chinese Medicine and homoeopathic medicine are also commonly practised in South Africa.

SIMILARITIES BETWEEN MEDICINE SYSTEMS. Each system of medicine is the art and science of diagnosing the cause of disease, treating diseases, and maintaining health in the broadest sense of physical, spiritual, social and psychological well-being. Each culture has found solutions to the preventive, promotive and curative aspects of health that resonate in harmony with the world view of that culture. Western medicine may diagnose a disease in terms of a bacterial infection, for example, and treat that infection effectively with antibiotics. An African traditional healer will seek to understand why the patient became ill in the first place, and the treatment administered will address the perceived cause, usually in addition to specific therapies to alleviate the signs and symptoms of the condition.

TRADITIONAL HEALING IN SOUTH AFRICA. There are an estimated 200 000 indigenous traditional healers in South Africa, and up to 60% of South Africans consult these healers, usually in addition to using modern biomedical services. Traditional healers in South Africa are most commonly known as "inyanga" and "isangoma" (Zulu; plural: "izinyanga" and "izangoma"), "ixwele" and "amaquira" (Xhosa), "nqaka" (Sotho), "bossiedokter" and "kruiedokter" (Western and Northern Cape). The terms "inyanga" and "sangoma" used to refer exclusively to herbalist and diviner respectively, but in modern times the distinction has become blurred, with some healers practising both arts. In addition to the herbalists and diviners who are believed to be spiritually empowered, there are traditional birth attendants, prophets, spiritual healers (Zulu: "abathandazi"), spirit mediums, intuitives and dreamers. Most elderly folk in rural areas have a knowledge of herbal lore, and function as first-aid healers with a family repertoire of herbal remedies or "kruierate".

THE FUTURE. Indigenous systems of medicine are dynamic and adaptive, although firmly rooted in the traditions of the past. This can be seen in the incorporation of introduced medicinal herbs such as liquorice root (*Glycyrrhiza glabra*; Zulu: "mlomo mnandi") and calamus root (*Acorus calamus*; Zulu: "ikalamuzi") into the *materia medica*, the use of modern medicines by some indigenous healers, and the keen interest in modern Primary Health Care training programmes expressed by modern traditional healers' associations. This dynamism suggests that with appropriate official support and recognition, traditional medicine will survive well into the next century, strengthened by modern science, not subsumed by it.

Group of Zulu "izinyanga" and "izangoma", generally referred to as inyangas and sangomas

An experienced Cape "bossiedokter" holding a sample of "dawidjie-wortel" (*Cissampelos capensis*)

Pharmacists are scientifically trained to dispense medicine and herbal remedies

PLANT PARTS USED

The active ingredients (chemical compounds) in leaves, roots or bark are often quite different – one part may be very toxic and another quite harmless. The whole plant is therefore rarely used for medicine. Of the 132 species included in this book, roughly equal numbers are used primarily for their leaves and/or twigs, their stem bark and their underground parts. Interesting exceptions are the use of wood, fruits, seeds, gums, exudates and nectar.

ROOTS. The fleshy or woody roots of many species are used medicinally. Harvesting the roots can be very destructive, because the whole plant is often removed. In many cases, the outer root bark is used rather than the inner woody part. More than one third of the plants in this book are harvested mainly for their roots (excluding bulbs, rhizomes or tubers). Examples include the fleshy roots of devil's claw (*Harpagophytum procumbens*) and uzara (*Xysmalobium undulatum*).

BULBS. A bulb is a fleshy underground structure made up of numerous layers of fleshy scales, which are actually leaf bases. An onion is perhaps the best example. Bulbs are popular for medicinal use and the famous European squill (*Scilla maritima*) has numerous counterparts in South Africa, such as inguduza (*Scilla natalensis*) and sekanama (*Urginea sanguinea*), to name just two. Some bulbs are not much swollen and may be mistaken for fleshy stems, such as wild garlic (*Tulbaghia violacea*).

RHIZOMES. A rhizome is a woody or fleshy elongated stem that usually grows horizontally below the ground, forming leaves above the ground and roots into the ground. There are several examples of medicinal plants that are used primarily for their rhizomes, including ubani (*Agapanthus* spp.), bulrush (*Typha capensis*), piles root (*Sansevieria hyacinthoides*) and ikhathazo (*Alepidea amatymbica*).

TUBERS. A tuber is a swollen, fleshy structure below the ground, usually of stem origin but often partly stem and partly root. A potato is the best known example. With some extra care, it may be possible to harvest tubers without destroying the plant. Medicinally used tubers include isidakwa (*Dioscorea dregeana*) and imfingo (*Stangeria eriopus*).

BARK. Bark is the outer protective layer of a tree trunk, formed by layers of living cells just above the wood itself. High concentrations of active ingredients are found in bark, hence its frequent medicinal use. There are numerous examples in African traditional medicine, such as pepper-bark (*Warburgia salutaris*) and unukani (*Ocotea bullata*). It is possible to harvest bark on a sustainable basis without causing permanent damage to the tree.

LEAVES, STEMS AND FLOWERS. Leaves and twigs are rarely separated and both are normally used. Very often, the young vigorously growing tips are preferred above the thicker basal parts. Thick stems or the wood itself is only rarely used (see sneezewood, *Ptaeroxylon obliquum*). Flowers may be inadvertently included or may sometimes be considered an essential part of the medication, as in traditional honeybush tea (*Cyclopia* species).

FRUITS AND SEEDS. These parts are rarely used for medicinal purposes and there are only four examples in this book. They are the small dry fruits of fennel (*Foeniculum vulgare*), often wrongly referred to as seeds, the fleshy fruits of kukumakranka (*Gethyllis* spp.), and the true seeds (nuts) of the castor oil plant (*Ricinus communis*) and purging nut (*Jatropha curcas*).

GUMS, EXUDATES AND NECTAR. Gum sometimes flows from a damaged stem, as a defence mechanism of the plant to stop wood-boring insects and to seal off wounds so that wood-rotting fungi and bacteria are kept out. An example is Cape gum (from *Acacia karroo*), used in the pharmaceutical industry. The yellow exudate which flows from a cut leaf of bitter aloe (*Aloe ferox*) is dried to a resinous medicinal product of considerable commercial importance, known as Cape aloes. Syrups or strong sugar solutions are used in cough remedies or to mask the unpleasant taste of medicines. A South African example is the syrup produced by boiling the nectar of the sugarbush (*Protea repens*). The syrup is known as "bossiestroop" in the Cape.

Fleshy roots of *Harpagophytum procumbens*

Bulbs of *Drimia robusta*, showing the bulb scales

Rhizomes of *Acorus calamus*

Tuber of *Dioscorea dregeana*

Bark of *Calodendrum capense*, known as "white umemezi"

Leaves and stems of *Aptenia cordifolia*, known as "ibohlololo"

Leaves and stems of *Achyrocline stenoptera*, known as "imphepho" (see *Helichrysum species*)

Seeds of *Ricinus communis*, the source of castor oil

METHODS OF COLLECTION AND STORAGE

Wild medicinal plant resources are increasingly under threat from habitat destruction as a result of agricultural, industrial and housing developments. The activities of professional herb gatherers and traditional healers thus have an exaggerated impact on the remaining stock of wild plants. In former times, traditional healers, their families and apprentices collected and stored their medicinal plants in accordance with traditions and taboos. Plants were thereby protected from over-harvesting. The modern era has seen the advent of urbanised healers who may be less rigorously trained than their forebears, and who mainly purchase their *materia medica* from street markets and stores, providing an economic incentive for the destructive harvesting of vulnerable medicinal plants.

SELECTIVE HARVESTING. An experienced "inyanga" will generally seek the guidance of an ancestral spirit before embarking on a collecting trip. The healer, through dreams, or during prayers, will be advised of an auspicious time for collecting the plants, and in some cases will be advised which particular plants to collect for a particular patient, and where these plants may be found. The healer supplements this supernatural advice with his own knowledge, training and experience. Factors which may be taken into account include a particular favoured locality, the correct season of collection, the best aspect on a mountain slope, type of soil and its moistness, and time of day. These factors are known by the healers to influence the potency of their medicinal plants, and are well understood by scientists to have a significant influence on the chemistry of plants. Certain potentially very toxic plants, for example *Boophane disticha*, are sometimes collected from a single locality only so that the healer can anticipate the desired therapeutic effect.

CONSERVATION MEASURES. There are many traditions and taboos associated with the collection of plants. These can be interpreted as a means of preventing the over-harvesting of plant material. *Alepidea amatymbica*, for example, is generally only collected in winter, thereby ensuring that the plant is reserved for the season when coughs, colds, influenza and bronchitis are most prevalent. This tradition also ensures that plants are left in the field to set seed in the summer months. In Gazankulu, a Shangaan taboo dictates that if the remaining root system of *Elephantorrhiza elephantina* is not covered after a portion has been removed, the patients treated with it will not get better. Bark that is used for treating kidney diseases are sometimes only harvested from the eastern and western sides of the tree, traditionally symbolising the kidneys, thereby preventing ring-barking. In addition to the wise and sustainable use of the natural resource, cultivation on farms becomes necessary when new phytomedicines are developed. Some rare and valuable medicinal plants are already being cultivated to reduce pressure on the wild populations. Examples include buchu (*Agathosma betulina*), pepper-bark (*Warburgia salutaris*) and wild ginger (*Siphonochilus aethiopicus*).

STORAGE. While some whole plants, or parts of plants, can only be used in a fresh state, many can be dried and stored. Plant material may be dried in the sun or shade, or may be cut into slices and left to dry. Once dry, the plant material may be stored as is, or may be reduced to powder. Dry plant material is stored in paper bags, newspaper, glass jars or tin cans. With modern phytomedicines, care is taken to ensure that the active ingredients remain stable and that the packing materials do not degenerate and contaminate the medicine. Since it is unacceptable for the plant material to be left exposed to the sun, wind, dust, and potential contact with strangers, associations representing traditional healers are actively advocating the introduction of proper warehousing facilities for herbal remedies marketed in the cities.

Gatherer harvesting bark from an *Acacia caffra* tree

Traditional healers salvaging umganu bark (*Sclerocarya birrea*) from a tree felled during road construction

The traditional method of harvesting *Aloe ferox*

Harvested plant of *Aloe ferox*

Muti market in Durban, showing products displayed along the pavement

Plant medicines for sale on the "Parade" in Cape Town

DOSAGE FORMS AND METHODS OF PREPARATION

The method of preparation is critical, as it includes the amount of fresh or dry plant material to be used, the addition of appropriate volumes of solvents such as water or alcohol, and additional activities such as boiling for a specified length of time, or partial burning to achieve a desired colour. These activities can serve to neutralise certain toxins. Instructions on how to prepare and take the remedy is either given on the label or conveyed orally by the healer, but in the case of toxic plants, the medicine is professionally prepared and standardised (or the healer or doctor personally administers the appropriate dosage). The dosages will be adjusted after an appraisal of the physical and general condition of the patient. Contra-indications and side-effects are well known to an experienced healer. Different dosage forms are described below.

ENEMAS. Enemas are aqueous or oily solutions or suspensions intended for rectal injection. They are given for their anthelmintic, nutritive, purgative or sedative effect. They should be freshly prepared and any solid substances should be uniformly suspended.

EXTRACTS. Extracts are preparations containing the active principles of crude drugs, and are prepared by extracting the ingredients with suitable solvents, such as water or alcohol. **Liquid extracts** are usually of such a strength that one part by volume of the preparation is equivalent to one part by weight of the crude drug. **Soft extracts** are prepared by evaporating the extractive until a soft mass is produced.

INFUSIONS. Infusions are prepared by **macerating** the crude drug for a short period of time in cold or boiling water. Infusions are liable to fungus and bacterial growth and should be used within 12 hours of their preparation.

INHALATIONS. Inhalations are liquid preparations composed of, or containing, volatile ingredients which, when vaporised in a suitable manner, are intended to be brought into contact with the lining of the respiratory tract. The ingredients might be volatile at room temperature, in which case they might be inhaled from an absorbent pad on which they have been placed, or they may need to be added to water heated to about 65°C, but not boiling, and the vapour inhaled for 5 to 10 minutes.

LINCTUSES. Linctuses are viscous liquid preparations usually containing sugar and medicinal substances and possessing demulcent, expectorant or sedative properties. They should be sipped and swallowed slowly without the addition of water.

LINIMENTS. Liniments are usually liquid or semi-liquid preparations which are intended for external application and may contain substances possessing analgesic, rubefacient, soothing or stimulating properties.

LOTIONS. Lotions are liquid preparations intended for application to the skin. They may be aqueous or alcoholic solutions, or suspensions in aqueous vehicles.

MIXTURES. Mixtures are liquid preparations intended for administration by mouth, and can consist of combinations of medicaments dissolved, suspended or diffused in either water or some other aqueous vehicle such as an **infusion**.

NASAL DROPS. Nasal drops are liquid preparations intended for instillation into the nostrils by means of a pipette.

OINTMENTS. Ointments are semi-solid preparations consisting of a medicament or mixture of medicaments dissolved or dispersed in a suitable basis of animal, vegetable, mineral or synthetic origin. They are used as emollients, as protective preparations on the skin or as vehicles for the topical application of medicaments.

TINCTURES. Tinctures are alcoholic liquids usually containing, in comparatively dilute solutions, the active principles of vegetable drugs. They are commonly prepared by maceration or percolation; in other cases they are obtained by dilution of the corresponding liquid extract.

SNUFFS. Snuffs are preparations of finely powdered, dried medicinal plants that can be drawn up into the nostrils through inhalation.

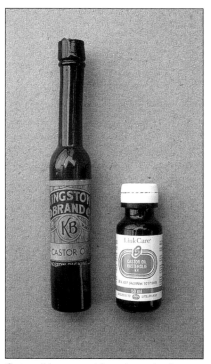

Castor oil is extracted from the seeds of
Ricinus communis

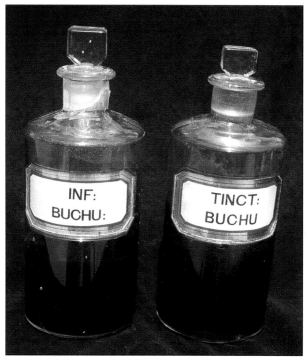

Infusion and tincture prepared from *Agathosma* leaves

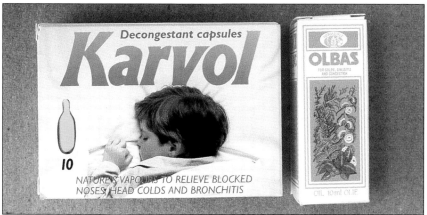

Examples of inhalations

Snuff prepared from dried *Xysmalobium* roots

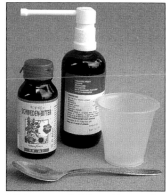

Mixtures are administered by mouth

METHODS OF ADMINISTRATION

The most common methods of administering plant medicines are outlined below.

ORALLY. Infusions, decoctions, syrups and tinctures are most often taken orally (by mouth). In some cases dried, powdered herbs, partially burned herbs, or the ash of burned herbs, are taken directly by mouth, usually followed by a mouthful of water. A common health practice among Zulus and other cultural groups is to drink a large volume (up to two litres) of a weak, luke-warm herbal infusion, and then to self-induce vomiting to cleanse and tone the system. This is called *"ukuphalaza"* or *"ukughabha"*. In some cases plants that are pharmacologically active emetics are used. Sea water is also commonly used.

SUBLINGUALLY. Some herbal remedies are taken sublingually (under the tongue). This part of the mucous membrane of the mouth is richly supplied with blood vessels, ensuring rapid absorption of soluble phytochemicals. Taken sublingually, the remedy avoids the acidic action of the stomach as well as the initial metabolism of the liver.

RECTALLY. Infusions and some decoctions are commonly administered as enemas, using modern enema syringes or tubes. In some rural areas a lubricated, truncated cow's horn is still used to administer the enema. Enemas are most commonly given to maintain general health, to remedy constipation, and for low back pain. The enema is the preferred route of administration of certain plant extracts, as it is believed that they are more effective when administered in this way. This may have a scientific rationale, as medicine is very rapidly absorbed through the delicate mucosa of the rectum and the large bowel, and the effects of the acidity of the stomach on the plant material is avoided.

TOPICALLY. Medicine may be applied directly to the skin, where the active compounds are absorbed into the underlying tissues. An example is the skin patches applied behind the ear for motion sickness. A common method in African medicine is to introduce extracts or powders of the herbs directly into small cuts made in the skin (Zulu: "umgaba"). Specific infusions, decoctions, tinctures, lotions, poultices and ointments may be applied directly to the skin, and to sprains, bruises, sores, burns, wounds and ulcers. Selected dried, powdered medicinal plants are also used topically to ulcers and open wounds, usually as dressings.

NASALLY. A large variety of plants are taken dried and powdered as snuffs. Some are taken to induce sneezing, which may traditionally be believed to aid the expulsion of disease. Others are taken for common conditions that have a parallel in modern medicine, such as headaches. The nasal route is an extremely effective method of introducing soluble phytochemicals directly into the cerebral circulation.

Plant medicines can be administered by other means as well:

SMOKING. Certain plants, including *Datura* spp. and *Pellaea* spp., are traditionally made into cigars, and the smoke inhaled to effectively relieve asthma. Smoke from other plants may also be used to make a patient cough to expel the perceived cause of disease, and to soothe the skin and affected parts. The plant material is burnt in a potsherd. The patient leans over the potsherd, his head covered by a blanket.

STEAMING. Medicinal herbs are commonly inhaled by steaming them in very hot water. A blanket or towel is used to cover the patient's head and the container. Hot rocks may be added to the mixture to make it boil. Herbal steaming is used to maintain general health, to improve the complexion by opening the pores and stimulating cutaneous circulation, and to make the patient sweat, thereby encouraging the expulsion of the perceived cause of disease. Herbal steaming is also used to introduce volatile phytochemicals and essential oils into the lungs for chest complaints, including asthma, and into the nose to relieve headaches, or the genitalia for the relief of post-partum pain.

BATHING. Herbal mixtures may also be added to bath water to relieve certain conditions, such as a rash in the case of measles, or simply to maintain good health.

Sublingual drops

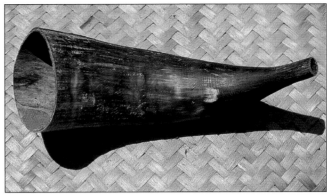

A traditional Zulu enema horn

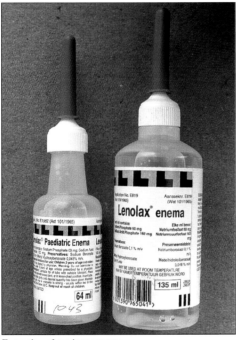

Examples of modern enemas

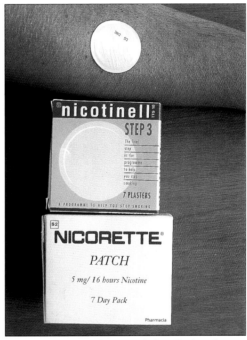

Skin patches are used for the topical application of nicotine

Pelargonium leaves inserted for earache

Traditional method of burning ritual incense ("imphepho") in a potsherd

ACTIVE INGREDIENTS

The active ingredients in medicinal plants are chemical compounds that act directly or indirectly to prevent or treat disease, and maintain health. The active compound may be extracted from the plant in a pure form, after which it is identified and tested. Natural, plant-based products are becoming increasingly popular nowadays. These phytomedicines ("phyto" means plant) are sold as extracts or powders in which the concentration of the active ingredient is standardised to ensure safety and efficacy. A brief and simplified overview of different classes of chemical compounds is given here.

SUGARS AND GUMS. The most common and well-known sugars are the **monosaccharides** glucose and fructose, and the **disaccharide** sucrose (see *Protea repens*). Sugar solutions are used medicinally for intravenous feeding and in cough syrups. **Syrups** are simply strong solutions of sugar in water. **Mucilages and gums** are formed when numerous sugar units are variously linked to each other to form long, chain-like structures. An example is Cape gum, collected from *Acacia karroo*, which has much of the same characteristics as the well-known North African gum arabic.

GLYCOSIDES AND AGLYCONES. A sugar molecule is often attached to some other molecule, and the resultant compound is then known as a glycoside. If the sugar part of the molecule is glucose, then we call it a glucoside; when it is fructose, then it is known as a fructoside, and so on.

AMINO ACIDS. Amino acids are the basic building blocks of proteins. They have a carboxyl group (-COOH) on the one end and an amino group ($-NH_2$) on the other end (see *Sutherlandia frutescens*). Compounds derived from amino acids are often of more pharmaceutical interest than the amino acids themselves. Examples are cyanogenic glycosides, such as amygdalin (see *Prunus africana*), the sulphur-containing compounds, such as alliin (see *Tulbaghia violacea*) and the so-called phenethylamines (see *Catha edulis*).

LECTINS. Lectins are specific types of proteins with the ability to bond with cell membranes. They are often toxic and occur mainly in seeds (see castor oil plant, *Ricinus communis*). The medicinal activity of mistletoe (*Viscum* spp.) is also ascribed to lectins.

GLYCOPROTEINS. A glycoprotein is a protein bonded to a sugar. They are believed to have wound-healing properties (see *Bulbine natalensis*).

FLAVONOIDS. These are phenolic compounds (that is, with one or more phenols in the structure), found almost universally as water-soluble pigments in plants. Different types of flavonoids are distinguished, such as **flavones** (see apigenin dimethylether from *Rhus undulata*), **flavonols** such as quercetin (see *Psidium guajava*), **flavanones** such as isosakuranetin (see *Cyclopia*), **chalcones** such as aspalathin (see *Aspalathus linearis*). Another group is the **anthocyanidins**, usually present as water-soluble pigments, with one or more sugar molecules bonded to them (then they are called anthocyanins). A typical example of an anthocyanidin is cyanidin, which contributes the red or purple colour to some of the medicinally important rhizomes and roots. Flavonoids have several proven medicinal properties, such as their ability to strengthen veins and to decrease their permeability. They also have anti-inflammatory, anti-oxidant, anti-allergic, antibacterial and antiviral effects.

TANNINS. Two basic groups of tannins are found in higher plants, namely hydrolysable tannins and condensed tannins. **Hydrolysable tannins** are compounds where one or more sugars (usually glucose) are bonded to phenolic acid molecules. The phenolic acids are either gallic acid or ellagic acid. For an example of a hydrolysable tannin, see geraniin, known from *Geranium* species. **Condensed tannins** (also called **proanthocyanidins**) are quite different. They are made up of two or more flavonoid units which break down into anthocyanidins when treated with acids at a high temperature. An example is procyanidin C_1 (see *Sclerocarya*). The pharmaceutical value of tannins is linked to their ability to form complexes with other molecules (to "detoxify" the digestive system, for example). They have antiseptic effects and are often used to treat diarrhoea.

QUINONES. This class of compounds is similar to phenolic compounds but they are oxidised, and have oxygen (-O) in the ring structure rather than hydroxyl (-OH) groups. Various types are distinguished, of which naphthoquinones

A pestle and mortar, used for grinding plant material before extraction

Various methods are used to filter crude extracts before they are analysed

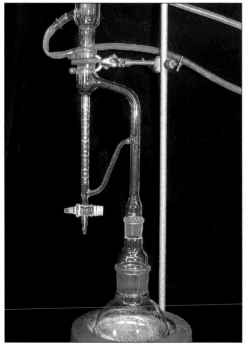

A clevenger apparatus is used for steam distillation of essential oils

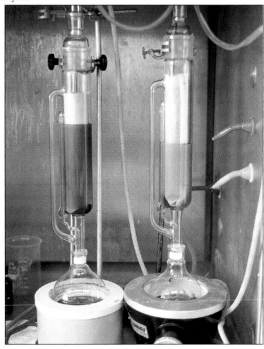

A soxhlet apparatus is commonly used for extracting plant material with organic solvents

and anthraquinones are the best known. The former has two aromatic rings, while the latter has three aromatic rings, with the middle one oxidised. An example of a **naphthoquinone** is plumbagin (see *Plumbago auriculata*). Examples of **anthraquinones** are chrysophanol (see *Bulbine natalensis*) and aloin, an anthrone *C*-glycoside (see *Aloe ferox*). Quinones have proven antibacterial and antifungal activity and various other properties.

COUMARINS. Coumarins are also phenolic compounds with a specific ring structure. There are **simple coumarins**, such as umckalin from *Pelargonium reniforme* or **furanocoumarins**, where there is an additional so-called furan ring attached to the first ring of the basic coumarin structure. Xanthotoxin is an example of this type of coumarin (see *Peucedanum galbanum*). Coumarins are sometimes present in essential oils because they are sufficiently volatile to be extracted through the process of steam distillation. Pharmaceutical effects are similar to those of flavonoids. Some furanocoumarins, however, may cause severe light-induced dermatitis (see *Peucedanum galbanum*).

TERPENOIDS AND STEROIDS. All terpenoids and steroids are formed by the linking together of a number of five carbon units, the so-called **isoprene units**. The various classes of terpenoids have the following numbers of isoprene units: **monoterpenoids** (two units) such as menthol (see *Mentha longifolia*); **sesquiterpenoids** (three units) such as zingiberene (see *Zingiber officinalis*), **triterpenoids** (six units) such as madecassic acid (see *Centella asiatica*). Some secondary modifications occur in **steroids**, so that the number of isoprene units is not immediately obvious. They all have a **steroid skeleton**, which is clearly seen in diosgenin (see *Dioscorea dregeana*) and typhasterol (see *Typha capensis*). Both triterpenoids and steroids are often present in plants in the form of **saponins**. This means that they have one or more sugar molecules attached to them, which make them water soluble. The presence of saponins in a watery extract is immediately evident from the foam which forms when the solution is shaken vigorously. Saponins, like other glycosides, can be hydrolysed to yield the triterpenoid or steroid as aglycone. Monoterpenoids and sesquiterpenoids are common constituents of volatile oils (essential oils) as obtained through steam distillation of leaves (see *Artemisia* and *Agathosma*, for example). **Iridoids** are a specific class of monoterpenoids with a so-called **iridane** skeleton. Various modifications of this basic skeleton may occur, as in harpagoside, the main iridoid of *Harpagophytum procumbens* and the main compounds of *Valeriana*, the so-called valopotriates, which are also iridoids. Another group of iridoids, the so-called **secoiridoids**, have a basic skeleton as in gentiopicroside, the main bitter principle in wild olive leaves (*Olea europaea*) and *Chironia* species. Another pharmaceutically important group of terpenoids is the **sesquiterpenoid lactones**, characterised by the presence of a lactone ring. These compounds are particularly common in the Asteraceae. Osmitopsin is an example from *Osmitopsis asteriscoides*; and glaucolide A an example from *Vernonia* species. Another large group of terpenoids is the **diterpenoids**. They are made up of four isoprene units but various modifications can occur. An example is *ent*-16-kaurenoic acid, the main kaurene of *Alepidea* and *Arctopus*. **Cardiac glycosides** are a specific group of steroidal glycosides comprising two basic types, the so-called cardenolide and bufadienolide types. The **cardenolides** have a five-member ring above the basic steroid skeletons (see uzarigenin from *Xysmalobium*). **Bufadienolides** differ in the presence of a six-member ring above the steroid skeleton. An example of this type is scillarenin, the main aglycone of *Urginea maritima* (see *Drimia robusta*).

ALKALOIDS. All alkaloids are basic, nitrogen-containing substances with a nitrogen atom (N) as a member of the ring system. Various classes of alkaloids are distinguished, depending on the ring system (skeleton) that is present. The best known example of **tropane alkaloids** is atropine (see *Datura stramonium*). **Pyrrolizidine alkaloids** are particularly common in *Senecio*. **Piperidine alkaloids** occur in many plants (see pelletierine, the main alkaloid of *Punica*). An example of an **isoquinoline alkaloid** (Amaryllidaceae type) is lycorine (see *Clivia*). **Indole alkaloids** include compounds such as ajmalicine (see *Rauvolfia*). **Imidazole alkaloids** are of limited pharmaceutical interest but note the presence of histamine in *Albizia* bark. There are many unusual alkaloids which are often not specifically grouped, such as the **tripeptide alkaloid** sanjoinine A (see *Ziziphus*). Most alkaloids are toxic and have a wide range of different pharmacological effects.

A glass TLC solvent chamber ("TLC" = thin layer chromatography) is used for routine analysis of plant extracts

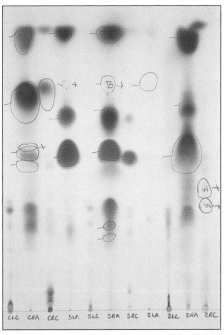

A TLC plate, showing the main compounds (visible as spots) of various extracts

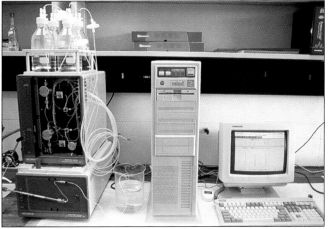

A modern HPLC system ("HPLC" = high performance liquid chromatography), used to analyse plant extracts

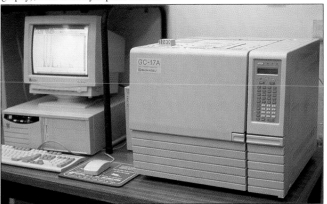

A modern GC system ("GC" = gas chromatography), used to analyse volatile compounds

ACACIA KARROO

Fabaceae

mookana (Northern Sotho); moshaoka (Tswana); umnga (Xhosa);
umunga (Zulu); soetdoring (Afrikaans); sweet thorn (English)

BOTANICAL DESCRIPTION. The sweet thorn varies from a multi-stemmed shrub to a tree of up to 15 metres in height. The dark brown to almost black bark is rough and somewhat flaky, revealing reddish underbark. When the trunk is damaged, a clear gum exudes from it. Pairs of large white spines are present on the twigs and branches. The leaves are divided into about five pairs of leaflets, and each is again divided into 10 or more pairs of smaller leaflets of about 5 mm long. Minute flowers are borne in attractive golden-yellow, ball-shaped heads. The fruit is a long, narrow, spirally twisted pod[1,2,3]. Due to its high tannin content, the bark was used in olden days for tanning. It is said to give leather a reddish colour, but disagreeable odour[4,5]. The gum, known commercially as Cape gum, was once exported from the Cape and Namibia[4].

PLANT PARTS USED. Bark, leaves and gum are used, and rarely the roots.

MEDICINAL USES. The bark and leaves are a Cape remedy for diarrhoea and dysentery[4,5,6]. The gum, bark and leaves have also been used as an emollient and astringent for colds, conjunctivitis and haemorrhage[4]. The gum is used as food and is also taken for oral thrush. Some other traditional uses have been recorded[6].

PREPARATION AND DOSAGE. Decoctions or infusions of the bark, leaves and gum are used.

ACTIVE INGREDIENTS. The bark and leaves are rich in tannins, but no detailed analyses are available[7]. Two biologically interesting gallotannins, known to control leaf movements, have been identified from *A. karroo*[7]. Cape gum is of the arabinose-galactose type[4,7,8] (similar to gum arabic) and is suitable for pharmaceutical use[4]. On partial acid hydrolysis, it yields two different L-arabinose units as hydrolysis products[7,8] (see below).

PHARMACOLOGICAL EFFECTS. A dried aqueous extract of the heartwood of different *Acacia* species was still official in the British Pharmaceutical Codex of 1949 under the name "black catechu". The presence of acacatechin, catechutannic acid and quercetin made it useful in the treatment of diarrhoea[9]. Gums have industrial value, particularly as additives in the food industry[10]. Medicinally, gum arabic and Cape gum have been used as emollients and as pharmaceutical aids: as emulsifiers, stabilisers of suspensions and additives for solid formulations[10,11].

DISTRIBUTION. *A. karroo* is perhaps the most widely distributed of all South African trees and can be found in practically all parts of the country[1,2].

3-O-ß-L-arabinopyranosyl-L-arabinose

3-O-α-D-galactopyranosyl-L-arabinose

1. **Ross, J.H. 1975.** Subfamily Mimosoideae. *Flora of Southern Africa 16(1).* Botanical Research Institute, Pretoria.
2. **Palmer, E. & Pitman, J. 1972.** *Trees of Southern Africa.* Balkema, Cape Town.
3. **Coates Palgrave, K. 1977.** *Trees of Southern Africa.* Struik, Cape Town.
4. **Watt, J.M. & Breyer-Brandwijk, M.G. 1962.** *The Medicinal and Poisonous Plants of Southern and Eastern Africa.* 2nd edition. Livingstone, London.
5. **Smith, C.A. 1966.** *Common Names of South African Plants. Memoirs of the Botanical Survey of South Africa 35*, pp. 642.
6. **Hutchings, A. 1996.** *Zulu Medicinal Plants.* Natal University Press, Pietermaritzburg.
7. **Dictionary of Natural Products on CD-ROM, release 4:2 (1996).** Chapman & Hall, London.
8. **Churms, S.C. *et al.* 1983.** New aspects of the molecular structure of *Acacia karroo* gum shown by Smith degradations. *S. Afr. J. Chem.* 36: 149-152.
9. **Martindale 1972.** *The Extra Pharmacopoeia.* 26th edition. Pharmaceutical Press, London.
10. **Merck 1989.** *The Merck Index.* 11th edition. Merck, Rahway.
11. **Bruneton, J. 1995.** *Pharmacognosy, Phytochemistry, Medicinal Plants.* Intercept, Hampshire.

Acacia karroo

Acacia karroo bark, with gum exuding from a wound

Flowering twigs of *Acacia karroo*

ACOKANTHERA OPPOSITIFOLIA

Apocynaceae

---

nthunguyembe (Xhosa); uhlunguyembe (Zulu); common poison-bush, bushman's poison bush (English); gewone gifboom, boesmansgif (Afrikaans)

BOTANICAL DESCRIPTION. *A. oppositifolia* is an evergreen shrub or small tree[1,2], usually about two to three metres in height but sometimes up to five metres. The leaves are thick and leathery, glossy dark green above and paler below, often tinged red, without any hairs but with conspicuous veins. The fragrant white flowers are about 10 mm long and occur in dense clusters almost throughout the year. The plum-like berries are 10 to 15 mm long and turn dark purple at maturity.

PLANT PARTS USED. Leaves and/or roots are used.

MEDICINAL USES. The dried leaves (or roots) are used to treat headaches[3,4] or as a treatment for snake bite. Weak leaf infusions are taken for abdominal pain. Other ailments[5] for which the plant has been used include toothache, colds, anthrax and tapeworm. *Acokanthera* species are best known as sources of extremely toxic arrow poisons[6,7].

PREPARATION AND DOSAGE. The leaves are dried, powdered and snuffed, or they may be soaked in water and the liquid used as a nasal spray. As a snake bite treatment, the leaves or roots are powdered and applied either directly to the bite or as a paste.

ACTIVE INGREDIENTS. The plant is extremely toxic since it contains several heart glycosides[7] of which acovenoside A is the major compound, with smaller amounts of acolongifloroside K and several other minor constituents. Amongst these are ouabain, the famous arrow poison from the East African *A. schimperi*[8].

PHARMACOLOGICAL EFFECTS. Toxic, analgesic and decongestant properties have been ascribed to *Acokanthera*. Ouabain (strophanthin-G) has been used as an injection in congestive heart failure[9].

DISTRIBUTION. This species is widely distributed along the eastern and northern parts of South Africa where it occurs in various habitats, from dense forest to open savanna, often in rocky places. It also occurs in Mozambique, Zimbabwe, Zambia, Zaire, Malawi, Tanzania and Kenya[1].

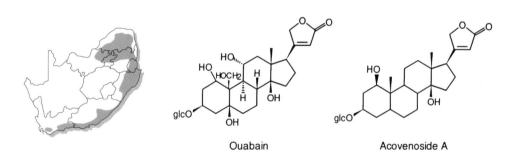

Ouabain   Acovenoside A

1. **Kupicha, F.K. 1982**. Studies on African Apocynaceae: the genus *Acokanthera. Kew Bull.* 37: 40-67.
2. **Codd, L.E. 1963**. Apocynaceae. In: *Flora of Southern Africa* 26: 244-250. Botanical Research Institute, Pretoria.
3. **Pujol, J. 1990**. *Naturafrica - the Herbalist Handbook.* Jean Pujol Natural Healers' Foundation, Durban.
4. **Hutchings, A. & Van Staden, J. 1994**. Plants used for stress-related ailments in traditional Zulu, Xhosa and Sotho medicine. Part 1: Plants used for headaches. *J. Ethnopharmacol.* 43: 89-124.
5. **Watt, J.M. & Breyer-Brandwijk, M.G. 1962**. *The Medicinal and Poisonous Plants of Southern and Eastern Africa.* 2nd edition. Livingstone, London.
6. **Forbes, V.S. (ed.) 1986**. *Carl Peter Thunberg Travels at the Cape of Good Hope 1772-1775.* Van Riebeeck Society, Cape Town.
7. **Neuwinger, H.D. 1994**. *Afrikanische Arzneipflanzen und Jagdgifte.* Wissenschaftliche Verlagsgesellschaft, Stuttgart.
8. **De Villiers, J.P. 1962**. The cardiac glycosides of *Acokanthera oblongifolia. J. S. Afr. Chem. Inst.* 15: 82-84 and references cited therein.
9. **Martindale 1958**. *The Extra Pharmacopoeia.* Pharmaceutical Press, London.

Acokanthera oppositifolia

Fruits of *Acokanthera oppositifolia*

Flowers of *Acokanthera oppositifolia*

ACORUS CALAMUS

Araceae

> **sweet-flag (English); makkalmoes (Afrikaans); ikalamuzi (Zulu)**

BOTANICAL DESCRIPTION. *A. calamus* is a reed-like, perennial, aquatic plant with long, thin, sword-shaped leaves growing from long creeping rhizomes. The leaves are reddish towards their bases. Inconspicuous flowers are compactly arranged on a long, fleshy axis, surrounded by a large leaf-like spathe. There are several varieties differing mainly in chemical composition[1] and chromosome number.

PLANT PARTS USED. All parts of the plant have a strong, pungent smell, but only the rhizomes are generally used. They contain an essential oil[2] in concentrations of 2 to 9%.

MEDICINAL USES. The plant has possibly been used since biblical times, but it is not certain if the "Calamus" of the Bible actually refers to this plant[3]. There are numerous traditional uses all over the world, mainly as a digestive and carminative, but sometimes as an emetic, anti-spasmodic, stimulant and anthelmintic. It appears to relieve stomach cramps, asthma and chronic dysentery. In the Cape, the use of the rhizome as a carminative and treatment for diarrhoea has been recorded[4].

PREPARATION AND DOSAGE. Alcoholic extracts (tinctures) are generally used. The dried or candied rhizomes may be directly chewed or taken as an infusion in boiling water. The use of *Acorus* in digestive medicines has been discontinued in most countries due to possible toxic and carcinogenic effects.

ACTIVE INGREDIENTS. The essential oil contains numerous monoterpenoids (e.g. camphene, *p*-cymene, linalool) and sesquiterpenoids (e.g. acorenone). Toxicity is ascribed to ß-asarone, a phenylpropanoid[1,2].

PHARMACOLOGICAL EFFECTS. The spasmolytic properties of the essential oil and central nervous system sedative effects of the main component of the Indian variety, ß-asarone, has been demonstrated[2]. The toxicity is due to ß-asarone and there is evidence that this compound may induce duodenal and liver cancer[2]. As a result, the ß-asarone content of extracts for internal use should be strictly controlled.

DISTRIBUTION. The plant originated from Asia, but is now widely distributed in wet places in Europe and eastern North America[2,3]. In South Africa it has been cultivated since early colonial times[5,6] and has become naturalised along a stream bank in the North West Province[7].

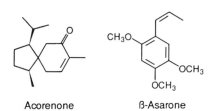

Acorenone   ß-Asarone

1. **Lander, V. & Schreier, P. 1990.** Acorenone and γ-Asarone: indicators of the origin of calamus oils (*Acorus calamus* L.). *Flavour Fragrance J.* 5: 75-79.
2. **Bruneton, J. 1995.** *Pharmacognosy, Phytochemistry, Medicinal Plants.* Intercept, Hampshire.
3. **Grieve, M. 1967.** *A Modern Herbal.* Hafner, London.
4. **Watt, J.M. & Breyer-Brandwijk, M.G. 1962.** *The Medicinal and Poisonous Plants of Southern and Eastern Africa.* 2nd edition. Livingstone, London.
5. **Marloth, R. 1917.** *The Flora of South Africa.* William Wesley, London.
6. **Smith, C.A. 1966.** *Common Names of South African Plants. Memoirs of the Botanical Survey of South Africa* 35.
7. **Ubbink, B. & Bredenkamp, G.J. 1985.** A new record of *Acorus calamus* in South Africa. *Bothalia* 15: 547.

Acorus calamus

Rhizome of *Acorus calamus*

Flower spike of *Acorus calamus*

Dried rhizomes of *Acorus calamus*, in segments or chopped

ADANSONIA DIGITATA

Bombacaceae

> **muvhuyu (Venda); shimuwu (Tsonga); movana (Tswana); kremetart (Afrikaans) baobab (English)**

BOTANICAL DESCRIPTION. This remarkable tree is a conspicuous feature of the Northern Province of South Africa. It is relatively short (up to about 15 metres in height), but develops a massive, unevenly folded trunk of more than 20 metres in circumference. The smooth bark is grey or yellowish-grey. The large leaves are divided into about five to seven leaflets, all borne on a single long, thin stalk. Each leaflet tapers to a sharp point and is up to 150 mm long. Large, pendulous white flowers are produced in early summer (October to December), followed by very large egg-shaped fruits of up to 150 mm long. The seeds are surrounded by a powdery white pulp ("cream of tartar") and the thin, hard outer shell of the fruit is covered with characteristic velvety, yellow hairs[1].

PLANT PARTS USED. The dried fruit pulp (mixed with water) or the bark are used, rarely the leaves or seeds.

MEDICINAL USES. A refreshing drink is prepared from the pale yellow or whitish fruit pulp, which has been regarded as "cream of tartar". This drink has been used to treat fevers, diarrhoea and apparently also haemoptysis[2]. In West Africa, the bark and leaves are claimed to have anti-inflammatory and dia-phoretic properties and are regarded as a remedy for urinary disorders and mild diarrhoea[3]. The leaves are reported to be used against fever, to reduce perspiration and as an astringent. In the Northern Province, the powdered seeds are given to children as a hiccup remedy[2]. The bark has been sold commercially in Europe under the name "cortex cael cedra" to treat fevers and as a substitute for cinchona bark[2]. It is, however, of limited interest in pharmacy[4]. Numerous non-medicinal uses have been recorded[2].

PREPARATION AND DOSAGE. The fruit pulp is mixed with water or a decoction made of the bark[2].

ACTIVE INGREDIENTS. The fruit pulp is rich in citric acid and tartaric acid[2]. The medicinal value may possibly be ascribed to one of several flavonols, such as quercetin-7-O-ß-$_D$-xylopyranoside or perhaps also to 7-baueren-3-acetate, a triterpenoid which has been isolated from the plant[5].

PHARMACOLOGICAL EFFECTS. Tartaric acid is mildly irritating in strong solution.

DISTRIBUTION. *A. digitata* is widely distributed in Africa, but in South Africa it is restricted to frost-free areas in the northern part of the country[1,6].

Quercetin-7-O-ß-$_D$-xylopyranoside

Tartaric acid

Citric acid

1. **Wickens, G.E. 1982.** The baobab – Africa's upside-down tree. *Kew Bull.* 37(2): 173-209.
2. **Watt, J.M. & Breyer-Brandwijk, M.G. 1962.** *The Medicinal and Poisonous Plants of Southern and Eastern Africa.* 2nd edition. Livingstone, London.
3. **Daziel, J.M. 1937.** *The Useful Plants of West Tropical Africa.* Crown Agents, London.
4. **Bruneton, J. 1995.** *Pharmacognosy, Phytochemistry, Medicinal Plants.* Intercept, Hampshire.
5. **Dictionary of Natural Products on CD-ROM, release 4:2 (1996).** Chapman & Hall, London.
6. **Von Breitenbach, F. 1986.** *National List of Indigenous Trees.* Dendrological Foundation, Pretoria.

Adansonia digitata

Leaf and flower of *Adansonia digitata*

Leaves and fruit of *Adansonia digitata*

Fruits of *Adansonia digitata*, showing the seeds surrounded by dry fruit pulp

AGAPANTHUS AFRICANUS

Amaryllidaceae (or Agapanthaceae)

> **ubani (Zulu); isicakathi (Xhosa); leta-la-phofu (Sotho); bloulelie (Afrikaans); blue lily (English)**

BOTANICAL DESCRIPTION. *Agapanthus* species are widely grown in gardens and are all rather similar in appearance. It is likely that most of them are used for similar medicinal purposes even though *A. africanus*, *A. campanulatus* and *A. praecox* appear to be the most popular. The species can be distinguished by their size and by details of the leaves and flowers[1]. They are all geophytes with thick tuberous rhizomes. The long, narrow, strap-shaped leaves are somewhat fleshy, dark green and about 0,4 m long in *A. africanus*. The flowers are characteristically borne in a dense cluster (umbel) on a long slender stalk. The flowers are usually pale to dark blue, but white forms of some species are also known.

PLANT PARTS USED. Rhizomes and roots are used.

MEDICINAL USES. *A. africanus* and other species are widely used in so-called "isicakathi", a decoction given orally or rectally as an antenatal and postnatal medicine, and also to the baby immediately after birth[2]. It is mildly purgative and may also be used to ease a difficult labour and to ensure that the placenta is expelled[3].

PREPARATION AND DOSAGE. Decoctions of the rhizome and roots are taken on their own or in combination with other plants (as "isicakathi")[2]. A plant is sometimes grown in water and this water is then used in the evening and morning from the fourth or fifth month of pregnancy[3].

ACTIVE INGREDIENTS. Several saponins and sapogenins of the furostane and spirostane types have been isolated from the rhizomes of *Agapanthus* species[4,5,6]. A typical example is the sapogenin agapanthagenin, which is known only from *A. africanus* and other *Agapanthus* species.

PHARMACOLOGICAL EFFECTS. A large number of biological activities and biochemical effects have been ascribed to saponins in the past few years. These include anti-inflammatory, anti-oedema, antitussive and immunoregulatory properties[7]. The precise activity of *Agapanthus* saponins are not known, but preliminary screening tests have shown definite uterotonic activity in crude decoctions[8].

DISTRIBUTION. *Agapanthus* species are widely distributed in the eastern parts of South Africa. Many of them are grown in gardens, so that the exact origin of plant material is often difficult to establish. The map shows the natural distribution area of the genus as a whole.

Agapanthagenin
(Spirostane-2,3,5-triol)

1. **Leighton, F.M. 1965.** The genus *Agapanthus* L'Heritier. *Jl S. Afr. Bot.* Suppl. 4.
2. **Bolofo, R.N. & Johnson, C.T. 1988.** The identification of 'Isicakathi' and its medicinal use in Transkei. *Bothalia* 18: 125-130.
3. **Watt, J.M. & Breyer-Brandwijk, M.G. 1962.** *The Medicinal and Poisonous Plants of Southern and Eastern Africa.* 2nd edition. Livingstone, London.
4. **Stephen, T. 1956.** Saponins and sapogenins. Part IV. Agapanthagenin, a new sapogenin from *Agapanthus* spp. *J. Chem. Soc.* 1956: 1167-1169.
5. **Gonzalez, A.G. *et al.* 1974.** 7-dehydroagapanthenin and 8(14)-dehydroagapanthagenin, two new spirostane sapogenins from *Agapanthus africanus*. *Phytochemistry* 13: 627-632.
6. **Dictionary of Natural Products on CD-ROM, release 4:2 (1996).** Chapman & Hall, London.
7. **Bruneton, J. 1995.** *Pharmacognosy, Phytochemistry, Medicinal Plants.* Intercept, Hampshire.
8. **Kaido, T.L., Veale, D.J.H. & Havlik, I. 1994.** *The preliminary screening of plants used as traditional herbal remedies during pregnancy and labour.* South African Pharmacological Society, 28th annual Congress, Cape Town, 22-24 September 1994.

Agapanthus africanus

Rhizomes and roots of *Agapanthus praecox*

Flowers of *Agapanthus africanus*

AGATHOSMA BETULINA

Rutaceae

buchu (Khoi, English), boegoe (Afrikaans), ibuchu (Xhosa)

BOTANICAL DESCRIPTION. The plant is a shrub of up to two metres in height. The leaves are about 20 mm long, characteristically very broad (less than twice as long as broad[1]), with a rounded apex which curves backwards. Conspicuous oil glands are present along the margins and lower surfaces of the leaves. The flowers are small, star-shaped and white or pale purple. This species is sometimes confused with *A. crenulata*, but in the latter the leaves are more than twice as long as they are broad[1].

PLANT PARTS USED. Dried leaves are used.

MEDICINAL USES. Buchu is part of the cultural heritage of the San and Khoi people[2]. *A. betulina* (and several related plants) were used to anoint the body (after mixing the powdered, dried leaves with sheep fat), probably both for cosmetic reasons and as an antibiotic protection[3]. For medicinal use, the leaves were chewed to relieve stomach complaints. These practises were later taken over by the early Dutch colonists and buchu or "boegoe" became a popular and famous Cape medicine. The leaves were steeped in brandy and the tincture (commonly known as Buchu brandy or "boegoebrandewyn") was an everyday remedy for stomach problems[4]. Buchu vinegar ("boegoe-asyn") was highly regarded for the washing and cleaning of wounds. Buchu is still a widely used household medicine in South Africa, with a great reputation for treating kidney and urinary tract diseases, for the symptomatic relief of rheumatism,

and also for external application on wounds and bruises[5]. Nowadays, an infusion of buchu is taken as a diuretic, often in supportive treatment of urinary infection[6] as it is thought to be a mild urinary antiseptic. The product is also used to treat minor digestive disturbances[5].

PREPARATION AND DOSAGE. Tinctures or infusions are used. A cup of boiling water is poured on 1 g of the drug and allowed to stand for 10 minutes before straining. The infusion is taken three times a day.

ACTIVE INGREDIENTS. The major compounds in the essential oils of *A. betulina* are isomenthone and diosphenol[7,8]. For use in the food industry, sulphur-containing minor compounds are important because they are partly responsible for the characteristic blackcurrant smell and flavour of buchu oil[8]. The closely related *A. crenulata* is less desirable because of the high levels of pulegone, a compound considered to be toxic.

PHARMACOLOGICAL EFFECTS. Essential oils are generally used because of their antiseptic and diuretic properties[6]. Buchu is taken as an antiseptic and urinary tract disinfectant.

DISTRIBUTION. *A. betulina* has a restricted natural distribution area in the mountains of the Western Cape[1].

Isomenthone   ψ-Diosphenol   Pulegone

1. **Spreeth, A.D. 1976.** A revision of the commercially important *Agathosma* species. *Jl S. Afr. Bot.* 42: 109-119.
2. **Smith, C.A. 1966.** *Common Names of South African Plants. Memoirs of the Botanical Survey of South Africa* 35.
3. **Forbes, V.S. (ed.) 1986.** *Carl Peter Thunberg Travels at the Cape of Good Hope 1772-1775.* Van Riebeeck Society, Cape Town.
4. **Dykman, E.J. 1891.** *Kook-, Koek- en Resepte Boek.* Paarlse Drukpers Maatskappy, Paarl.
5. **Watt, J.M. & Breyer-Brandwijk, M.G. 1962.** *The Medicinal and Poisonous Plants of Southern and Eastern Africa.* 2nd edition. Livingstone, London.
6. **Bruneton, J. 1995.** *Pharmacognosy, Phytochemistry, Medicinal Plants.* Intercept, Hampshire.
7. **Kaiser, R. et al. 1975.** Analysis of buchu leaf oil. *J. Agric. Food Chem.* 23: 943-950.
8. **Posthumus, M.A. et al. 1996.** Chemical composition of the essential oils of *Agathosma betulina, A. crenulata* and an *A. betulina* x *A. crenulata* hybrid (buchu). *J. Essent. Oil Res.* 8: 223-228.

Agathosma crenulata – oval leaf buchu

Agathosma betulina – round leaf buchu

Dried leaves of *Agathosma crenulata*

Agathosma betulina plantation

Examples of buchu products

ALBIZIA ADIANTHIFOLIA

Fabaceae

umgadankawu (Zulu); umhlandlothi (Xhosa);
platkroon (Afrikaans); flat-crown (English)

BOTANICAL DESCRIPTION[1]. The flat-crown is a large tree of up to 20 metres in height with a characteristic flattened and spreading crown. The smooth or rough bark is grey to yellowish-brown. Young branches are densely covered with reddish-brown hairs. Each leaf is divided into four to eight, and each of the divisions have six to 15 pairs of leaflets. The leaflets are about 10 to 20 mm long and markedly asymmetrical. Several flowers are grouped together to form rounded, fluffy inflorescences which appear in spring (mainly September to October). Each flower is whitish in colour, with the stamens partly fused to form a tube. The oblong pods are thin and leaf-like in appearance, with prominent veins.

PLANT PARTS USED. The bark is mainly used, rarely the roots or leaves.

MEDICINAL USES. A. adianthifolia is mainly used in Zulu medicine, for the cleansing of blood, treatment of skin diseases, as a body wash ("geza") or as a facial sauna ("gquma")[2]. A cold infusion is locally applied to treat inflammation of the eye[3]. The powdered bark is used as a snuff to relieve headaches[4]. Another species, A. anthelmintica, is a well known African anthelmintic and the powdered bark has been used in South Africa to treat tapeworm infestations[5].

The traditional headache remedy suggests analgesic and decongestant effects[4].

PREPARATION AND DOSAGE. The powdered bark is used as snuff[4]. A decoction of the bark is sometimes used as an emetic or to clean the skin. A weak infusion (one tablespoon of powdered bark in half a litre of water) is said to be helpful to treat stomach ailments[2].

ACTIVE INGREDIENTS. The presence of histamine and other imidazole derivatives in the bark of Albizia species may have some effect when the bark is used as headache snuff[4] and perhaps also for hyposensitisation effects when applied to the skin. Other beneficial activities may possibly be due to various saponins and sapogenins (such as acacic acid) which have been isolated from the bark of Albizia species[6].

PHARMACOLOGICAL EFFECTS. Histamine is a potent vasodilator found in normal tissues and blood. It is sometimes used in hyposensitisation therapy[7].

DISTRIBUTION. A. adianthifolia occurs along the eastern parts of South Africa, from the Eastern Cape to the Northern Province. It is also widely distributed in tropical Africa, as far north as Kenya and Gambia[1].

Histamine

Acacic acid

1. **Ross, J.H. 1975.** Subfamily Mimosoideae. *Flora of Southern Africa* 16(1). Botanical Research Institute, Pretoria.
2. **Pujol, J. 1990.** *Naturafrica – the Herbalist Handbook.* Jean Pujol Natural Healers' Foundation, Durban.
3. **Watt, J.M. & Breyer-Brandwijk, M.G. 1962.** *The Medicinal and Poisonous Plants of Southern and Eastern Africa.* 2nd edition. Livingstone, London.
4. **Hutchings, A. & Van Staden, J. 1994.** Plants used for stress-related ailments in traditional Zulu, Xhosa and Sotho medicine. Part 1: Plants used for headaches. *J. Ethnopharmacol.* 43: 89-124.
5. **Teichler, G.H. 1971.** *Albizia anthelmintica* (monogo) – a good worm medicine. *Botswana Notes and Records* 3: 6-7.
6. **Dictionary of Natural Products on CD-ROM, release 4:2 (1996).** Chapman & Hall, London.
7. **Merck 1989.** *The Merck Index.* 11th edition. Merck, Rahway.

Albizia adianthifolia

Leaves and flowers of *Albizia adianthifolia*

Pieces of bark and pounded bark of *Albizia adianthifolia*

ALEPIDEA AMATYMBICA

Apiaceae

ikhathazo (Zulu); lesoko (Sotho); iqwili (Xhosa); kalmoes (Afrikaans)

BOTANICAL DESCRIPTION[1]. The plant is a robust perennial with dark green rosettes of oblong, markedly toothed leaves arising from a single or branched rhizome. The flowering stalk is hollow and up to two metres in height, with numerous small flowers arranged in dense, rounded heads. The shape of the basal leaves and the serrations and hairs along the leaf margins are important to distinguish the different species of *Alepidea*. There are two distinct forms of *A. amatymbica*: the typical form from the Eastern Cape, with leaves which gradually taper towards their bases; a northern form with distinctly heart-shaped leaves (the leaf base is lobed and does not gradually merge with the petiole).

PLANT PARTS USED. Rhizomes and roots are used.

MEDICINAL USES. The rhizomes and roots are sold commercially in many parts of South Africa and are widely used for colds and chest complaints[1,2,3,4,5,6], as well as for asthma, influenza and abdominal cramps.

PREPARATION AND DOSAGE. Fresh rhizomes and roots are chewed[4,5] or a decoction is made of the dried product, to which honey is normally added[1]. It is also administered as snuff or burned and inhaled[5]. The smoke from burning roots is used as a mild sedative. An infusion is made, together with *Cannabis sativa*, for treating asthma.

ACTIVE INGREDIENTS. The rhizomes and roots contain very high concentrations (up to 27% dry weight) of several diterpenoids of the kaurene type[7,8]. The major compounds are dehydrokaurenoic acids and kaurenoic acids, of which *ent*-16-kauren-19-oic acid is usually present in the greatest quantity[8]. The activity of the medicine can most likely be attributed to these diterpenoids, although they have not been tested individually.

PHARMACOLOGICAL EFFECTS. Screening tests indicated antimicrobial, antihypertensive and diuretic activity[4].

DISTRIBUTION. *A. amatymbica* grows in grassland areas and occurs from the Eastern Cape northwards to Mpumalanga, the Northern Province and eastern Zimbabwe[1].

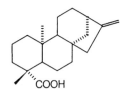

ent-16-Kauren-19-oic acid

1. **De Castro, A. & Van Wyk, B-E. 1994.** Diagnostic characters and geographical distribution of *Alepidea* species used in traditional medicine. *S. Afr. J. Bot.* 60: 345-350.
2. **Watt, J.M. & Breyer-Brandwijk, M.G. 1962.** *The Medicinal and Poisonous Plants of Southern and Eastern Africa.* 2nd edition. Livingstone, London.
3. **Hutchings, A. 1989a.** A survey and analysis of traditional medicinal plants as used by the Zulu, Xhosa and Sotho. *Bothalia* 19: 111-123.
4. **Hutchings, A. 1989b.** Observations on plant usage in Xhosa and Zulu medicine. *Bothalia* 19: 225-235.
5. **Hutchings, A. & Van Staden, J. 1994.** Plants used for stress-related ailments in traditional Zulu, Xhosa and Sotho medicine. Part 1: Plants used for headaches. *J. Ethnopharmacol.* 43: 89-124.
6. **Pujol, J. 1990.** *Naturafrica – the Herbalist Handbook.* Jean Pujol Natural Healers' Foundation, Durban.
7. **Rustaiyan, A. & Sadjada, A.S. 1987.** Kaurene derivatives from *Alepidea amatynsia* [= *A. amatymbica*]. *Phytochemistry* 26: 2106-2107.
8. **Holzapfel, C.W. *et al.* 1995.** A chemotaxonomic survey of kaurene derivatives in the genus *Alepidea* (Apiaceae). *Biochem. Syst. Ecol.* 23: 799-803.

Alepidea amatymbica

Flower heads of *Alepidea amatymbica*

Single flower head of *Alepidea amatymbica*

Dried rhizomes of *Alepidea amatymbica*

ALOE FEROX

Asphodelaceae

> **bitteraalwyn, Kaapse aalwyn (Afrikaans); bitter aloe (English); umhlaba (Xhosa, Zulu, Sotho)**

BOTANICAL DESCRIPTION. This aloe is a robust plant with persistent dry leaves on the lower portion of the single stem. The broad, fleshy leaves are dull green or reddish-green, with dark brown spines along the edges and sometimes on the lower surface. Bright red or orange flowers (rarely yellowish or white) appear from May to August and are arranged in erect, candle-shaped clusters[1,2].

PLANT PARTS USED. The bitter yellow juice which exudes from just below the surface of the leaf is dried by an age-old method[3,4] to form a dark brown resinous solid, known commercially as aloe lump or Cape aloes. This product should not be confused with aloe gel, which originates from the inner fleshy part of the leaf. Aloe gel is a watery mixture of pectic substances, amino acids, minerals, trace elements, organic acids and various minor compounds. It is used in hair and skin care products.

MEDICINAL USES. Cape aloes is still an important commercial laxative medicine. The larger part of the annual production is exported, but substantial quantities are marketed and used locally. The popular self-care remedies "Lewensessens" and "Schweden bitters" contain Cape aloes. *A. ferox* and other species are used to a great extent in traditional human and livestock medicines. The leaves or roots, boiled in water, are taken as a laxative, but also for arthritis, eczema, conjunctivitis[5,6], hypertension and stress[7].

Leaf sap of several species such as *A. arborescens* and *A. greatheadii* is applied externally to treat skin irritations, bruises and burns. The dry leaves of *A. marlothii* are popular in snuff mixtures.

PREPARATION AND DOSAGE. A small crystal of the crude drug, about twice the size of a match head, is taken orally as a laxative. The product should not be used during pregnancy. Half the laxative dose is taken for arthritis. The fresh bitter sap is instilled directly for conjunctivitis and sinusitis.

ACTIVE INGREDIENTS. The main purgative principle is the anthrone *C*-glucoside aloin (=barbaloin). The aloin content in exudate varies between 8,5 and 32%[8], but 18% is the minimum requirement[9,10] for export. The wound-healing properties of aloe gel are ascribed to glycoproteins (see *Bulbine*) and to hydrating, insulating and protective effects[11].

PHARMACOLOGICAL EFFECTS. At therapeutic doses, the anthraquinone derivatives act as stimulant laxatives[11]. Aloin is only a prodrug while aloe-emodin anthrone, formed in the colon under the influence of bacterial enzymes, is responsible for the laxative action. It is said to increase peristalsis and to affect the absorption of water and electrolytes[11].

DISTRIBUTION. *A. ferox* is widely distributed along the eastern parts of South Africa[2].

Aloin A

Aloe-emodin anthrone

1. **Reynolds, G.W. 1950.** *The Aloes of South Africa.* The Trustees of the Aloes of South Africa Book Fund, Johannesburg.
2. **Van Wyk, B-E. & Smith, G.F. 1996.** *Guide to the Aloes of South Africa.* Briza Publications, Pretoria.
3. **Forbes, V.S. (ed.) 1986.** *Carl Peter Thunberg Travels at the Cape of Good Hope 1772-1775.* Van Riebeeck Society, Cape Town.
4. **Hodge, W.H. 1953.** The drug aloes of commerce, with special reference to the Cape species. *Econ. Bot.* 7: 99-129.
5. **Watt, J.M. & Breyer-Brandwijk, M.G. 1962.** *The Medicinal and Poisonous Plants of Southern and Eastern Africa.* 2nd edition. Livingstone, London.
6. **Bruce, W.G.G. 1975.** Medicinal properties in the aloe. *Excelsa* 5: 57-68.
7. **Pujol, J. 1990.** *Naturafrica – the Herbalist Handbook.* Jean Pujol Natural Healers' Foundation, Durban.
8. **Van Wyk, B-E. *et al.* 1995.** Geographical variation in the major compounds of *Aloe ferox* leaf exudate. *Planta Med.* 61: 250-253.
9. **European Pharmacopoeia 1993.** 2nd edition, part 2, p. 258. Maisonneuve, Sainte-Ruffine.
10. **British Pharmacopoeia 1993.** vol.1, p. 30. HMSO, London.
11. **Bruneton, J. 1995.** *Pharmacognosy, Phytochemistry, Medicinal Plants.* Intercept, Hampshire.

Aloe ferox

Aloe arborescens

The traditional method of tapping *Aloe ferox* leaves

Cape aloes, the dried leaf exudate of *Aloe ferox*

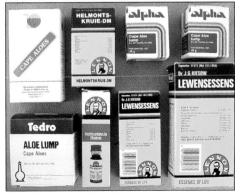

Cape aloes – examples of products

ARCTOPUS ECHINATUS

Apiaceae

Kaapse platdoring, sieketroos (Afrikaans)

BOTANICAL DESCRIPTION. This peculiar plant is quite unlike any other and most people would not recognise it as a member of the family Apiaceae (Umbelliferae). The plant has a thick, tuberous root with a rosette of spiny leaves which is borne flat on the ground. Male and female flowers are formed on different plants. The inconspicuous greenish-yellow flowers appear in the middle of the rosettes, followed, in female plants, by dry, spiny fruits.

PLANT PARTS USED. Roots are used (or the white resinous gum which oozes from it).

MEDICINAL USES. "Sieketroos" was a popular early Cape remedy[1] for numerous diseases and the use of the plant probably had its origin in the Khoi culture[2]. The vernacular name is derived from the medicinal value of the tuberous rootstock, which brings comfort (Afrikaans: "troos") to the sick (Afrikaans: "sieke")[3]. Decoctions, infusions or tinctures of the root have been used to treat venereal diseases[4]. The medicine is said to be diuretic, demulcent and pur-

gative, and is widely used to treat bladder ailments and skin irritations[4]. Other traditional uses include the treatment of epilepsy[5].

PREPARATION AND DOSAGE. Infusions are used internally or locally for the treatment of venereal diseases while decoctions are taken orally for epilepsy and bladder problems.

ACTIVE INGREDIENTS. The resinous gum in the roots is chemically very similar to the resin from *Alepidea* rhizomes. The same mixture of diterpenoids (kaurene derivatives) has been found, such as *ent*-16-kauren-19-oic acid and other kaurenoic acids[6].

PHARMACOLOGICAL EFFECTS. Biological activity is probably – at least partly – due to kaurenoic acids (see *Alepidea amatymbica*).

DISTRIBUTION. *A. echinatus* is widely distributed in the Cape fynbos region, from Nieuwoudtville in the north to Port Elizabeth in the east[6].

ent-16-Kauren-19-oic acid

1. **Forbes, V.S. (ed.) 1986.** *Carl Peter Thunberg Travels at the Cape of Good Hope 1772-1775.* Van Riebeeck Society, Cape Town.
2. **Pappe, L. 1857.** *Florae Capensis Medicae Prodromus,* 2nd edition. Cape Town.
3. **Smith, C.A. 1966.** *Common Names of South African Plants. Memoirs of the Botanical Survey of South Africa* 35.
4. **Watt, J.M. & Breyer-Brandwijk, M.G. 1962.** *The Medicinal and Poisonous Plants of Southern and Eastern Africa.* 2nd edition. Livingstone, London.
5. **Watt, J.M. 1967.** African plants potentially useful in mental health. *Lloydia* 30: 1-22.
6. **De Castro, A., Van Wyk, B-E., Witte, L. & Tilney, P.M.** *Generic relationships in Southern African Saniculoideae (Apiaceae).* (in preparation).

Arctopus echinatus

Arctopus monacanthus, a closely related species used in the same way as *A. echinatus*

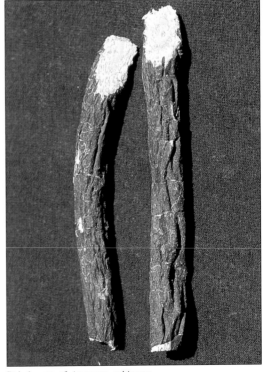

Dried roots of *Arctopus echinatus*

ARTEMISIA AFRA

Asteraceae

> **umhlonyane (Xhosa, Zulu); lengana (Sotho, Tswana); als, alsem, wildeals (Afrikaans); African wormwood (English)**

BOTANICAL DESCRIPTION. This highly aromatic plant is an erect multi-stemmed perennial shrub of up to two metres in height. The feathery leaves are finely divided and usually have a greyish-green colour. Flowers are borne along the branch ends. They are pale yellowish and inconspicuous. In cold regions, the branches die back in winter but rapidly regenerate from the base.

PLANT PARTS USED. The leaves are mainly used, but sometimes also the roots.

MEDICINAL USES. "Wildeals" is one of the most widely used traditional medicines in South Africa. Numerous ailments are treated with it – mainly coughs, colds and influenza[1,2,3] – but also fever, loss of appetite, colic, headache, earache, malaria and intestinal worms, amongst others[2,3,4,5,6]. The most common practise is to insert fresh leaves into the nostrils to clear blocked nasal passages. The roots, known as "inyathelo", are used to treat colds and fever[7].

PREPARATION AND DOSAGE. An infusion or decoction is generally used, often made syrupy with the addition of honey or sugar[2,3] to mask the natural bitter taste. To treat a blocked nose, plugs of fresh leaves may be inserted in the nostrils[2,3,4,5] or the leaves may be boiled in water and the fumes inhaled[5,8].

ACTIVE INGREDIENTS. The volatile oil, which contains mainly 1,8-cineole, α-thujone, ß-thujone, camphor and borneol, has definite antimicrobial and anti-oxidative properties[9]. Toxic and hallucinogenic effects have been associated with thujone, so that overdoses or continued use over long periods are potentially harmful[10]. Also present are terpenoids of the eudesmadien- and germacratien types, as well as coumarins and acetylenes[11], but the contribution of these compounds to biological activity is not known.

PHARMACOLOGICAL EFFECTS. Decongestant and antibacterial effects of volatile oils are well known[12]. In addition, narcotic, analgesic and antihistamine activity have been demonstrated in preliminary tests[4].

DISTRIBUTION. *A. afra* is a very common species in South Africa and its natural distribution extends northwards into tropical east Africa, as far north as Ethiopia.

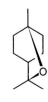

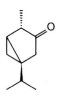

| 1,8-Cineole | α-Thujone | ß-Thujone | Borneol | Camphor |

1. **Dykman, E.J. 1891.** *Kook-, Koek- en Resepte Boek.* Paarlse Drukpers Maatskappy, Paarl.
2. **Watt, J.M. & Breyer-Brandwijk, M.G. 1962.** *The Medicinal and Poisonous Plants of Southern and Eastern Africa.* 2nd edition. Livingstone, London.
3. **Rood, B. 1994.** *Uit die Veldapteek.* Tafelberg, Cape Town.
4. **Hutchings, A. 1989.** Observations on plant usage in Xhosa and Zulu medicine. *Bothalia* 19: 225-235.
5. **Hutchings, A. & Van Staden, J. 1994.** Plants used for stress-related ailments in traditional Zulu, Xhosa and Sotho medicine. Part 1: Plants used for headaches. *J. Ethnopharmacol.* 43: 89-124.
6. **Iwu, M.M. 1993.** *Handbook of African Medicinal Plants.* CRC Press, Boca Raton.
7. **Williams, V.L. 1996.** The Witwatersrand Muti Trade. *Veld & Flora*, March 1996: 12-14.
8. **Bhat, R.B. & Jacobs, T.V. 1995.** Traditional herbal medicine in Transkei. *J. Ethnopharmacol.* 48: 7-12.
9. **Graven, E.H. *et al.* 1992.** Antimicrobial and antioxidative properties of the volatile (essential) oil of *Artemisia afra* Jacq. *Flavour Fragrance J.* 7: 121-123.
10. **Arnold, W.N. 1989.** Absinthe. *Scientific American*, June 1989, 86-91.
11. **Dictionary of Natural Products on CD-ROM, release 4:2 (1996).** Chapman & Hall, London.
12. **Bruneton, J. 1995.** *Pharmacognosy, Phytochemistry, Medicinal Plants.* Intercept, Hampshire.

Artemisia afra

Flower heads of *Artemisia afra*

Traditional products from *Artemisia afra*

Dried leaves and stems of *Artemisia afra*

ASCLEPIAS FRUTICOSA

Asclepiadaceae

umsinga-lwesalukazi (Zulu); lebegana, lereke-la-ntja (Sotho);
modimolo (Southern Sotho); melkbos, tontelbos (Afrikaans); milkweed (English)

BOTANICAL DESCRIPTION. This is an erect, multi-stemmed shrublet of up to two metres in height, with long, thin stems and narrow, opposite leaves. All parts of the plant produce a white, milky latex when broken. The greenish-yellow flowers are borne in pendulous clusters, followed by large, bladdery seed pods. Each pod is much inflated, but ends in a narrow tip; the surface is covered with sparse, wiry hairs. Attached to the seeds are parachutes of long, silky hairs, which have been used for tinder (Afrikaans: "tontel"). Other species are also used medicinally, especially *A. physocarpa* and *A. crispa*. The former has the same Zulu vernacular name as *A. fruticosa* and the two species may easily be confused. The fruits are more strongly inflated and rounded, however, and lack the narrower tips. *A. crispa* (Afrikaans: "bitterwortel") can easily be distinguished by its smaller size and prominently wavy leaf margins.

PLANT PARTS USED. The leaves are mainly used, sometimes the roots.

MEDICINAL USES. The dried leaves of *A. fruticosa* and *A. physocarpa* are finely ground and used as snuff, not only for headache[1], but also to treat tuberculosis[2] and as an emetic to strengthen the body[3]. The roots of *A. fruticosa* are reported to relieve stomach pain and a general ache in the body[3]. *A. crispa* roots are used in much the same way as those of *Xysmalobium undulatum*. A decoction or infusion of the roots of *A. crispa*[4] is said to be diuretic, purgative and emetic[2]. In Europe and the United States, the roots of *A. tuberosa* and *A. syrica* have been used as a powder or infusion, to treat asthma and typhus fever, as it relieves cough and pain[5].

PREPARATION AND DOSAGE. Leaves (or aboveground parts) are dried, powdered and snuffed[1,2,3]. For use of the root see *Xysmalobium undulatum*.

ACTIVE INGREDIENTS. Poisonous cardiac glycosides such as 15ß-hydroxygomphoside and 19-deoxyuscharin have been isolated from *A. fruticosa*[6] but it is not clear if these compounds are responsible for the reported pharmacological effects.

PHARMACOLOGICAL EFFECTS. The toxicity[7] of cardiac glycosides, which may lead to death in both humans and livestock[8], is well known. Decongestant and analgesic effects[1] have not been reported.

DISTRIBUTION. *A. fruticosa* is an indigenous plant that has become a weed in disturbed places such as roadsides and abandoned fields. It occurs practically all over South Africa.

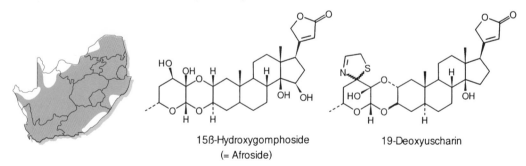

15ß-Hydroxygomphoside
(= Afroside)

19-Deoxyuscharin

1. **Hutchings, A. & Van Staden, J. 1994.** Plants used for stress-related ailments in traditional Zulu, Xhosa and Sotho medicine. Part 1: Plants used for headaches. *J. Ethnopharmacol.* 43: 89-124.
2. **Watt, J.M. & Breyer-Brandwijk, M.G. 1962.** *The Medicinal and Poisonous Plants of Southern and Eastern Africa.* 2nd edition. Livingstone, London.
3. **Pujol, J. 1990.** *Naturafrica – the Herbalist Handbook.* Jean Pujol Natural Healers' Foundation, Durban.
4. **Smith, C.A. 1966.** *Common Names of South African Plants. Memoirs of the Botanical Survey of South Africa* 35. - in early days, the roots of *Asclepias crispa* were known to Dutch apothecaries as the *radix Asclepiadis crispae*.
5. **Grieve, M. 1967.** *A Modern Herbal.* Hafner, London.
6. **Dictionary of Natural Products on CD-ROM, release 4:2 (1996).** Chapman & Hall, London.
7. **Bruneton, J. 1995.** *Pharmacognosy, Phytochemistry, Medicinal Plants.* Intercept, Hampshire.
8. **Vahrmeijer, J. 1981.** *Poisonous Plants of Southern Africa That Cause Stock Losses.* Tafelberg, Cape Town.

Asclepias fruticosa

Dried roots of *Asclepias fruticosa*

Asclepias physocarpa

Dried leaves and flowers of *Asclepias fruticosa*

ASPALATHUS LINEARIS

Fabaceae

rooibostee (Afrikaans); rooibos tea (English)

BOTANICAL DESCRIPTION. *A. linearis*[1] is a shrub of half a metre to two metres in height, with bright green, needle-shaped leaves which turn a rich reddish-brown colour upon fermentation. The small, yellow, typically pea-shaped flowers are produced in spring and early summer. Morphologically[2], chemically[3] and genetically[4] speaking, the species is exceptionally variable. Only one type is commercially cultivated: the so-called Red type or Rocklands type – originally from the Pakhuis Pass area. Rooibos tea should not be confused with honeybush tea (*Cyclopia* species). Rooibos tea is a traditional beverage of the Khoi-descended people of the Clanwilliam region in the Cape, and is one of only a few indigenous plants that have become an important commercial crop[5]. Local people harvested the wild plants and produced tea by a process of cutting (the twigs and leaves) with axes, bruising them with wooden hammers, fermenting the product in heaps and finally drying it.

PLANT PARTS USED. Leaves and twigs are used.

MEDICINAL USES. The main medicinal use of rooibos tea is as a milk substitute for infants who are prone to colic[6]. It is considered to have significant antispasmodic activity[7]. Rooibos tea is also popular as a health beverage, because it contains no harmful stimulants and is totally devoid of caffeine[8]. There is growing evidence that flavonoids contribute substantially to a reduction in heart disease and other ailments associated with ageing. Rooibos tea is also used as an ingredient in cosmetics, as there have been claims that it is beneficial in cases of eczema.

PREPARATION AND DOSAGE. Rooibos tea is popular as a health beverage, prepared and used in much the same way as black tea. It has gained popularity as an excellent iced tea.

ACTIVE INGREDIENTS. The health properties of rooibos tea are ascribed mainly to the low tannin content, the high levels of minerals and the free-radical capturing properties of some unique flavonoids[3], of which the *C*-glucoside dihydrochalcones aspalathin and nothofagin are the most important[9].

DISTRIBUTION. The plant is endemic to the western parts of the Cape[1], and occurs naturally from the Cape Peninsula northwards to Nieuwoudtville. Commercial cultivation is centred in the Nieuwoudtville, Clanwilliam, Citrusdal and Piquetberg districts.

Aspalathin

Nothofagin

1. **Dahlgren, R. 1988.** Crotalarieae (*Aspalathus*). In: *Flora of Southern Africa* 16,3(6): 1-430. Botanical Research Institute, Pretoria.
2. **Dahlgren, R. 1968.** Revision of the genus *Aspalathus* II. The species with ericoid and pinoid leaflets. Subgenus *Nortieria*. With remarks on Rooibos Tea Cultivation. *Bot. Notiser* 121: 165-208.
3. **Rabe, C. *et al.* 1994.** Phenolic metabolites from Rooibos Tea (*Aspalathus linearis*). *Phytochem.* 35: 1559-1565.
4. **Van der Bank, M. *et al.* 1995.** Biochemical genetic variation in four wild populations of *Aspalathus linearis* (Rooibos Tea). *Biochem. Syst. Ecol.* 23(3): 257-262.
5. **Van der Walt, A. & Machado, R. 1992.** *New Marketing Success Stories.* Southern Book Publishers, Halfway House.
6. **Rooi Tea Control Board. 1973.** *Eighty Rooi Tea Wonders.* Muller & Retief, Cape Town.
7. **Snyckers, F.O. & Salemi, G. 1974.** Studies of South African medicinal plants. Part. 1. Quercetin as the major in vitro active component of rooibos tea. *J. S. Afr. Chem. Inst.* 27: 5-7.
8. **Blommaert, K.L.J. & Steenkamp, J. 1978.** Tannien- en moontlike kafeïeninhoud van Rooibostee, *Aspalathus linearis. Agroplantae* 10: 49.
9. **Joubert, E. 1996.** HPLC quantification of the dihydrochalcones, aspalathin and nothofagin in rooibos tea (*Aspalathus linearis*) as affected by processing. *Food Chemistry* 55: 403-411.

Aspalathus linearis plantation

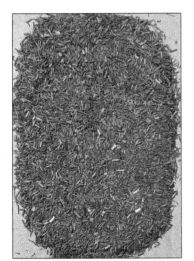

The dry product from *Aspalathus linearis*, known as rooibos tea

Flower and green fruit of *Aspalathus linearis*

Examples of the packed product

ASTER BAKERANUS

Asteraceae

> **udlutshana (Zulu); unozixekana (Xhosa); phoa (Sotho)**

BOTANICAL DESCRIPTION. The plant is a herbaceous perennial with one to several annual stems of up to about half a metre in height, developing from a perennial woody base[1]. The leaves are about 80 mm long and variable in size and shape, with coarse hairs on the surface and sparse, minute teeth along the margins. The flower heads are blue, mauve or rarely white[1]. *A. bakeranus* is closely related to *A. pleiocephalus* and *A. harveyanus* but can be distinguished from these species by the presence of hairs on the bracts around the flower head[1].

PLANT PARTS USED. The dense cluster of roots, each of which is elongated and tapering on both ends (fusiform), is used.

MEDICINAL USES. As a traditional headache remedy, the dried roots are powdered and used as snuff to induce sneezing[2]. *A. muricatus* has been used for the same purpose[3]. The roots may also be pounded and mixed with water to clean the nostrils[2]. Decoctions are strongly emetic and have a purgative action[3]. It has been used as a snake-bite remedy and for venereal disease and stomach complaints. It may also be injected as an enema to treat severe stomach pain and intestinal parasites[3].

PREPARATION AND DOSAGE. Dried, powdered roots are snuffed or decoctions are taken orally. The medicine is most often applied as an enema, but details are not available.

ACTIVE INGREDIENTS. The roots contain mainly diterpenoids of the kaurene type, of which *ent*-kaurenic acid and the corresponding aldehyde are the main compounds, together with smaller quantities of triterpenoids, such as friedelin[4]. A monoterpenoid, 6,7-dihydro-6,7-ocimenediol was found in the leaves[4]. The pain-killing and anti-inflammatory activity[5] can possibly be ascribed to the terpenoids (see *Alepidea*). The roots are reported to be poisonous[3] but the cause of the toxicity is unknown.

PHARMACOLOGICAL EFFECTS. Anti-inflammatory activity has been induced in rats[5] but there is no published evidence for the reported analgesic properties[2] and toxicity[3].

DISTRIBUTION. *A. bakeranus* is widely distributed in the grassland areas of South Africa, from George in the Eastern Cape eastwards and northwards as far as Tanzania[1].

ent-16-Kauren-18-oic-acid
(*ent*-Kaurenic acid)

Friedelin

6,7-Dihydro-6,7-ocimenediol

1. **Hilliard, O.M. 1977.** *Compositae in Natal.* University of Natal Press, Pietermaritzburg.
2. **Hutchings, A. & Van Staden, J. 1994.** Plants used for stress-related ailments in traditional Zulu, Xhosa and Sotho medicine. Part 1: Plants used for headaches. *J. Ethnopharmacol.* 43: 89-124.
3. **Watt, J.M. & Breyer-Brandwijk, M.G. 1962.** *The Medicinal and Poisonous Plants of Southern and Eastern Africa.* 2nd edition. Livingstone, London.
4. **Tsankova, E. & Bohlman, F. 1983.** A monoterpene from *Aster bakeranus*. *Phytochemistry* 22: 1285-1286.
5. **Benoit, P.S. et al. 1976.** Biological and phytochemical evaluation of plants, 24. Anti-inflammatory evaluation of 163 species of plants. *Lloydia* 39: 160-171.

Aster bakeranus

Fresh roots of *Aster harveyanus*

Leaves and flower heads of *Aster bakeranus*

Dried roots of *Aster bakeranus*

BALANITES MAUGHAMII

Balanitaceae

umgobandlovu (Zulu); umnulu (Swazi); fakkelhout, groendoring (Afrikaans); torchwood (English)

BOTANICAL DESCRIPTION. Torchwood is a relatively tall tree of up to 20 metres in height and occurs in open savanna, often along rivers. The bark is grey and smooth. Distinctive characteristics are the unevenly forked, green thorns and the paired leaflets, which are densely velvety when young, but become smooth on the upper surface at maturity. Inconspicuous greenish-yellow flowers are produced in spring, followed by edible, yellowish fruit in summer[1,2,3].

PLANT PARTS USED. The stem bark or root bark is used.

MEDICINAL USES. The roots are a popular ingredient of ritual emetics[4,5] and the bark is reported to be applied in the form of cutaneous implantations to strengthen the body. The fruits are lethal to freshwater snails and other organisms and have been recommended for the eradication of bilharzia[4].

Balanites species are potential sources of starting materials for the steroid industry[6,7]. The fruits are used to treat coughs[8].

PREPARATION AND DOSAGE. The root bark is mixed with other ingredients for use as emetics but details are not available.

ACTIVE INGREDIENTS. *Balanites* species contain numerous steroidal glycosides derived from diosgenin and structurally related sapogenins[9]. An example is cryptogenin.

PHARMACOLOGICAL EFFECTS. Activities that have been ascribed to saponins include anti-fungal, anti-viral, spermicidal and molluscicidal effects[7].

DISTRIBUTION. *B. maughamii* is confined to the extreme eastern parts of South Africa[10] but has a much wider distribution in tropical Africa.

Cryptogenin

1. **Palmer, E. & Pitman, J. 1972.** *Trees of Southern Africa*. Balkema, Cape Town.
2. **Coates Palgrave, K. 1977.** *Trees of Southern Africa*. Struik, Cape Town.
3. **Van Wyk, P. 1995.** *Field Guide to the Trees of the Kruger National Park*. Struik, Cape Town.
4. **Watt, J.M. & Breyer-Brandwijk, M.G. 1962.** *The Medicinal and Poisonous Plants of Southern and Eastern Africa*. 2nd edition. Livingstone, London.
5. **Ngwenya, A. 1994.** Tribute to an amateur: Jobe Mafuleka. Part 1. *Plantlife* 11: 13.
6. **Bruneton, J. 1995.** *Pharmacognosy, Phytochemistry, Medicinal Plants*. Intercept, Hampshire.
7. **Iwu, M.M. 1993.** *Handbook of African Medicinal Plants*. CRC Press, Boca Raton.
8. **Iwu, M.M. 1986.** *African ethnomedicine*. USP Press, Enugu, Nigeria.
9. **Dictionary of Natural Products on CD-ROM, release 4:2 (1996).** Chapman & Hall, London.
10. **Von Breitenbach, F. 1986.** *National List of Indigenous Trees*. Dendrological Foundation, Pretoria.

Balanites maughamii

Leaves and thorny branches of *Balanites maughamii*

Fruit of *Balanites maughamii*

Trunk of *Balanites maughamii* from which bark has been harvested

BALLOTA AFRICANA

Lamiaceae

> **kattekruid, kattekruie (Afrikaans)**

BOTANICAL DESCRIPTION. Kattekruie is an erect or spreading shrublet of up to 1,2 m in height. The slender stems bear sparsely hairy, opposite leaves with a rounded shape and a conspicuous pattern of sunken veins. The pink or purple flowers appear in dense clusters above each leaf pair. Even when no open flowers are present, the plant can still be recognised by the persistent calyx with its 10 to 20 teeth and the aromatic, somewhat drooping foliage[1].

PLANT PARTS USED. The leaves are used.

MEDICINAL USES. The medicinal use of this plant probably originates from the Khoi (and Nama) cultures, who used the leaves (often with the addition of various *Salvia* species) to treat fevers and measles[2]. Children along the west coast used to dance around the plant, singing "kattekruie, kattekruie, daar staan die kattekruie, dis 'n lekker kruie" ("kattekruie, kattekruie, there is the kattekruie, what a lovely herb"). To this day, infusions or brandy tinctures are popular in the Western Cape for the treatment of colds and influenza, asthma, bronchitis, hoarseness, heart trouble, hysteria, insomnia, typhoid fever, headaches, liver problems, piles and as a foot bath for arthritis[2,3,4,5,6]. It is interesting to note that the closely re-lated European species, *B. nigra* (black horehound) is traditionally used in France[7] for minor cases of insomnia and the symptomatic treatment of coughs. In Britain, *B. nigra* has been used as an antispasmodic, stimulant and vermifuge[8].

PREPARATION AND DOSAGE. The leaves are steeped in hot water for 10 minutes[4] and taken as a tea. An alcoholic tincture[5] may also be prepared, of which a single tot is taken in the evening, particularly for the treatment of haemorrhoids[6].

ACTIVE INGREDIENTS. *B. nigra* contains several diterpenoid lactones of the labdane type[7,9,10,11] such as ballotenol. These diterpenoids are similar to marrubiin (see *Leonotis*). It is not known if *B. africana* produces similar compounds.

PHARMACOLOGICAL EFFECTS. The traditional use of *Ballota* species suggests antispasmodic and sedative effects[7], but there is no reliable published information (see *Leonotis*).

DISTRIBUTION. *B. africana*, the only indigenous species of the genus, is widely distributed in the western and southern parts of South Africa[1].

Ballotenol

1. **Codd, L.E. 1985.** Lamiaceae. *Flora of Southern Africa* 28(4). Botanical Research Institute, Pretoria.
2. **Watt, J.M. & Breyer-Brandwijk, M.G. 1962.** *The Medicinal and Poisonous Plants of Southern and Eastern Africa*. 2nd edition. Livingstone, London.
3. **Smith, C.A. 1966.** Common Names of South African Plants. Memoirs of the Botanical Survey of South Africa 35.
4. **Rood, B. 1994.** *Uit die Veldapteek*. Tafelberg, Cape Town.
5. **Cillié, A.M. 1992.** *Kruie op Witblits, Rate, Resepte en Feite*, pp. 43. Unpublished notes, Worcester Museum.
6. **Dykman, E.J. 1891.** *Kook-, Koek- en Resepte Boek*. Paarlse Drukpers Maatskappy, Paarl.
7. **Bruneton, J. 1995.** *Pharmacognosy, Phytochemistry, Medicinal Plants*. Intercept, Hampshire.
8. **Grieve, M. 1967.** *A Modern Herbal*. Hafner, London.
9. **Savona, G. et al. 1976.** Structure of ballotinone, a diterpenoid from *Ballota nigra*. *J. Chem. Soc., Perkin Trans. I*, 1976: 1607-1609.
10. **Savona, G. et al. 1977.** Structures of three new diterpenoids from *Ballota* species. *J. Chem. Soc., Perkin Trans. I*, 1977: 322-324.
11. **Savona, G. et al. 1977.** The structure of ballotenol, a new diterpenoid from *Ballota nigra*. *J. Chem. Soc., Perkin Trans. I*, 1977: 497-499.

Ballota africana

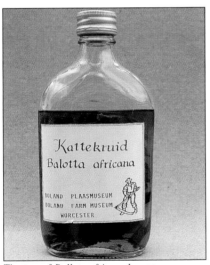

Tincture of *Ballota africana* leaves

Leaves and flowers of *Ballota africana*

Dried stems and leaves of *Ballota africana*

BERSAMA LUCENS

Melianthaceae

isindiyandiya (Xhosa, Zulu); undiyaza (Zulu); glossy bersama (English);
blinkblaarwitessenhout (Afrikaans)

BOTANICAL DESCRIPTION. B. lucens is a shrub or small tree with dense leaf clusters at the tips of the branchlets. The leaves each have three to seven glossy, green, hairless leaflets. Whitish flowers are borne in erect clusters in early spring, followed by rounded hairy capsules in summer. Each capsule contains four seeds, each with a yellowish-green, fleshy aril[1,2]. B. tysoniana has more than seven leaflets per leaf and the capsule has an uneven, wart-like surface[1,2].

PLANT PARTS USED. Bark and roots are used.

MEDICINAL USES. The stem bark and/or roots are used to relieve menstrual pain[3,4,5] and to treat impotency and infertility[3]. It is also ground to a fine powder and snuffed to treat headaches[4,5] and strokes[5]. A tincture of the bark is used as an emetic to calm nervous disorders[5] and it is interesting to note that the bark of the closely related B. tysoniana has been used to treat hysteria[6].

PREPARATION AND DOSAGE. Bersama species should be treated with caution, as they are known to contain highly toxic heart glycosides[7].

ACTIVE INGREDIENTS. The poisonous compounds in Bersama are heart glycosides, such as melianthugenin, for example, which has been isolated from B. abyssinica[7].

PHARMACOLOGICAL EFFECTS. The toxic effects of heart glycosides are well known but it is not known if the relief of pain is also due to these compounds.

DISTRIBUTION. B. lucens is fairly widely distributed along the eastern parts of South Africa[8].

Melianthugenin

1. Palmer, E. & Pitman, J. 1972. *Trees of Southern Africa.* Balkema, Cape Town.
2. Coates Palgrave, K. 1977. *Trees of Southern Africa.* Struik, Cape Town.
3. Watt, J.M. & Breyer-Brandwijk, M.G. 1962. *The Medicinal and Poisonous Plants of Southern and Eastern Africa.* 2nd edition. Livingstone, London.
4. Pujol, J. 1990. *Naturafrica – the Herbalist Handbook.* Jean Pujol Natural Healers' Foundation, Durban.
5. Hutchings, A. & Van Staden, J. 1994. Plants used for stress-related ailments in traditional Zulu, Xhosa and Sotho medicine. Part 1: Plants used for headaches. *J. Ethnopharmacol.* 43: 89-124.
6. Watt, J.M. 1967. African plants potentially useful in mental health. *Lloydia* 30: 1-22.
7. Dictionary of Natural Products on CD-ROM, release 4:2 (1996). Chapman & Hall, London.
8. Von Breitenbach, F. 1986. *National List of Indigenous Trees.* Dendrological Foundation, Pretoria.

Flowers of *Bersama lucens*

Fruits of *Bersama lucens*

Bark of *Bersama lucens*

Fruits of *Bersama tysoniana*

BERULA ERECTA

Apiaceae

> **tandpynwortel (Afrikaans); water parsnip (English); lehlatso (Sotho)**

BOTANICAL DESCRIPTION. This is a herbaceous plant common in wet areas. It is often found in mud banks along rivers, sometimes growing in shallow water. The leaf-bearing stems are connected to each other below the ground by numerous thin, white, root-like rhizomes. The leaves are compound, with numerous toothed leaflets. The small, white flowers are arranged in characteristic umbels, typical of the family Apiaceae. There is only one species of the genus *Berula*, but the southern African form has been described as a distinct subspecies, namely *B. erecta* subsp. *thunbergii*[1]. It differs from the other subspecies in Europe and Asia in the more regular and less deeply divided teeth of the leaflets. *B. erecta* may be confused with *Sium* species, but the latter have distinct ribs on the fruits[2].

PLANT PARTS USED. The rhizomes, generally referred to as "roots", are used.

MEDICINAL USES. As the Afrikaans common name suggests, the rhizome has been highly regarded as a remedy for toothache[3,4].

PREPARATION AND DOSAGE. The fresh rhizome ("wortel" = root) is held in the mouth or chewed[3]. It has also been used as a body wash to treat headaches[3].

ACTIVE INGREDIENTS. Berulide, a triglyceride, and erectene, a long-chain diene, have been isolated from the rhizomes of *B. erecta*[5].

PHARMACOLOGICAL EFFECTS. The plant is reported to be poisonous to cattle under certain conditions[3]. The claimed analgesic and anaesthetic effects could not be confirmed experimentally[5].

DISTRIBUTION. *B. erecta* is widely distributed in Africa, Europe, Asia and North America. The subspecies *thunbergii* is confined to southern Africa[1] and is widespread throughout the region.

$$CH_3(CH_2)_{14}COO-\overset{\displaystyle CH_2-OCO-(CH_2)_7CH=CHCH_2CH=CH(CH_2)_4CH_3}{\underset{\displaystyle CH_2-OCO-(CH_2)_7CH=CHCH_2CH=CH(CH_2)_4CH_3}{C}}$$

Berulide

$$CH_3CH_2CH=CHCH_2CH=CH(CH_2)_{14}CH_3$$

Erectene

1. **Burtt, B.L. 1991.** Umbelliferae of Southern Africa: an introduction and annotated checklist. *Edinb. J. Bot.* 48: 133-282.
2. **Cannon, J.F.M. 1978.** Umbelliferae. In: E. Launert (ed.), *Flora Zambesiaca* 4. Flora Zambesiaca Management Committee, London.
3. **Watt, J.M. & Breyer-Brandwijk, M.G. 1962.** *The Medicinal and Poisonous Plants of Southern and Eastern Africa.* 2nd edition. Livingstone, London.
4. **Smith, C.A. 1966.** *Common Names of South African Plants. Memoirs of the Botanical Survey of South Africa* 35.
5. **Durand, W.C. & Breytenbach, J.C. 1988.** A pharmacochemical investigation of *Berula erecta*. *S. Afr. J. Sci.* 84: 297-299.

Berula erecta

Rhizomes of *Berula erecta*

BOOPHANE DISTICHA

Amaryllidaceae

---

incwadi (Xhosa); incotha (Zulu); leshoma (Southern Sotho, Tswana); muwandwe (Shona); gifbol (Afrikaans); bushman poison bulb (English)

BOTANICAL DESCRIPTION. This bulbous plant has large, strap-like leaves arranged in a very distinctive fan-shaped manner. The bulb is partly exposed above the surface of the ground and has numerous papery scales around the fleshy part. The rounded inflorescence has numerous pink flowers all at an equal distance from the main flowering stalk. When dry, the inflorescence rolls about in the wind, distributing the seeds.

PLANT PARTS USED. The bulb scales are used.

MEDICINAL USES. The dry outer scales of the bulb are used as an outer dressing after circumcision[1] and are also applied to boils[1] or septic wounds (often mixed with water, milk or oil[2]) to alleviate pain and to "draw out" the pus. Weak decoctions of the bulb scales are administered by mouth or as an enema[3] for various complaints such as headaches, abdominal pain, weakness and eye conditions[1]. In the Karoo near Touws River there is an old belief that sleeping on a mattress filled with bulb scales will relieve hysteria and insomnia[4]. Very weak decoctions of the bulb scales are used as an effective sedative. Higher doses induce visual hallucinations, which are sometimes used for divination and even higher doses can be fatal.

PREPARATION AND DOSAGE. Gifbol and other Amaryllidaceae contain extremely toxic alkaloids and several human deaths have been recorded. Internal use is dangerous and should be avoided.

ACTIVE INGREDIENTS. Numerous alkaloids have been isolated from *B. disticha*, including buphanidrin, undulatin, buphanisine, nerbowdin and others[5]. Buphanidrin is usually one of the main compounds.

PHARMACOLOGICAL EFFECTS. Amaryllidaceae alkaloids are known mainly for their extreme toxicity, but also show narcotic, hypotensive, vasodilatory and analgesic activity[6]. The analgesic effect of buphanidrin is at a level of 6,2 mg/kg in mice and the lethal dose of 8,9 mg/kg makes it much too toxic for therapeutic use[6]. An important traditional use of the gifbol is as a source of arrow poison[7,8]. Plants growing in the shade are said to be more potent than those growing in full sun[7].

DISTRIBUTION. *B. disticha* is widely distributed in the southern and eastern parts of South Africa and further north into tropical Africa. It is usually found in open grassland.

Buphanidrin

---

1. **Watt, J.M. & Breyer-Brandwijk, M.G. 1962.** *The Medicinal and Poisonous Plants of Southern and Eastern Africa.* 2nd edition. Livingstone, London.
2. **Rood, B. 1994.** *Uit die Veldapteek.* Tafelberg, Cape Town.
3. **Hutchings, A. & Van Staden, J. 1994.** Plants used for stress-related ailments in traditional Zulu, Xhosa and Sotho medicine. Part 1: Plants used for headaches. *J. Ethnopharmacol.* 43: 89-124.
4. **Watt, J.M. 1967.** African plants potentially useful in mental health. *Lloydia* 30: 1-22.
5. **Dictionary of Natural Products on CD-ROM, release 4:2 (1996).** Chapman & Hall, London.
6. **Eddy, N.B. *et al.* 1950.** *J. Pharmacol. Exptl Therap.* 98: 121.
7. **Forbes, V.S. (ed.) 1986.** *Carl Peter Thunberg Travels at the Cape of Good Hope 1772-1775.* Van Riebeeck Society, Cape Town.
8. **Neuwinger, H.D. 1994.** *Afrikanische Arzneipflanzen und Jagdgifte.* Wissenschaftliche Verlagsgesellschaft, Stuttgart.

Boophane disticha

Bulb scales of *Boophane disticha*

Flowering plant of *Boophane disticha*

Bulb of *Boophane disticha*

BOWIEA VOLUBILIS

Hyacinthaceae

igibisila, gifisila (Zulu); umagaqana (Xhosa); knolklimop (Afrikaans);
climbing potato (English)

BOTANICAL DESCRIPTION. This plant has a green-ish-white, fleshy tuberous bulb, without any papery or fibrous outer scales. The upper ends of the fleshy scales form distinctive rings around the middle of the bulb, from where the thin green, leafless climbing and creeping flowering stems arise. The flowers are small, greenish in colour and rather inconspicuous.

PLANT PARTS USED. The bulb or bulb scales are used.

MEDICINAL USES. Igibisila has been used to treat a wide variety of ailments[1], including headaches[2]. A hot water extract of the roasted bulb is taken as a purgative[1]. The fresh bulb is taken for oedema (dropsy) and infertility in women[1]. The fresh juice may be rubbed into the skin of a sick person or a decoction applied as a lotion for sore eyes[1]. A hot water extract of the fresh outer bulb scales is a Zulu remedy for ascites, sterility and bladder complaints[1,3,4].

PREPARATION AND DOSAGE. All parts of the plant are extremely poisonous and internal use is potentially lethal.

ACTIVE INGREDIENTS. Several cardiac glycosides have been found in *B. volubilis*. They are all glycosides of bovogenin A and structurally related bufa-dienolides[5].

PHARMACOLOGICAL EFFECTS. The main pharma-codynamic properties of cardiac glycosides are their ability to increase the force of heart muscle contraction, hence its therapeutic benefit in congestive heart failure. Toxic concentrations of cardiac glycosides can cause abnormalities of cardiac rhythm and disturbances of atrio-ventricular conduction, including complete atrio-ventricular block[6].

DISTRIBUTION. *B. volubilis* is widely distributed in the eastern parts of South Africa.

Bovogenin A

1. **Watt, J.M. & Breyer-Brandwijk, M.G. 1962.** *The Medicinal and Poisonous Plants of Southern and Eastern Africa*. 2nd edition. Livingstone, London.
2. **Hutchings, A. & Van Staden, J. 1994.** Plants used for stress-related ailments in traditional Zulu, Xhosa and Sotho medicine. Part 1: Plants used for headaches. *J. Ethnopharmacol.* 43: 89-124.
3. **Pujol, J. 1990.** *Naturafrica – the Herbalist Handbook*. Jean Pujol Natural Healers' Foundation, Durban.
4. **Hutchings, A. 1996.** *Zulu Medicinal Plants*. Natal University Press, Pietermaritzburg.
5. **Dictionary of Natural Products on CD-ROM, release 4:2 (1996).** Chapman & Hall, London.
6. **Goodman, L.S. & Gilman, A. 1992.** *The Pharmacological Basis of Therapeutics*. 8th edition. Pergamon Press, New York.

Bowiea volubilis

Flowers of *Bowiea volubilis*

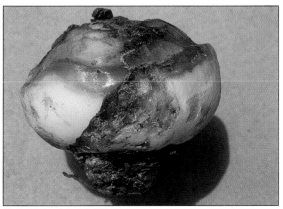

Bulb of *Bowiea volubilis*

BULBINE NATALENSIS

Asphodelaceae

---

ibhucu (Zulu); rooiwortel (Afrikaans)

BOTANICAL DESCRIPTION. This species is an aloe-like plant with a rosette of fleshy, thornless, yellowish-green leaves. The yellow flowers are borne in elongated clusters on long, thin flowering stems. The hairy stamens are an easy way to distinguish *Bulbine* species from other similar plants. There are several species that are used medicinally, such as *B. asphodeloides* (Afrikaans: "wildekopiva"), *B. alooides* (Afrikaans: "rooistorm"), *B. frutescens* (Afrikaans: "balsemkopiva") and *B. narcissifolia* (Afrikaans: "geelslangkop"). *B. natalensis* is known to many people as *B. latifolia*, but the latter is a distinct species from the Eastern Cape Province, with dark green, firm-textured leaves and densely grouped flowers. It often co-occurs with *B. natalensis* in the Eastern Cape and is also used medicinally.

PLANT PARTS USED. The fresh leaves and roots are used.

MEDICINAL USES. The leaf sap of *Bulbine* species is widely used for the treatment of wounds, burns, rashes, itches, ringworm, cracked lips[1,2,3] and herpes. The roots of *B. natalensis, B. latifolia, B. alooides, B. asphodeloides* and *B. narcissifolia* are taken orally in the form of infusions to quell vomiting and diarrhoea[3] and also to treat convulsions, venereal diseases, diabetes, rheumatism, urinary complaints and blood disorders[1,2,3].

PREPARATION AND DOSAGE. Leaf sap is applied directly to the skin or in the form of a warm poultice. For internal use, an infusion of the roots (or sometimes a brandy tincture[1]) is taken two or three times a day.

ACTIVE INGREDIENTS. Stems and roots of *Bulbine* species contain anthraquinones such as chrysophanol and knipholone[4,5], but these compounds are probably of minor importance in the healing of wounds.

PHARMACOLOGICAL EFFECTS. Chrysophanol has antibacterial properties[6]. The healing effect is likely to be due mainly to glycoproteins in the leaf gel, such as aloctin A and aloctin B, which have been found in the leaf gel of *Aloe arborescens*[7].

DISTRIBUTION. *B. natalensis* is widely distributed in the eastern and northern parts of South Africa.

Chrysophanol   Knipholone

1. **Watt, J.M. & Breyer-Brandwijk, M.G. 1962.** *The Medicinal and Poisonous Plants of Southern and Eastern Africa.* 2nd edition. Livingstone, London.
2. **Rood, B. 1994.** *Uit die Veldapteek.* Tafelberg, Cape Town.
3. **Pujol, J. 1990.** *Naturafrica – the Herbalist Handbook.* Jean Pujol Natural Healers' Foundation, Durban.
4. **Van Staden, L.F. & Drewes, S.E. 1994.** Knipholone from *Bulbine latifolia* and *Bulbine frutescens. Phytochemistry* 35: 685-686.
5. **Van Wyk, B-E. *et al.* 1995.** Chemotaxonomic significance of anthraquinones in the roots of Asphodeloideae (Asphodelaceae). *Biochem. Syst. Ecol.* 23: 277-281.
6. **Bruce, W.G.G. 1975.** Medicinal properties in the aloe. *Excelsa* 5: 57-68.
7. **Suzuki, I.** *Antiinflammatory agent.* Eur. Pat. Apl. 25, 873 (CIA61K35/78), 01 April 1981.

Bulbine natalensis

Flowers of *Bulbine frutescens*

Broken leaf of *Bulbine frutescens*, showing the leaf gel

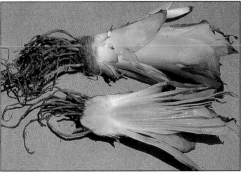

Bulbine natalensis as sold on the muti markets

CANNABIS SATIVA

Cannabaceae (or Cannabinaceae)

> **dagga (Afrikaans); marijuana (English); umya (Xhosa);**
> **matokwane (Sotho); nsangu (Zulu)**

BOTANICAL DESCRIPTION. This well-known narcotic plant is an erect annual herb of up to four metres in height[1,2]. The somewhat drooping leaves are divided into several (three to eleven) leaflets, all radiating from the same point. Each leaflet is up to 150 mm long, pale green, minutely hairy, with distinctly toothed margins. Male and female flowers are borne on different plants. Both are greenish-yellow and inconspicuous. This ancient crop plant is probably indigenous to temperate Asia and has been domesticated since the early history of mankind[3,4]. Two groups of cultivars are distinguished: plants grown for fibre and seed oil (subsp. *sativa*) and those grown for their intoxicant potential (subsp. *indica*)[1].

PLANT PARTS USED. The female flowering tops and associated leaves, commonly referred to as marijuana, are smoked. The dried resin produced by glands (mainly on the flowers of the female plant) is known as "hashish". This product can be smoked or eaten and has the most powerful effect. In South Africa, however, the name "hashish" has not come into general use[5].

MEDICINAL USES. In South Africa, the plant was an early treatment for snake bite, malaria and blood poisoning[5]. *Cannabis* was still included in the 1949 British Pharmaceutical Codex[6] and tinctures and extracts have been used to a limited extent. Nowadays, it is used in the treatment of glaucoma, to alleviate the nausea caused by chemotherapy and to stimulate appetite and a sense of well-being in AIDS patients. It is also used in the treatment of asthma, depression and numerous other conditions[4,7].

PREPARATION AND DOSAGE. The product is usually smoked. The main active compound, THC (see below), may be administered orally, intravenously or by topical application.

ACTIVE INGREDIENTS. More than 90 chemical compounds have been described in *Cannabis*[8], of which the so-called cannabinoids (phenolic terpenoids) are the most interesting. These compounds are absent from the seeds and stems, but occur in the leaves and particularly in the bracts and the resin. The tetrahydrocannabinols, particularly Δ^9-THC and Δ^1-THC are the main psychotropic substances[7].

PHARMACOLOGICAL EFFECTS. Despite the low toxicity, THC has powerful effects on the central nervous system, including euphoria, relaxation, loss of coordination, slow speech and, with chronic use, a loss of motivation. THC is a bronchodilator, induces hypotension and decreases intra-ocular pressure[7].

DISTRIBUTION. *C. sativa* is widely distributed in South Africa[2]. Cultivation is illegal but the plant commonly grows as a weed along roadsides and in gardens and abandoned fields.

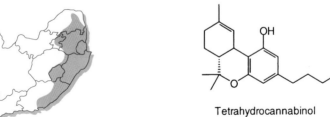

Tetrahydrocannabinol

1. **Small, E. & Cronquist, A. 1976.** A practical and natural taxonomy for *Cannabis. Taxon* 25: 405-435.
2. **Henderson, M. & Anderson, J.G. 1966.** *Common Weeds in South Africa. Memoirs of the Botanical Survey of South Africa* 37.
3. **Small, E. 1995.** Hemp. Chapter 9 in Smartt, J. & Simmonds, N.W. (eds), *Evolution of Crop Plants*, 2nd edition, pp. 28-32. Longman, London.
4. **Robinson, R. 1996.** *The Great Book of Hemp*. Park Street Press, Vermont (see numerous scientific references on pages 218-233).
5. **Watt, J.M. & Breyer-Brandwijk, M.G. 1962.** *The Medicinal and Poisonous Plants of Southern and Eastern Africa*. 2nd edition. Livingstone, London.
6. **Martindale 1958.** *The Extra Pharmacopoeia*. Pharmaceutical Press, London.
7. **Bruneton, J. 1995.** *Pharmacognosy, Phytochemistry, Medicinal Plants*. Intercept, Hampshire (see references cited therein).
8. **Dictionary of Natural Products on CD-ROM, release 4:2 (1996).** Chapman & Hall, London.

Cannabis sativa

Flowers of *Cannabis sativa*

Cannabis sativa product – dried flowering stems and seeds

CAPPARIS TOMENTOSA

Capparaceae

iqwaningi, umabusane (Zulu); gwambadzi, mubadali (Venda);
woolly caper-bush (English); wollerige kapperbos (Afrikaans)

BOTANICAL DESCRIPTION. This popular medicinal plant is usually a scrambling shrub and rarely becomes a small tree of up to 10 metres in height[1]. The young twigs and leaves are yellowish-green and covered in soft, velvety hairs. The oblong leaves are about 50 by 20 mm long and there is a pair of sharp, hooked thorns (modified stipules) at the base of each leaf where it is attached to the stem. The flowers are white or pinkish and rather showy, with masses of stamens. The rounded orange or pink fruits are characteristically stalked, with a greyish, fleshy fruit pulp surrounding the seeds[1].

PLANT PARTS USED. The roots or root bark are used.

MEDICINAL USES. *Capparis* roots are a popular medicine for a variety of ailments, mainly rheumatism, but also insanity, snake-bite, chest pains, jaundice, malaria, headache, coughs and pneumonia[2,3,4,5,6], and as a laxative. The use of several species of *Capparis* in different parts of the world suggests that further study and evaluation would be worthwhile[5].

PREPARATION AND DOSAGE. The root is boiled in water and half a cupful of the infusion is taken three times a day[3] for coughs and chest pain. The powdered, burnt root is rubbed into skin scarifications[2] for the relief of headache[2]. In view of reported human poisoning[2], the indiscriminate use of this plant is not recommended.

ACTIVE INGREDIENTS. Two alkaloids are known from *C. tomentosa* and are likely to be at least partly responsible for the beneficial and toxic effects: stachydrine[7] and 3-hydroxy-4-methoxy-3-methyl-oxindole[8]. The isolated oxindole compound had weak antispasmodic activity[8].

PHARMACOLOGICAL EFFECTS. Anti-inflammatory and anticonvulsive activity is ascribed to some *Capparis* species[5]. Stachydrine-containing plants are widely used against rheumatism and many other diseases[7].

DISTRIBUTION. *C. tomentosa* occurs naturally along the extreme eastern parts of South Africa[1].

Stachydrine   3-Hydroxy-4-methoxy-3-methyl-oxindole

1. **Coates Palgrave, K. 1977.** *Trees of Southern Africa.* Struik, Cape Town.
2. **Watt, J.M. & Breyer-Brandwijk, M.G. 1962.** *The Medicinal and Poisonous Plants of Southern and Eastern Africa.* 2nd edition. Livingstone, London.
3. **Pujol, J. 1990.** *Naturafrica – the Herbalist Handbook.* Jean Pujol Natural Healers' Foundation, Durban.
4. **Watt, J.M. 1967.** African plants potentially useful in mental health. *Lloydia* 30: 1-22.
5. **Hutchings, A. & Van Staden, J. 1994.** Plants used for stress-related ailments in traditional Zulu, Xhosa and Sotho medicine. Part 1: Plants used for headaches. *J. Ethnopharmacol.* 43: 89-124 (and references cited therein).
6. **Iwu, M.M. 1993.** *Handbook of African Medicinal Plants.* CRC Press, Boca Raton.
7. **Dictionary of Natural Products on CD-ROM, release 4:2 (1996).** Chapman & Hall, London.
8. **Dekker, T.G. *et al.* 1987.** An oxindole from the roots of *Capparis tomentosa*. *Phytochemistry* 26: 1845-1846.

Capparis tomentosa

The thorny, hairy stems of *Capparis tomentosa*

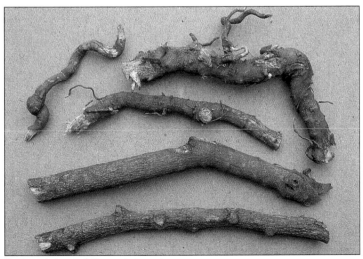

Roots and stems of *Capparis tomentosa*

CARPOBROTUS EDULIS

Mesembryanthemaceae

> **suurvy, perdevy, vyerank (Afrikaans);**
> **gaukum or ghaukum (Khoi); sour fig (English)**

BOTANICAL DESCRIPTION. This fleshy succulent is a perennial, mat-like creeper[1]. The smooth fleshy leaves are erect, triangular in cross-section and often reddish-green in colour. The yellow flowers are large and fleshy, and soon develop into a fragrant fleshy fruit with a jelly-like, somewhat slimy, sour-sweet fruit pulp which contains a multitude of small, brown seeds. The ripe fruits are often sold on street markets in the Cape and are popular for jams and curry dishes. The two most commonly used species are *C. edulis* and *C. acinaciformis*, for which the common names listed above are nowadays used indiscriminately[2]. Other medicinally important members of this family include *Sceletium* species (Afrikaans: "kougoed") and *Aptenia cordifolia* (Zulu: "ibohlololo").

PLANT PARTS USED. Leaf juice or leaf pulp are used.

MEDICINAL USES. The leaf juice is traditionally gargled to treat infections of the mouth and throat[3]. It is also taken orally for dysentery[3], digestive troubles, tuberculosis and as a diuretic and styptic[4]. It is highly astringent and is applied externally to treat eczema, wounds and burns[4,5]. It is also said to be effective against toothache, earache and oral and vaginal thrush.

PREPARATION AND DOSAGE. The fresh juice is taken orally or gargled. The leaf pulp may be applied to the skin to treat wounds and infections[4,5].

ACTIVE INGREDIENTS. The juice is said to be mildly antiseptic and highly astringent, so that the beneficial effects are probably due to the presence of tannins. It contains malic acid and citric acid[4].

PHARMACOLOGICAL EFFECTS. The biological properties of tannins are associated with their ability to form complexes with proteins (such as digestive enzymes and fungal or viral toxins)[6]. In addition to their antiseptic (antibacterial and antifungal) activity, tannins have a vasoconstrictor effect and reduce fluid loss from wounds and burns, thereby enhancing tissue regeneration[6].

DISTRIBUTION. *C. edulis* originally occurred in sandy areas in the Western Cape Province and along the Cape south coast to the Eastern Cape[1], but it is now commonly grown in many parts of the world, often as a ground cover to stabilise sandy banks. *C. acinaciformis* has a restricted distribution and is more or less confined to the Western Cape[1].

$$HOCHCOOH$$
$$CH_2COOH$$

Malic acid

$$CH_2COOH$$
$$HOCCOOH$$
$$CH_2COOH$$

Citric acid

1. **Wisura, W. & Glen, H.F. 1993.** The South African species of *Carpobrotus* (Mesembryanthema, Aizoaceae). *Contr. Bol. Herb.* 15: 76-107.
2. **Smith, C.A. 1966.** *Common Names of South African Plants. Memoirs of the Botanical Survey of South Africa 35.*
3. **Forbes, V.S. (ed.) 1986.** *Carl Peter Thunberg Travels at the Cape of Good Hope 1772-1775.* Van Riebeeck Society, Cape Town.
4. **Watt, J.M. & Breyer-Brandwijk, M.G. 1962.** *The Medicinal and Poisonous Plants of Southern and Eastern Africa.* 2nd edition. Livingstone, London.
5. **Rood, B. 1994.** *Uit die Veldapteek.* Tafelberg, Cape Town.
6. **Bruneton, J. 1995.** *Pharmacognosy, Phytochemistry, Medicinal Plants.* Intercept, Hampshire.

Leaves of *Carpobrotus edulis*

Flower and young fruit of *Carpobrotus edulis*

Carpobrotus acinaciformis

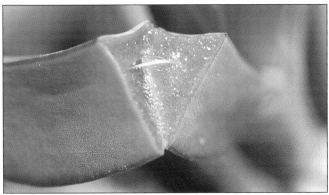

Broken leaf of *Carpobrotus edulis*, showing the fleshy interior

Ripe fruits of *Carpobrotus edulis*

CASSINE TRANSVAALENSIS

Celastraceae

**ingwavuma (Zulu); Transvaalsaffraan (Afrikaans);
Transvaal saffronwood (English)**

BOTANICAL DESCRIPTION. This plant is a shrub or small, multi-branched tree, usually around five metres in height but may reach 10 metres or more[1]. The bark is generally smooth and has a very characteristic pale, grey colour. Tufts of leaves are crowded on the ends of rigid side shoots. The leaves are oblong in shape, about 50 mm long and 20 mm wide, with a firm texture and conspicuous venation on the upper and lower surfaces. The leaf margin is sometimes toothed. Small and inconspicuous greenish flowers are produced in summer, followed by oblong, yellow to dark orange, berry-like fruits, which are edible.

PLANT PARTS USED. The bark is used.

MEDICINAL USES. An infusion of the bark is taken as a stomach cleanser and used as an enema for stomach ache and fever[2] and to treat intestinal cramps and diarrhoea[3]. The bark of *C. papillosa*, known as "isithundu", may also be used to clean the stomach[3]. The leaves are chewed and the juice swallowed for a sore throat[4].

PREPARATION AND DOSAGE. A teaspoon of powdered bark is boiled in water and no more than two cups are taken per day[3]. The powdered bark may also be licked from the palm of the hand, and washed down with a small amount of water – a technique known as "khotha"[3]. The bark is known to be toxic[4] so the dosage should be carefully controlled.

ACTIVE INGREDIENTS. The beneficial effects of the bark have been ascribed to its high tannin content[5]. An interesting phenolic compound, elaeocyanidin, has been isolated from both *C. transvaalensis* and *C. papillosa*[6]. The latter also contains gallotannins and ouratea proanthocyanidin A, and it is likely that these or similar compounds will be present in *C. transvaalensis*, together with the reported triterpenoids[6].

PHARMACOLOGICAL EFFECTS. Tannins are sometimes used for their astringent and antidiarrhoeal properties[7] so that the activity of *C. transvaalensis* and *C. papillosa* bark can at least partly be explained by the presence of these phenolic compounds.

DISTRIBUTION. The species is widely distributed in the north-eastern parts of South Africa. It occurs along the coastal parts of KwaZulu-Natal and in Mpumalanga, Gauteng and the Northern Province[1,8]. The Ingwavuma area in KwaZulu-Natal is named after this tree.

Elaeocyanidin   Ouratea proanthocyanidin A

1. **Coates Palgrave, K. 1977.** *Trees of Southern Africa.* Struik, Cape Town.
2. **Watt, J.M. & Breyer-Brandwijk, M.G. 1962.** *The Medicinal and Poisonous Plants of Southern and Eastern Africa.* 2nd edition. Livingstone, London.
3. **Pujol, J. 1990.** *Naturafrica – the Herbalist Handbook.* Jean Pujol Natural Healers' Foundation, Durban.
4. **Von Koenen, E. 1996.** *Heil-, Gift- u Essbare Pflanzen in Namibia.* Klaus Hess Verlag, Göttingen.
5. **Frost, C. 1941.** An investigation of the active constituents and pharmacological effects of the bark of the *Pseudocassine transvaalensis*. *S. Afr. Med. Sci.* 6: 57-58.
6. **Drewes, S.E. & Mashimbye, M.J. 1993.** Flavanoids and triterpenoids from *Cassine papillosa* and the absolute configuration of 11,11-dimethyl-1,3,8,10-tetrahydroxy-9-methoxypeltogynan. *Phytochemistry* 32: 1041-1044, and references cited therein.
7. **Bruneton, J. 1995.** *Pharmacognosy, Phytochemistry, Medicinal Plants.* Intercept, Hampshire.
8. **Von Breitenbach, F. 1986.** *National List of Indigenous Trees.* Dendrological Foundation, Pretoria.

Cassine transvaalensis

Bark of *Cassine transvaalensis*

Leaves and fruits of *Cassine transvaalensis*

CATHA EDULIS

Celastraceae

---

boesmanstee (Afrikaans); bushman's tea (English); khat (Arabic)

BOTANICAL DESCRIPTION. *C. edulis* is usually a shrub or small tree of two to five metres in height, but it may reach a height of more than 10 metres under favourable conditions. The bark is pale grey and smooth in young trees, but becomes brown and rough in old specimens. The leaves are bright green and shiny above, paler below, firm in texture, with an evenly toothed margin. They have a characteristic drooping appearance. The small white flowers, which usually appear in early winter (April to June) are arranged in dense clusters along the twigs. The fruit are small dry capsules.

PLANT PARTS USED. Fresh leaves (generally known as khat) are chewed.

MEDICINAL USES. Khat chewing is an ancient tradition of the Afro-Arabian culture, probably originating in the Harar area of Ethiopia[1,2]. The fresh leaves relieve fatigue and sleepiness and have a stimulating and euphoric effect. In South Africa there are early records of the use of the leaves as a stimulant[3,4], but also to treat coughs, asthma and other chest ailments[4,5]. The production, marketing and use of this plant is generally prohibited as a result of its potential for causing dependency[6].

PREPARATION AND DOSAGE. In the traditional khat-chewing areas of north-eastern Africa, twigs are harvested and the fresh leaves chewed within 24 hours[6]. In South Africa, as the common name suggests, infusions have been made of the leaves and twigs[3,4]. However, leaf chewing has also been recorded in South Africa[3].

ACTIVE INGREDIENTS. The stimulating effect of *Catha* is due to several phenethylamines (also known as khatamines), of which cathinone is the major compound in fresh leaves[7].

PHARMACOLOGICAL EFFECTS. Cathinone is closely related to ephedrine and amphetamine and has a similar pharmacological activity[8]. It reduces fatigue and increases mental power and communication skills, but also leads to hypertension and other potentially harmful effects[9]. Compulsive users may become aggressive and develop personality problems[8].

DISTRIBUTION. The plant is widely distributed in East Africa, as far north as Ethiopia, the horn of Africa and South Yemen[10]. In South Africa, it occurs from the Eastern Cape northwards to Mpumalanga and the Northern Province[11].

Cathinone   D-Amphetamine

1. **Getahun, A. & Krikorian, A.D. 1973.** Chat: coffee's rival from Harar, Ethiopia. *Econ. Bot.* 27: 353-389.
2. **Krikorian, A.D. 1983.** Khat and its use: an historic perspective. *Proceedings of the International Conference on Khat, Antananarivo, Madagascar, 17-21 January 1983*, pp. 7-71. International Council on Alcohol and Addictions, Lausanne, Switzerland.
3. **Smith, C.A. 1966.** *Common Names of South African Plants. Memoirs of the Botanical Survey of South Africa 35.*
4. **Watt, J.M. & Breyer-Brandwijk, M.G. 1962.** *The Medicinal and Poisonous Plants of Southern and Eastern Africa.* 2nd edition. Livingstone, London.
5. **Cawston, F.G. 1933.** Native medicines of Natal. *S.A. Med. J.*, 10 June 1933: 370-371.
6. **Bruneton, J. 1995.** *Pharmacognosy, Phytochemistry, Medicinal Plants.* Intercept, Hampshire.
7. **Crombie, L. *et al.* 1990.** Alkaloids of Khat (*Catha edulis*). In Brossi, A. (ed.), *The Alkaloids, Chemistry and Pharmacology*, vol. 39, pp. 139-164. Academic Press, San Diego.
8. Other side effects include anorexia, arrhythmia, hyperthermia, mydriasis and respiratory stimulation.
9. **Kalix, P. 1991.** The pharmacology of psycoactive alkaloids from *Ephedra* and *Catha. J. Ethnopharmacol.* 32: 201-208.
10. **Demisew, S. 1984.** Botanical aspects of "khat" *Catha edulis* (Celastraceae). *Proceedings of the International Symposium on Khat, Addis Ababa, Ethiopia, 15 December 1984*, pp. 5-11. NAPRECA, Addis Ababa.
11. **Von Breitenbach, F. 1986.** *National List of Indigenous Trees.* Dendrological Foundation, Pretoria.

Catha edulis

Flowers of *Catha edulis*

Fresh leaves of *Catha edulis* are traditionally used for chewing

CATHARANTHUS ROSEUS

Apocynaceae

Madagascar periwinkle (English); isisushlungu (Zulu)

BOTANICAL DESCRIPTION. The plant is a perennial herb of up to one metre in height, with a somewhat woody base. The leaves are dark green and glossy, with a prominent white midrib. Flower colour varies from pink to white, or white with a pink centre. This popular and attractive garden plant has become a weed in some parts of South Africa[1].

PLANT PARTS USED. The roots or more commonly the leaves are used.

MEDICINAL USES. The plant is traditionally used in South Africa as a remedy for diabetes and to treat rheumatism[2]. A preparation called Vinculin was marketed in England as a diabetes "treatment"[3]. The roots are an official drug in France[4] for the supportive treatment of diabetes. Alkaloid extracts of the aerial parts are used to treat various forms of cancer, including breast cancer, uterine cancer and Hodgkin's and non-Hodgkin's lymphoma[4].

PREPARATION AND DOSAGE. An infusion of the leaf has been used to treat diabetes, but even dilute mixtures can be extremely toxic. The two main alkaloids of the plant are used in combined chemotherapy and small doses are injected weekly or monthly.

ACTIVE INGREDIENTS. The compounds responsible for the hypoglycemic effects are various alkaloids such as catharanthine, leurosine and vindolinine[3]. In cancer chemotherapy, however, the two binary indole alkaloids vincristine and vinblastine are well known for their antitumour activity[4]. A large number of other indole alkaloids have also been found in the plant[5].

PHARMACOLOGICAL EFFECTS. The binary alkaloids (or various semisynthetic derivatives) prevent cell division in the metaphase by binding to the protein tubulin and blocking its ability to polymerise into microtubules[4,6].

DISTRIBUTION. The plant originates from Madagascar but has become naturalised in tropical and subtropical regions of the world. It is commonly grown in gardens in South Africa and has become a weed, often found at roadsides and in other disturbed areas, particularly in KwaZulu-Natal and Mpumalanga.

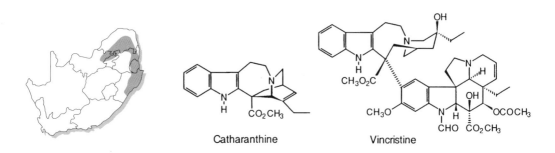

Catharanthine   Vincristine

---

1. **Codd, L.E. 1963.** Apocynaceae. 7. *Catharanthus. Flora of Southern Africa* 26, pp. 267-268. Botanical Research Institute, Pretoria.
2. **Watt, J.M. & Breyer-Brandwijk, M.G. 1962.** *The Medicinal and Poisonous Plants of Southern and Eastern Africa.* 2nd edition. Livingstone, London.
3. **Marles, R.J. & Farnsworth, N.R. 1995.** Antidiabetic plants and their active constituents. *Phytomedicine* 2: 137-189.
4. **Bruneton, J. 1995.** *Pharmacognosy, Phytochemistry, Medicinal Plants.* Intercept, Hampshire.
5. **Dictionary of Natural Products on CD-ROM, release 4:2 (1996).** Chapman & Hall, London.
6. **Goodman, L.S. & Gilman, A. 1992.** *The Pharmacological Basis of Therapeutics.* 8th edition. Pergamon Press, New York.

Catharanthus roseus – form with white flowers

Catharanthus roseus – typical pink-flowered form

CENTELLA ASIATICA

Apiaceae
(= *Hydrocotyle asiatica*)

pennywort (English); varkoortjies (Afrikaans); brahmi (Hindi)

BOTANICAL DESCRIPTION. *C. asiatica* (the old name *Hydrocotyle asiatica* is still often used) is a perennial weed often found in moist places. It is a creeping plant forming thin stems with characteristically round or kidney-shaped leaves on long, slender stalks. The flowers are small and inconspicuous, borne in groups of three. The species varies considerably in different parts of the world and is sometimes treated as several distinct species[1].

PLANT PARTS USED. Dried aboveground parts (mainly leaves) are used.

MEDICINAL USES. In South Africa and elsewhere, *Centella* has been used to treat leprosy[2,3,4], wounds and cancer. It is widely used for wound treatment, fever, syphilis and as a diuretic and purgative[2,5]. *Centella* is an important constituent of dermatological products[6]. Between 40 and 60 tons are exported annually from Madagascar to Europe[7]. It is taken orally to relieve the symptoms of venous and lymphatic vessel insufficiency[6]. It is also a popular constituent of homoeopathic remedies claimed to be useful for treating acne and allergies.

PREPARATION AND DOSAGE. Extracts and tinctures of the plant material are used, or the active components may be isolated for use in standardised products.

ACTIVE INGREDIENTS. The wound-healing activity is associated with a triterpenoid saponin known as asiaticoside[8], which has asiatic acid as aglycone, with a trisaccharide bonded to it. This and several other triterpenoids such as madecassic acid[8] may be responsible for the antitumour properties[9] of *Centella* by acting as spindle poisons and thus preventing cell division. The volatile oil contains several monoterpenoids and some sesquiterpenoids[10].

PHARMACOLOGICAL EFFECTS. The wound-healing activity has been evaluated clinically and there is *in vitro* and *in vivo* evidence of antitumour activity[9]. Other activities that have been reported include antibacterial, antifungal, anti-inflammatory, tranquilising, anti-allergic, hypotensive, antipyretic and peptic ulcer healing[11].

DISTRIBUTION. *C. asiatica* has a pantropical distribution and is found in Africa, Asia, Australia, South America and the southern part of North America. In South Africa, it is widely distributed, from the Cape Peninsula northwards along the moist eastern parts.

Asiatic acid   Madecassic acid

1. **Nannfeldt, J. A. 1924.** Revision des verwandtschaftkreises von *Centella asiatica* (L.) Urb. *Svensk Bot. Tidskr.* 18: 297-426.
2. **Watt, J.M. & Breyer-Brandwijk, M.G. 1962.** *The Medicinal and Poisonous Plants of Southern and Eastern Africa.* 2nd edition. Livingstone, London.
3. **Bailey, E. 1945.** Treatment of leprosy. *Nature* 155: 601.
4. **Boiteau, P. *et al.* 1949.** Derivatives of *Centella* used against leprosy, chemical constitution of asiaticoside. *Nature* 163: 258-259.
5. **Iwu, M.M. 1993.** *Handbook of African Medicinal Plants.* CRC Press, Boca Raton.
6. **Bruneton, J. 1995.** *Pharmacognosy, Phytochemistry, Medicinal Plants.* Intercept, Hampshire.
7. **Rasoanaivo, P. 1993.** Introducing "Institut Malagache de Recherches Appliquees (IMRA)". *Extended Abstracts of the Fifth NAPRECA Symposium on Natural Products, 19-23 September 1993, Antananarivo, Madagascar,* p. 147.
8. **Dictionary of Natural Products on CD-ROM, release 4:2 (1996).** Chapman & Hall, London.
9. **Babu, T.D. *et al.* 1995.** Cytotoxic and anti-tumor properties of certain taxa of Umbelliferae with special reference to *Centella asiatica* (L.) Urban. *J. Ethnopharmacol.* 48: 53-57.
10. **Yoshinori, A. *et al.* 1982.** Mono- and sesquiterpenoids from *Hydrocotyle* and *Centella* species. *Phytochemistry* 21: 2590-2592.
11. **Ponglux, D. *et al.* (eds) 1987.** *Medicinal Plants.* The first Princess Chulabhorn Science Congress, Bangkok, Thailand.

Centella asiatica

Examples of *Centella asiatica* products

Young plant of *Centella asiatica*, showing fruits

CHIRONIA BACCIFERA

Gentianaceae

---

aambeibossie, bitterbossie (Afrikaans); Christmas berry (English)

BOTANICAL DESCRIPTION. The plant is a rounded dense shrub of up to one metre in height, with multi-branched, angular twigs and small narrow leaves. The attractive pink flowers appear in spring, followed by bright red berries in summer. This common species can easily be recognised by the narrow, spreading leaves, small flowers and rounded berries[1].

PLANT PARTS USED. The whole plant is used.

MEDICINAL USES. This is an important medicine in South Africa, traditionally used by the Khoi as a purgative and to treat boils[2]. The purgative use, especially for haemorrhoids, is widely known[3,4,5]. A decoction of the whole plant is taken as a blood purifier to treat acne, sores and boils. Infusions may be used as a remedy for diarrhoea, or for leprosy[3]. The plant is bitter and is said to cause perspiration and sleepiness[3].

PREPARATION AND DOSAGE. Decoctions, tinctures or infusions are taken, but the plant is potentially toxic and uncontrolled use can be dangerous.

For external application, the plant is fried in butter, and is then applied to the sores[3]. Infusions are also applied topically to haemorrhoids.

ACTIVE INGREDIENTS. *C. baccifera* roots contain various secoiridoids, of which gentiopicroside is the main component, together with smaller amounts of swertiamarine, chironioside and others[6]. Other species of the family Gentianaceae, such as *Gentiana lutea* (yellow gentian) and *C. krebsii* are known to contain gentiopicroside[7] and chironioside[6] respectively. These are bitter substances, traditionally used in the liquor industry[8].

PHARMACOLOGICAL EFFECTS. The bitter iridoids are known to stimulate appetite, but the compounds responsible for the healing properties of *Chironia* appear to be unknown.

DISTRIBUTION. *C. baccifera* occurs from the Cape Peninsula northwards to the Khamiesberg and eastwards to the Eastern Cape and KwaZulu-Natal. It often grows in the shade of other plants[1].

Gentiopicroside

---

1. **Marais, W. & Verdoorn, I.C. 1963.** Gentianaceae. *Flora of Southern Africa* 26, pp. 171-243. Botanical Research Institute, Pretoria.
2. **Laidler, P.W. 1928.** The magic medicine of the Hottentots. *S. Afr. J. Sci.* 25: 433-447.
3. **Watt, J.M. & Breyer-Brandwijk, M.G. 1962.** *The Medicinal and Poisonous Plants of Southern and Eastern Africa.* 2nd edition. Livingstone, London.
4. **Smith, C.A. 1966.** *Common Names of South African Plants. Memoirs of the Botanical Survey of South Africa 35.*
5. **Rood, B. 1994.** *Uit die Veldapteek.* Tafelberg, Cape Town.
6. **Wolfender, J.-L. et al. 1993.** Search for bitter principles in *Chironia* species by LC-MS and isolation of a new secoiridoid diglycoside from *Chironia krebsii. J. Nat. Prod.* 56: 682-689.
7. **Dictionary of Natural Products on CD-ROM, release 4:2 (1996).** Chapman & Hall, London.
8. **Bruneton, J. 1995.** *Pharmacognosy, Phytochemistry, Medicinal Plants.* Intercept, Hampshire.

Chironia baccifera

Flowers of *Chironia baccifera*

Berries of *Chironia baccifera*

Chironia baccifera as it is sold for medicinal use

CICHORIUM INTYBUS

Asteraceae

> chicory (English); sigorei (Afrikaans)

BOTANICAL DESCRIPTION. Chicory is an erect, somewhat woody perennial herb of up to one metre in height, with a strong tap root and large basal leaves. The leaves are oblong in shape with strongly and irregularly dentate margins. All parts of the plant exude a milky latex when broken. The pale blue to bright blue flower heads are distinctive and quite attractive[1].

PLANT PARTS USED. The roots are mainly used.

MEDICINAL USES. In Europe, the roots are used medicinally as a tonic, laxative and diuretic[2,3]. It is used as a choleretic and cholagogue, to enhance kidney function and to relieve the symptoms of digestive disturbances[4]. In South Africa, it is a traditional tonic to purify the blood, liver and kidneys and to improve appetite and indigestion[5]. Inulin derivates are nowadays used as sucrose substitutes[4].

PREPARATION AND DOSAGE. For jaundice, an infusion may be prepared from 30 to 40 g of leaves, stems and roots boiled in one litre of water for five minutes. A small wine glass of the preparation is taken three times a day for three days[5]. As a traditional tonic and purifying medicine for infants, chicory syrup is made from equal quantities of root juice and sugar, slowly boiled until syrupy. Ten millilitres are used three times a day[5].

ACTIVE INGREDIENTS. Chicory root has a very high inulin content but the link between the chemical constituents and activity is not clear. The bitterness is due to sesquiterpenoid lactones, such as lactucin[6].

PHARMACOLOGICAL EFFECTS. The activity of this traditional medicine is not clearly linked to any specific compound[4]. Inulin is used as a diagnostic aid for renal function[7].

DISTRIBUTION. The plant is indigenous to Europe and Asia, but it has become a widespread weed along roadsides in the dry parts of South Africa[1].

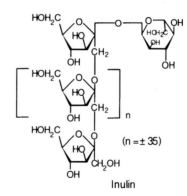

Inulin

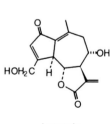

Lactucin

1. **Henderson, M. & Anderson, J.G. 1966.** *Common Weeds in South Africa. Memoirs of the Botanical Survey of South Africa 37.*
2. **Grieve, M. 1967.** *A Modern Herbal.* Hafner, London.
3. **Watt, J.M. & Breyer-Brandwijk, M.G. 1962.** *The Medicinal and Poisonous Plants of Southern and Eastern Africa.* 2nd edition. Livingstone, London.
4. **Bruneton, J. 1995.** *Pharmacognosy, Phytochemistry, Medicinal Plants.* Intercept, Hampshire.
5. **Rood, B. 1994.** *Uit die Veldapteek.* Tafelberg, Cape Town.
6. **Dictionary of Natural Products on CD-ROM, release 4:2 (1996).** Chapman & Hall, London.
7. **Merck 1989.** *The Merck Index.* 11th edition. Merck, Rahway.

Flower heads of *Cichorium intybus*

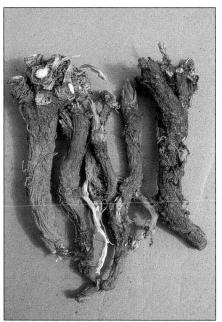
Roots of *Cichorium intybus*

Leaves and flower heads of *Cichorium intybus*

CINNAMOMUM CAMPHORA

Lauraceae

> camphor tree (English); kanferboom (Afrikaans); uroselina (Zulu)

BOTANICAL DESCRIPTION. It is a large tree, up to 26 metres in height in South Africa, usually heavily branched low down. The bark is pale brown with a characteristically coarse, fissured appearance. The leaves are dark green to yellowish-green, with three main veins arising near the base. Inconspicuous white flowers are followed by small round purple berries. All parts of the plant have a strong camphor smell, making it easy to recognise[1].

PLANT PARTS USED. The essential oil (gum) is distilled from the wood. It has a strong penetrating odour and a pungent bitter taste.

MEDICINAL USES. In Europe, camphor has mainly been used for colds and inflammatory complaints[2], but there are numerous other ailments that have been treated with camphor from time to time, including heart conditions, infections, fevers, pneumonia (used as an antibacterial), hysteria and diarrhoea[2,3]. Externally it has been used as a counter-irritant and antiseptic[2]. In addition to the long-established medicinal use of gum camphor in South Africa, the bark of the tree has become popular in the treatment of fevers, colds and influenza. An infusion of the dried leaves is used as a Zulu ritual emetic. Camphor is commonly used in modern medicine, as a topical anti-infective and antipruritic and internally as a stimulant and carminative[4]. A synthetic form of camphor is also a cardiac and respiratory analeptic[5] preparation.

PREPARATION AND DOSAGE. Camphor is toxic in large doses and should not be used internally without proper supervision.

ACTIVE INGREDIENTS. Natural camphor, (+)-(1R)-camphor, is distilled from the wood of the camphor tree[6]. Racemic camphor is nowadays obtained by synthesis (usually from pinene)[4].

PHARMACOLOGICAL EFFECTS. Antiseptic, counter-irritant, stimulant, carminative and analeptic (see above) properties have been identified.

DISTRIBUTION. Camphor trees occur naturally in China, Taiwan and Japan. It is an early introduction to South Africa which has adapted well to local conditions and has become very popular as an ornamental tree in gardens and parks[1]. The tree has recently become naturalised at two localities (see map).

(+) - (1R) - Camphor
(= *d*-Camphor)

1. **Poynton, R.J. 1975.** *Suid-Afrikaanse Boomgids.* Tafelberg, Cape Town.
2. **Grieve, M. 1967.** *A Modern Herbal.* Hafner, London.
3. **Watt, J.M. & Breyer-Brandwijk, M.G. 1962.** *The Medicinal and Poisonous Plants of Southern and Eastern Africa.* 2nd edition. Livingstone, London.
4. **Merck 1989.** *The Merck Index.* 11th edition. Merck, Rahway.
5. **Bruneton, J. 1995.** *Pharmacognosy, Phytochemistry, Medicinal Plants.* Intercept, Hampshire.
6. **Dictionary of Natural Products on CD-ROM, release 4:2 (1996).** Chapman & Hall, London.

Cinnamomum camphora

Bark of *Cinnamomum camphora*

Leaves and berries of *Cinnamomum camphora*

Dried and pounded leaves of *Cinnamomum camphora*

CISSAMPELOS CAPENSIS

Menispermaceae

dawidjiewortel (Afrikaans)

BOTANICAL DESCRIPTION. This plant is a perennial climber with twining stems and rounded, bright green leaves[1]. The plant does not have tendrils but supports itself by twining around the stems of other plants. The small, hairy, greenish flowers are produced in clusters, followed by small orange berries. It should not be confused with *Zehneria scabra* (Cucurbitaceae), which is in some parts known by the same vernacular[2]. The latter resembles a cucumber and can be distinguished by the spirally coiled tendrils.

PLANT PARTS USED. The rhizomes and roots are used.

MEDICINAL USES. This is a well known and much used medicinal plant, particularly in the Western Cape Province[2,3,4,5,6]. It is traditionally taken as a blood purifier, for boils and syphilis, but also for bladder ailments, diarrhoea, colic and cholera[6]. A paste of the leaves may be applied to boils and sores[6]. Many members of the Menispermaceae are recorded in African traditional medicine[7] of which *C. pareira* is perhaps the best known example.

PREPARATION AND DOSAGE. The medicine is traditionally used as a brandy tincture[3,4] but sometimes taken as infusions or decoctions and externally applied as poultices[4].

ACTIVE INGREDIENTS. A large number of biologically active alkaloids of the bisbenzyltetrahydroisoquinoline type have been isolated from several *Cissampelos* species (and various other genera of the Menispermaceae), of which cissampareine is a typical example[8]. There appears to be no information on *C. capensis* but the activity of the medicine is likely to be at least partly due to these or similar alkaloids.

PHARMACOLOGICAL EFFECTS. Sedative, antispasmodic and antitumour properties have been ascribed to Menispermaceae alkaloids[8,9], which are often the active ingredients of various types of curares, the famous dart and arrow poisons of South America.

DISTRIBUTION. The plant is widely distributed in the western part of South Africa.

Cissampareine

1. **Botha, D.J. 1980.** The identity of *Antizoma harveyana* Miers ex Harv. and *A. capensis* (L.f.) Diels. *Jl S. Afr. Bot.* 46: 1-5.
2. **Smith, C.A. 1966.** *Common Names of South African Plants. Memoirs of the Botanical Survey of South Africa 35.*
3. **Cillié, A.M. 1992.** *Kruie op Witblits, Rate, Resepte en Feite.* Unpublished notes, Worcester Museum.
4. **Dykman, E.J. 1891.** *Kook-, Koek- en Resepte Boek.* Paarlse Drukpers Maatskappy, Paarl.
5. **Rood, B. 1994.** *Uit die Veldapteek.* Tafelberg, Cape Town.
6. **Watt, J.M. & Breyer-Brandwijk, M.G. 1962.** *The Medicinal and Poisonous Plants of Southern and Eastern Africa.* 2nd edition. Livingstone, London.
7. **Iwu, M.M. 1993.** *Handbook of African Medicinal Plants.* CRC Press, Boca Raton.
8. **Dictionary of Natural Products on CD-ROM, release 4:2 (1996).** Chapman & Hall, London.
9. **Bruneton, J. 1995.** *Pharmacognosy, Phytochemistry, Medicinal Plants.* Intercept, Hampshire.

Cissampelos capensis

Leaves and flowers of *Cissampelos capensis*

Rhizome of *Cissampelos capensis* – the traditional product

CLIVIA MINIATA

Amaryllidaceae

---

umayime (Zulu); boslelie (Afrikaans); bush lily, orange lily (English)

BOTANICAL DESCRIPTION. This attractive plant is a shade-loving perennial with a fleshy, tuberous rhizome and dark-green, strap-shaped leaves[1]. The flowers are usually orange (rarely yellow[2]) and all arise from the same point on the flowering stalk. Due to the exceptionally beautiful flowers, *C. miniata* is a popular garden plant and it is also commonly grown as a pot plant in many parts of the world[1]. There are four species of *Clivia*, but it seems that only *C. miniata* and *C. nobilis* are used to any extent in traditional medicine.

PLANT PARTS USED. The whole plant is used, including the rhizome, roots and leaves.

MEDICINAL USES. The rhizome is used by the Zulu to treat fever. The whole plant is used to help with childbirth and to hasten parturition[3,4,5]. The rhizome is also a snake-bite remedy[3] and it is claimed to relieve pain[3].

PREPARATION AND DOSAGE. The rhizomes of *Clivia* species are extremely toxic due to the presence of numerous alkaloids. Their continued use should be strongly discouraged.

ACTIVE INGREDIENTS. The toxicity is due to several so-called Amaryllidaceae alkaloids, of which lycorine is the best known compound[6,7]. Several structurally related alkaloids have been isolated from *C. miniata*, such as clivacetine, clivonine, cliviasine and clividine[7].

PHARMACOLOGICAL EFFECTS. Lycorine occurs in *C. miniata* at levels of up to 0,4% of the dry weight and causes salivation, vomiting and diarrhoea at low doses; paralysis and collapse at high doses[8]. Leaf extracts were shown to have uterotonic effects[9].

DISTRIBUTION. *C. miniata* occurs naturally along the eastern coastal parts of South Africa.

Lycorine

1. **Dyer, R.A. 1921.** *Clivia miniata. Flower. Pl. S. Afr.* 1: Plate 13.
2. **Dyer, R.A. 1931.** *Clivia miniata* var. *flava. Flower. Pl. S. Afr.* 11: Plate 411.
3. **Watt, J.M. & Breyer-Brandwijk, M.G. 1962.** *The Medicinal and Poisonous Plants of Southern and Eastern Africa.* 2nd edition. Livingstone, London.
4. **Pujol, J. 1990.** *Naturafrica – the Herbalist Handbook.* Jean Pujol Natural Healers' Foundation, Durban.
5. **Hutchings, A. 1996.** *Zulu Medicinal Plants.* University of Natal Press, Pietermaritzburg.
6. **Merck 1989.** *The Merck Index.* 11th edition. Merck, Rahway.
7. **Dictionary of Natural Products on CD-ROM, release 4:2 (1996).** Chapman & Hall, London.
8. **Bruneton, J. 1995.** *Pharmacognosy, Phytochemistry, Medicinal Plants.* Intercept, Hampshire.
9. **Veale, D.J.H. *et al.* 1989.** Preliminary isolated organ studies using an aqueous extract of *Clivia miniata* leaves. *J. Ethnopharmacol.* 27: 341-346.

Clivia miniata

Rhizome of *Clivia miniata* as it is sold for medicinal use

Clivia nobilis

CNICUS BENEDICTUS

Asteraceae

karmedik (Afrikaans); holy thistle (English)

BOTANICAL DESCRIPTION. This annual plant grows up to 0,7 metres high and has characteristically indented and spiny leaves, initially forming a basal rosette, but later becoming dispersed along the stem. The yellow flowers are borne in a terminal flower head surrounded by a circle of spiny bracts[1].

PLANT PARTS USED. The whole plant is used.

MEDICINAL USES. The plant is used as a cholagogue, stomachic and tonic[2,3]. Externally it is used to treat wounds and ulcers[3]. The recorded uses in South Africa include the use of brandy tinctures for internal cancers; use as a stomachic[4,5,6]; and for diabetes and arthritis. The German Commission E monograph allows the indication, lack of appetite and dyspeptic complaints, for the drug.

PREPARATION AND DOSAGE. Boiling water is poured over 1,5 to 2 g of powdered material and strained after five to 10 minutes. A cup of the unsweetened infusion is taken half an hour before meals.

ACTIVE INGREDIENTS. One of the constituents, a bitter lactone, cnicin, is most probably the main active ingredient[3,7]. This sesquiterpenoid lactone was already isolated from the plant in 1837. Lignan lactones such as trachelogenin also contribute to the bitterness of the plant. It contains up to 0,3% volatile oil with the terpenoids *p*-cymene, fenchone and citral and the aromatic substances cinnamaldehyde and benzoic acid, all of which can contribute towards the pharmacological activity of the phytomedicine[8,9].

PHARMACOLOGICAL EFFECTS. The medicine is used as an aromatic bitter to stimulate the secretion of gastric juice and increase the appetite. There is no scientific evidence to support other traditional uses.

DISTRIBUTION. *C. benedictus* is widely distributed in Asia and the Mediterranean region and was introduced to South Africa more than 150 years ago[1,4]. It has become a weed in the Cape and also on the Highveld.

Cnicin

1. Henderson, M. & Anderson, J.G. 1966. *Common Weeds in South Africa. Memoirs of the Botanical Survey of South Africa 37*.
2. Grieve, M. 1967. *A Modern Herbal*. Hafner, London.
3. Bruneton, J. 1995. *Pharmacognosy, Phytochemistry, Medicinal Plants*. Intercept, Hampshire.
4. Smith, C.A. 1966. *Common Names of South African Plants. Memoirs of the Botanical Survey of South Africa 35*.
5. Watt, J.M. & Breyer-Brandwijk, M.G. 1962. *The Medicinal and Poisonous Plants of Southern and Eastern Africa*. 2nd edition. Livingstone, London.
6. Rood, B. 1994. *Uit die Veldapteek*. Tafelberg, Cape Town.
7. Merck 1989. *The Merck Index*. 11th edition. Merck, Rahway.
8. **Dictionary of Natural Products on CD-ROM, release 4:2 (1996).** Chapman & Hall, London.

Cnicus benedictus

Flower head of *Cnicus benedictus*

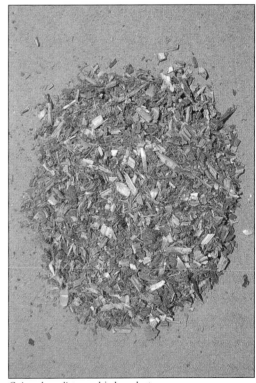

Cnicus benedictus – dried product

COTYLEDON ORBICULATA

Crassulaceae

---

imphewula (Xhosa); seredile (Sotho, Tswana); plakkie (Afrikaans);
kouterie (Afrikaans, Khoi); pigs's ear (English)

BOTANICAL DESCRIPTION. This common succulent is a small shrub with woody branches and thick, fleshy leaves. The leaves are bright green to grey, often with a reddish margin and usually covered with a waxy layer on the surface. Orange or red tubular flowers are borne on a long, slender stalk. *C. orbiculata* is a very variable species and several different varieties have been described[1].

PLANT PARTS USED. The leaves or leaf juice is used.

MEDICINAL USES. The plant is widely used for medicinal purposes. The fleshy part of the leaf is applied to corns and warts to soften and remove them[2,3,4]. A single leaf is eaten as a vermifuge. The warmed leaf juice is used as drops for earache and toothache[3,4]. It may also be applied in the form of a hot poultice to treat boils, earache or inflammation[3,4,5]. The juice has been used to treat epilepsy[2,6].

PREPARATION AND DOSAGE. The warmed leaf juice is directly applied. Internal use is dangerous and potentially lethal, and the toxicity is affected by the moisture content of the leaves.

ACTIVE INGREDIENTS. The plant contains several cardiac glycosides[7] of the bufadienolide type, such as orbicuside A.

PHARMACOLOGICAL EFFECTS. There is no clear link between bufadienolides and the reported analgesic effects.

DISTRIBUTION. *C. orbiculata* is widely distributed over practically the whole of southern Africa[1].

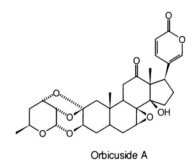

Orbicuside A

---

1. **Tölken, H.R. 1985.** Crassulaceae. *Flora of Southern Africa* 14. Botanical Research Institute, Pretoria.
2. **Smith, C.A. 1966.** *Common Names of South African Plants. Memoirs of the Botanical Survey of South Africa 35.*
3. **Watt, J.M. & Breyer-Brandwijk, M.G. 1962.** *The Medicinal and Poisonous Plants of Southern and Eastern Africa.* 2nd edition. Livingstone, London.
4. **Rood, B. 1994.** *Uit die Veldapteek.* Tafelberg, Cape Town.
5. **Bhat, R.B. & Jacobs, T.V. 1995.** Traditional herbal medicine in Transkei. *J. Ethnopharmacol.* 48: 7-12.
6. **Watt, J.M. 1967.** African plants potentially useful in mental health. *Lloydia* 30: 1-22.
7. **Steyn, P.S. *et al.* 1986.** Bufadienolide glycosides of the Crassulaceae. Structure and stereochemistry of orbicusides A-C, novel toxic metabolites of *Cotyledon orbiculata*. *J. Chem. Soc., Perkin Trans.* I, 1986: 1633-1636.

Cotyledon orbiculata – West Coast

Cotyledon orbiculata – Little Karoo

Cotyledon orbiculata – Southern Cape

CRINUM MACOWANII

Amaryllidaceae

umduze (Zulu)

BOTANICAL DESCRIPTION. This widely distributed geophyte has a large bulb of about 200 mm in diameter, with long, strap-shaped leaves radiating from it. The leaf margins are undulating and the tips end abruptly as a result of frost damage. The wide open, trumpet-shaped flowers with their black anthers are characteristic of this species[1].

PLANT PARTS USED. The bulbs and leaves are used.

MEDICINAL USES. The plant is a Zulu remedy for various complaints, mainly scrofula, micturition and rheumatic fever[2]. It is also used for blood cleansing, kidney and bladder diseases, glandular swelling, fever and skin problems such as sores, boils and acne[3,4]. A related species, *C. bulbispermum*, is used by the Southern Sotho people for colds and scrofula[2]. Various species have been used as arrow poisons[5].

PREPARATION AND DOSAGE. The plant is not usually taken alone but is mixed with other ingredients.

Since the bulbs contain highly toxic alkaloids, continued use of *Crinum* species is not recommended.

ACTIVE INGREDIENTS. Numerous Amaryllidaceae alkaloids have been isolated from *Crinum* species, of which lycorine is perhaps the best known (for structure see *Clivia*). Some of these compounds have antitumour properties. Many species also contain crinamine, which is a respiratory depressant and a powerful transient hypotensive agent in dogs[6]. Two other alkaloids, pratorimine and pratorinine have been isolated from the bulbs of *C. bulbispermum* and several other *Crinum* species[6].

PHARMACOLOGICAL EFFECTS. Various effects have been ascribed to *Crinum* alkaloids, such as antitumour, hypotensive and analgesic activity[6].

DISTRIBUTION. *C. macowanii* is the most widely distributed of all the *Crinum* species indigenous to southern Africa[1]. *C. bulbispermum* is also very widely distributed in the northern parts of South Africa.

Crinamine   Pratorimine

1. **Verdoorn, I.C. 1973.** The genus *Crinum* in southern Africa. *Bothalia* 11: 27-52.
2. **Watt, J.M. & Breyer-Brandwijk, M.G. 1962.** *The Medicinal and Poisonous Plants of Southern and Eastern Africa.* 2nd edition. Livingstone, London.
3. **Pujol, J. 1990.** *Naturafrica – the Herbalist Handbook.* Jean Pujol Natural Healers' Foundation, Durban.
4. **Hutchings, A. 1996.** *Zulu Medicinal Plants.* University of Natal Press, Pietermaritzburg.
5. **Neuwinger, H.D. 1994.** *Afrikanische Arzneipflanzen und Jagdgifte.* Wissenschaftliche Verlagsgesellschaft, Stuttgart.
6. **Dictionary of Natural Products on CD-ROM, release 4:2 (1996).** Chapman & Hall, London.

Crinum macowanii

Flowers of *Crinum macowanii*

Flowers of *Crinum bulbispermum*

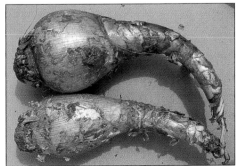

Bulbs of *Crinum macowanii*

CROTON GRATISSIMUS

Euphorbiaceae

**umahlabekufeni (Zulu); maquassie (San); lavender croton (English);
bergboegoe, laventelkoorsbessie (Afrikaans)**

BOTANICAL DESCRIPTION. This is a shrub or small tree of up to 10 metres in height, with a rough, grey bark. The aromatic leaves are dark green above but have a characteristic silver, shiny lower surface, dotted with brown glands. The flowers are cream-coloured and rather inconspicuous. Small yellow fruit (3-lobed capsules) are produced in autumn[1,2].

PLANT PARTS USED. The bark is used.

MEDICINAL USES. The bark of *C. gratissimus* and *C. sylvaticus* are used for the same purposes and both are known by the same Zulu common name. As the Afrikaans name "koorsbessie" ("koors" = fever, "bessie" = berry) suggests, these trees are much used for fever[3]. Leaf infusions are also used for coughs. Numerous other ailments are treated with the bark, including bleeding gums, rheumatism, chest complaints, indigestion and oedema (dropsy)[3,4]. "Maquassie" is said to be the original Bushman name for the species[5]. The powdered leaves have been used as a perfume (similar to the use of real buchu, see *Agathosma*) and hot water extracts have served as a substitute for lavender water[5]. The Boegoeberg in the Northern Cape Province and the small town of Makwassie in the North West Province are both named after this species[5]. The oil of *C. tiglium* has been used commercially.

PREPARATION AND DOSAGE. Several species are known to contain toxic substances and their medicinal use is potentially dangerous.

ACTIVE INGREDIENTS. *Croton* is a genus of great chemical complexity and a wide range of compounds have been isolated from different species, including alkaloids, flavonoids, cardenolides, saponins, monoterpenoids and diterpenoids[7]. The chemical constituents of *C. gratissimus* and *C. sylvaticus* appear to be unknown. Two examples of typical *Croton* compounds[8] are crotonin and crotofolin A.

PHARMACOLOGICAL EFFECTS. The diterpenoids of *Croton* are toxic irritants of the skin and mucosas[6] and they produce a burning sensation in the throat and mouth[3].

DISTRIBUTION. *C. gratissimus* occurs naturally over a large area in the north of South Africa. *C. sylvaticus* is restricted to the east coast, Mpumalanga and the Northern Province[1,2,9].

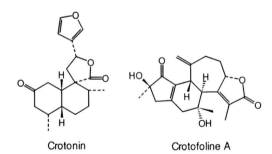

Crotonin   Crotofoline A

---

1. **Palmer, E. & Pitman, J. 1972.** *Trees of Southern Africa.* Balkema, Cape Town.
2. **Coates Palgrave, K. 1977.** *Trees of Southern Africa.* Struik, Cape Town.
3. **Watt, J.M. & Breyer-Brandwijk, M.G. 1962.** *The Medicinal and Poisonous Plants of Southern and Eastern Africa.* 2nd edition. Livingstone, London.
4. **Pujol, J. 1990.** *Naturafrica – the Herbalist Handbook.* Jean Pujol Natural Healers' Foundation, Durban.
5. **Smith, C.A. 1966.** *Common Names of South African Plants. Memoirs of the Botanical Survey of South Africa 35.*
6. **Bruneton, J. 1995.** *Pharmacognosy, Phytochemistry, Medicinal Plants.* Intercept, Hampshire.
7. **Stuart, K.L. 1970.** Chemical and biological investigations of the *Croton* genus. *Rev. Latinoamer. Quim.* 1: 140-147.
8. **Dictionary of Natural Products on CD-ROM, release 4:2 (1996).** Chapman & Hall, London.
9. **Von Breitenbach, F. 1986.** *National List of Indigenous Trees.* Dendrological Foundation, Pretoria.

Croton gratissimus

Flowers of *Croton gratissimus*

Leaves of *Croton sylvatica*

Bark and foliage of *Croton gratissimus*

CURTISIA DENTATA

Cornaceae

---

umlahleni (Xhosa, Zulu); assegaai (Afrikaans); assegai (English)

BOTANICAL DESCRIPTION. This is a medium to large-sized tree, usually around 10 metres but sometimes up to 20 metres in height. The bark is brown and smooth but becomes dark brown and rough in older trees. The leaves occur in opposite pairs on the twigs. They are dark green and glossy on the upper surface, covered with brown hairs below, with a distinct pattern of veins. Large, regular teeth are present along the leaf margins. The inconspicuous, cream-coloured, hairy flowers are followed by round, white berries of about 10 mm in diameter[1,2].

PLANT PARTS USED. Bark is used.

MEDICINAL USES. This important Zulu medicine is used for stomach ailments and diarrhoea[3,4,5]. It is also traditionally used as an aphrodisiac and to "purify the blood"[4]. The medicine is poorly recorded[5] but is very popular and forms an important part of the commercial trade in KwaZulu-Natal[6].

PREPARATION AND DOSAGE. The bark was commonly included in bark mixtures (Zulu: "khubalo") but it has become scarce and is now only put in "special" mixes[6]. No details are available on the exact methods of preparation.

ACTIVE INGREDIENTS. Nothing appears to be known about the chemical constituents of *Curtisia*[7]. It is interesting to note that other members of the family Cornaceae are rich sources of tannins. *Cornus officinalis,* for example, has yielded about 20 different gallotannins and ellagitannins[7]. An example is cornustannin 2.

PHARMACOLOGICAL EFFECTS. Tannins are usually responsible for the activity of antidiarrhoeal medicines through their antiseptic and vasoconstrictor effects, and the way in which they form protective layers on the skin and mucous membranes.

DISTRIBUTION. *C. dentata* occurs in the afromontane forests of South Africa, from the Cape Peninsula to the Northern Province[1,2]. It has become threatened in some localities as a result of over-exploitation[6].

Cornustannin 2

1. **Palmer, E. & Pitman, J. 1972.** *Trees of Southern Africa.* Balkema, Cape Town.
2. **Coates Palgrave, K. 1977.** *Trees of Southern Africa.* Struik, Cape Town.
3. **Pujol, J. 1990.** *Naturafrica – the Herbalist Handbook.* Jean Pujol Natural Healers' Foundation, Durban.
4. **Hutchings, A. 1996.** *Zulu Medicinal Plants.* Natal University Press, Pietermaritzburg.
5. **Watt, J.M. & Breyer-Brandwijk, M.G. 1962.** *The Medicinal and Poisonous Plants of Southern and Eastern Africa.* 2nd edition. Livingstone, London.
6. **Cunningham, A.B. 1988.** *An Investigation of the Herbal Medicine Trade in Natal/KwaZulu.* Investigational report no 29, Institute of Natural Resources, University of Natal.
7. **Dictionary of Natural Products on CD-ROM, release 4:2 (1996).** Chapman & Hall, London.

Leaves and berries of *Curtisia dentata*

Leaves of *Curtisia dentata*, showing the toothed margins

Bark of *Curtisia dentata*

CYCLOPIA INTERMEDIA

Fabaceae

heuningbostee (Afrikaans); honeybush tea (English)

BOTANICAL DESCRIPTION. Originally the name "heuningbostee" or "heuningtee"[1] referred to *C. genistoides*, but this species is no longer used commercially. *C. intermedia* (so-called "bergtee", or mountain tea), currently the main commercial source, is a multi-branched woody shrub of up to about one metre in height. The young twigs have a characteristically golden colour. Each leaf comprises three separate leaflets. The attractive yellow flowers are followed by flat, brown seed pods. The original source, *C. genistoides*, may be distinguished by its smaller size and narrow, needle-like leaflets. *C. subternata*, (so-called "vleitee") is also used commercially nowadays. The leaves and flowers are very similar to those of *C. intermedia* but the plant is an erect, sparsely branched shrub of 1,5 metres or more. It regenerates from seed after fire, while *C. intermedia* resprouts from its woody base[2,3,4].

PLANT PARTS USED. Leaves, twigs and (traditionally) also the flowers are processed.

Production of the tea involves cutting the plant into small lengths, adding some water and then fermenting or "sweating" it in heaps (the phenolic compounds are oxidised, and a sweet honey-like scent is produced). A fermentation oven may enhance the process and improve the colour and aroma. It is finally spread out in the sun to dry.

MEDICINAL USES. This uniquely South African (Cape) herbal drink is mainly used as a tea substitute and health drink, because it contains no harmful substances such as caffeine. It has also been used since early times for its direct positive effects on the urinary system and is valued as a stomachic that aids weak digestion without affecting the heart[5,6].

PREPARATION AND DOSAGE. Honeybush tea is used and enjoyed very much like ordinary tea. One or two teaspoons of the product per cup are steeped or more commonly boiled for several minutes. Boiling is said to improve the quality and taste, unlike ordinary tea.

ACTIVE INGREDIENTS. Mangiferin, a xanthone-*C*-glycoside, is a major constituent, together with flavanone-*O*-glycosides, mainly of the aglycones hesperitin (compare *Mentha*) and isosakuranetin[7].

PHARMACOLOGICAL EFFECTS. Apart from the absence of stimulants, it is likely that some beneficial effects may be linked to the free-radical capturing properties of phenolic compounds.

DISTRIBUTION. *Cyclopia* species are restricted to the fynbos region of the Cape. *C. genistoides* occurs in the west; *C. intermedia* and *C. subternata* in the southern and eastern parts[2,3].

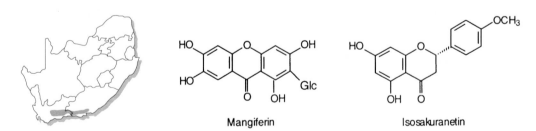

Mangiferin   Isosakuranetin

1. **Forbes, V.S. (ed.) 1986.** *Carl Peter Thunberg Travels at the Cape of Good Hope 1772-1775.* Van Riebeeck Society, Cape Town.
2. **Schutte, A.L. 1995.** *A Taxonomic Study of the Tribes Podalyrieae and Liparieae (Fabaceae).* Ph.D. thesis, Rand Afrikaans University, Johannesburg.
3. **Schutte, A. L. 1997.** A revision of the genus *Cyclopia* (Fabaceae). *Edinb. J. Bot.* (in press).
4. **Schutte, A.L. *et al.* 1995.** Fire-survival strategy – a character of taxonomic, ecological and evolutionary importance in fynbos legumes. *Pl. Syst. Evol.* 195: 243-259.
5. **Marloth, R. 1925.** *The Flora of Southern Africa*, Vol 2(1), pp. 69-72. Darter, Cape Town.
6. **Watt, J.M. & Breyer-Brandwijk, M.G. 1962.** *The Medicinal and Poisonous Plants of Southern and Eastern Africa.* 2nd edition. Livingstone, London.
7. **De Nysschen, A.M. *et al.* 1996.** The major phenolic compounds in the leaves of *Cyclopia* species (honeybush tea). *Biochem. Syst. Ecol.* 24: 243-246.

Cyclopia intermedia

Leaves and flowers of *Cyclopia genistoides*

Leaves and flowers of *Cyclopia intermedia*

Honeybush tea, made from *Cyclopia intermedia*

DATURA STRAMONIUM

Solanaceae

thornapple (English); stinkblaar (Afrikaans); ijoyi, umhlabavuthwa (Xhosa); iloyi, iloqi (Zulu); lethsowe (Sotho); lechoe (Southern Sotho); zaba-zaba (Tsonga)

BOTANICAL DESCRIPTION. This exotic weed is a robust annual of up to 1,5 metres in height. The large, bright green leaves are irregularly toothed and have an unpleasant smell when crushed. Each leaf axil in the mature plant has a single large, white or purplish tubular flower, followed by a characteristic four-locular fruit capsule. These capsules are 50 mm in length and covered with numerous thin spines of about 10 mm long. Inside them are numerous brown, kidney-shaped seeds of about 3 mm long[1].

PLANT PARTS USED. The leaves or more rarely the green fruit are used.

MEDICINAL USES. The plant is much used in traditional medicine, mainly to relieve asthma and to reduce pain. Weak infusions are used as hypnotics by the elderly and as aphrodisiacs by adults. The fresh warmed leaf may be used as a poultice to relieve the pain of rheumatism, gout, boils, abscesses and wounds[2]. The fresh green fruit is sometimes applied locally for toothache, a sore throat and tonsillitis[2]. The leaf is rolled up and smoked to relieve asthma and bronchitis[2,3,4]. Extracts have been included in antitussive syrups and the leaves to treat respiratory difficulties, but these uses have mostly been discontinued. The two major alkaloids of the plant are still used commercially: atropine is an ingredient of eyedrops, while the main use of hyoscine is to treat motion sickness, but it may also be used as an injection to treat Parkinsonism and painful visceral spasms[5,6].

PREPARATION AND DOSAGE. For hyoscine (scopolamine), the maximum dose per injection is 0,25 mg (0,5 mg maximum per day)[5]. For motion sickness, 1,5 mg of the alkaloid is applied behind the ear in the form of a skin patch, releasing 0,5 mg alkaloid in 72 hours[5]. There is a danger of harmful side effects and treatment should never be given without medical advice.

ACTIVE INGREDIENTS. *Datura* species contain several tropane alkaloids, of which atropine (± hyoscyamine) and (-)-hyoscine (scopolamine) are the two major ones[7].

PHARMACOLOGICAL EFFECTS. The alkaloids are highly toxic and have numerous effects on a wide range of receptors. Atropine increases the heart rate, relaxes smooth muscles, decreases saliva, sweat, and other secretions, paralyses certain eye muscles and increases intra-ocular pressure. At low doses, it is a depressant and sedative, but high doses may lead to hallucinations, mental confusion and insomnia. Hyoscine has similar effects[5,6].

DISTRIBUTION. The plant is probably indigenous to tropical America but has become a cosmopolitan weed and is now also widely distributed in South Africa[1].

Atropine
= (±) - Hyoscyamine

(-) - Hyoscine
= (-) - Scopolamine

1. **Henderson, M. & Anderson, J.G. 1966.** *Common weeds in South Africa. Memoirs of the Botanical Survey of South Africa* 37.
2. **Watt, J.M. & Breyer-Brandwijk, M.G. 1962.** *The Medicinal and Poisonous Plants of Southern and Eastern Africa.* 2nd edition. Livingstone, London.
3. **Hutchings, A. & Van Staden, J. 1994.** Plants used for stress-related ailments in traditional Zulu, Xhosa and Sotho medicine. Part 1: Plants used for headaches. *J. Ethnopharmacol.* 43: 89-124.
4. **Iwu, M.M. 1993.** *Handbook of African Medicinal Plants.* CRC Press, Boca Raton.
5. **Bruneton, J. 1995.** *Pharmacognosy, Phytochemistry, Medicinal Plants.* Intercept, Hampshire.
6. **Martindale 1993.** *The Extra Pharmacopoeia.* 30th edition. Pharmaceutical Press, London.
7. **Dictionary of Natural Products on CD-ROM, release 4:2 (1996).** Chapman & Hall, London.

Datura stramonium

Leaves and flowers of *Datura stramonium*

Flower and green fruit of *Datura stramonium*

Dried leaves of *Datura stramonium*

DICOMA CAPENSIS

Asteraceae

---

wilde karmedik, koorsbossie (Afrikaans)

BOTANICAL DESCRIPTION. This indigenous herb is a small plant with creeping branches spreading from a woody, perennial rootstock[1]. The leaves are variable in shape, often oblong but sometimes very narrow, greyish-green in colour and covered with short, dense, white hair. The flower heads are pale mauve and inconspicuous, with a neat halo of numerous spreading bracts. These are long, thin and somewhat spiny, superficially resembling those of true karmedik (see *Cnicus*). Another species, *D. anomala* (Afrikaans: "swartstorm" or "maagbossie") is also used medicinally. It differs in the bright green upper surfaces of the leaves and the larger flower heads.

PLANT PARTS USED. The leaves and twigs are mainly used, but the roots are often included.

MEDICINAL USES. As the Afrikaans vernacular suggests, the plant is widely used to treat fever[2] ("koors" = fever) but also for an upset stomach[3] and numerous other ailments, including influenza, high blood pressure, diarrhoea and even cancer. *D. anomala* is used for similar conditions[2,4]. In addition to the use of aboveground parts, the roots of *D. anomala* are ground and snuffed as a treatment for colds, or a decoction of it in gin has been used to treat haemorrhoids and fever[2]. Anecdotes exist for several other species of *Dicoma*[2].

PREPARATION AND DOSAGE. For an upset stomach and fever, an infusion of the leaves is used[2], but precise details are not available.

ACTIVE INGREDIENTS. There is no scientific evidence to substantiate the reported beneficial effects of this traditional medicine. Several lactones were isolated from aerial parts of *D. capensis*[5], of which 15-acetoxy-14-hydroxycostunolide was the main ingredient, together with small amounts of an acetate of brachylaenolide and various minor compounds. These lactones have not yet been associated with any biological activity.

PHARMACOLOGICAL EFFECTS. As a treatment for fever, the infusion is said to induce perspiration[2] but the pharmacology of the medicine appears to be unknown.

DISTRIBUTION. *D. capensis* is widely distributed in the dry interior of South Africa and is often found in sandy soil along seasonal streams and in disturbed places[1,3].

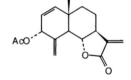

15-Acetoxy-14-hydroxycostunolide   3-Acetoxy-brachylaenolide

---

1. **Pope, G.V. 1992.** Compositae (*Dicoma*). *Flora Zambesiaca* 6(2): 41-42.
2. **Watt, J.M. & Breyer-Brandwijk, M.G. 1962.** *The Medicinal and Poisonous Plants of Southern and Eastern Africa*. 2nd edition. Livingstone, London.
3. **Shearing, D. 1994.** *Karoo. South African Wild Flower Guide 6*. Botanical Society of South Africa, Claremont.
4. **Rood, B. 1994.** *Uit die Veldapteek*. Tafelberg, Cape Town.
5. **Zdero, C. & Bohlmann, F. 1990.** Sesquiterpene lactones from *Dicoma* species. *Phytochemistry* 29: 183-187.

Dicoma capensis

Leaves and flower heads of *Dicoma anomala*

Leaves and flower heads of *Dicoma capensis*

Dicoma capensis product – dried flowering stems

DIOSCOREA DREGEANA

Dioscoreaceae

---

isidakwa (Zulu); wild yam (English); wildejam (Afrikaans)

BOTANICAL DESCRIPTION. The plant is a climber (vine) with a large underground fleshy tuber of up to 300 mm in diameter. Thick robust hairy climbing (twining) stems are produced in spring and tend to die back in the dry winter months. The leaves are divided into three egg-shaped leaflets with distinctive drawn out tips. The inconspicuous flowers are followed by winged fruit. Other species of medicinal interest are *D. sylvatica*, recognised by its relatively smooth tubers and simple, heart-shaped leaves and *D. elephantipes* with its characteristic corky tuber[1,2]. These and several other species have been eradicated in the past, mainly to evaluate them as sources of commercially valuable steroids (see below).

PLANT PARTS USED. The large, fleshy tubers are used.

MEDICINAL USES. The tuber is used in different ways for different purposes[3,4]. It may be hollowed out and the water which is heated in it is used as a lotion for cuts and sores[3]. The plant is also a Zulu remedy for hysteria, convulsions and epilepsy[3,5,6]. The Zulu name "isidakwa" means "the drunkard", referring to the reported effects that it may have[3]. It is also used topically for scabies.

None of the South African species are used commercially, but there are several Central American, Indian and Chinese species of importance in the extraction of steroidal saponins which are hydrolysed to diosgenin. The compound is used as a starting material in steroid hormone semi-synthesis, to produce cortisone and contraceptives[7].

PREPARATION AND DOSAGE. A small piece of the root is boiled in water[5] but the exact dosage and method of preparation are critical because the plant is known to be toxic[3].

ACTIVE INGREDIENTS. The activity of *Dioscorea* species have been ascribed to the action of various steroidal saponins (diosgenin is a well-known aglycone) and also to dioscorine and other alkaloids derived from nicotinic acid[7,8,9].

PHARMACOLOGICAL EFFECTS. Semi-synthetic plant-derived steroids are used as contraceptives and as anti-inflammatory agents, androgens, estrogens and progestins[7].

DISTRIBUTION. *D. dregeana* occurs in the eastern parts of South Africa, mainly in KwaZulu-Natal, Mpumalanga and the Northern Province[1].

Diosgenin   Dioscorine

1. **Von Teichman, I.** *et al.* **1975.** The genus *Dioscorea* L. in South Africa. *Boissiera* 24: 215-224.
2. **Archibald, E.E.A. 1967.** The genus *Dioscorea* in the Cape Province west of East London. *Jl S. Afr. Bot.* 33: 1-46.
3. **Watt, J.M. & Breyer-Brandwijk, M.G. 1962.** *The Medicinal and Poisonous Plants of Southern and Eastern Africa.* 2nd edition. Livingstone, London.
4. **Rood, B. 1994.** *Uit die Veldapteek.* Tafelberg, Cape Town.
5. **Pujol, J. 1990.** *Naturafrica – the Herbalist Handbook.* Jean Pujol Natural Healers' Foundation, Durban.
6. **Watt, J.M. 1967.** African plants potentially useful in mental health. *Lloydia* 30: 1-22.
7. **Bruneton, J. 1995.** *Pharmacognosy, Phytochemistry, Medicinal Plants.* Intercept, Hampshire.
8. **Merck 1989.** *The Merck Index.* 11th edition. Merck, Rahway.
9. **Dictionary of Natural Products on CD-ROM, release 4:2 (1996).** Chapman & Hall, London.

Dioscorea sylvatica

Dioscorea dregeana

Tuber of *Dioscorea dregeana*

Tuber of *Dioscorea elephantipes*

DODONAEA ANGUSTIFOLIA

Sapindaceae

> sandolien, ysterhouttoppe (Afrikaans); sand olive (English);
> mutata-vhana (Venda); mutepipuma (Shona)

BOTANICAL DESCRIPTION. Although previously included in *Dodonaea viscosa*, the South African plant is now considered to be a distinct species closely related to it. The sand olive is a shrub or small tree of about five metres in height, occurring in a wide range of habitats, from deserts to forest margins. The long, narrow leaves are pale green and shiny as a result of a resinous exudate on the surface. The inconspicuous flowers are yellowish-green, followed by small, winged papery fruits, resembling those of *Combretum* species[1,2].

PLANT PARTS USED. The leaves and tips of the twigs are used.

MEDICINAL USES. A decoction of the leaves is an early Cape remedy for fever[3]. It is still used for colds, influenza, stomach trouble and even measles[4,5], for arthritis, and as a gargle for a sore throat and oral thrush. Other early uses include the treatment of pneumonia, tuberculosis and externally as an antipruritic in skin rashes[4].

PREPARATION AND DOSAGE. Fresh leaves and twigs are boiled in water, steeped for a while and then filtered[5].

ACTIVE INGREDIENTS. Dodonic acid[6], hautriwaic acid and structurally related diterpenoids[7] have been isolated from several *Dodonaea* species but there is no direct link between these acids and the reported beneficial effects. Of interest is also the presence of ß-sitosterol, stigmasterol and a glycoside of ß-sitosterol[6]. Several favonoids are known from the plant, of which santin is a typical example[8].

PHARMACOLOGICAL EFFECTS. The plant acts as a febrifuge but details of its exact action are not available. It is possible that the diterpenoids and flavonoids contribute to the activity of the medicine.

DISTRIBUTION. The species is widely distributed except for the central part of South Africa (see map)[9].

Dodonic acid   Hautriwaic acid   Santin

1. **Palmer, E. & Pitman, J. 1972.** *Trees of Southern Africa.* Balkema, Cape Town.
2. **Coates Palgrave, K. 1977.** *Trees of Southern Africa.* Struik, Cape Town.
3. **Forbes, V.S. (ed.) 1986.** *Carl Peter Thunberg Travels at the Cape of Good Hope 1772-1775.* Van Riebeeck Society, Cape Town.
4. **Watt, J.M. & Breyer-Brandwijk, M.G. 1962.** *The Medicinal and Poisonous Plants of Southern and Eastern Africa.* 2nd edition. Livingstone, London.
5. **Rood, B. 1994.** *Uit die Veldapteek.* Tafelberg, Cape Town.
6. **Sachev, K. & Kulshreshtha, D.K. 1984.** Dodonic acid, a new diterpenoid from *Dodonaea viscosa. Planta Med.* 50: 448-449.
7. **Dictionary of Natural Products on CD-ROM, release 4:2 (1996).** Chapman & Hall, London.
8. **Sachev, K. & Kulshreshtha, D.K. 1984.** Flavonoids from *Dodonaea viscosa. Phytochemistry* 22: 1253-1256, and references cited therein.
9. **Von Breitenbach, F. 1986.** *National List of Indigenous Trees.* Dendrological Foundation, Pretoria.

Dodonaea angustifolia

Leaves of *Dodonaea angustifolia*

Fruits of *Dodonaea angustifolia*

Dodonaea angustifolia leaves, as they are sold for medicinal use

DOMBEYA ROTUNDIFOLIA

Sterculiaceae

---

inhlizya enkulu (Zulu); motubane (Tswana); mulanga (Venda); mohlabaphala (Northern Sotho); dikbas (Afrikaans); wild pear (English)

BOTANICAL DESCRIPTION. This is a small, usually single-stemmed tree of about six metres in height. The bark is dark brown and furrowed. The large, leathery leaves are rounded in shape with a dark green upper surface and a paler, hairy lower surface with five main veins arising from the base. Attractive white or rarely pale pink flowers are produced in masses in spring (before the leaves appear), followed by small spherical capsules in summer[1,2]. The tree has become a popular garden subject.

PLANT PARTS USED. The bark is mainly used, but sometimes also the wood or the roots.

MEDICINAL USES. Infusions are used orally or as enemas to treat internal ulcers[3], but also for haemorroids, diarrhoea and stomach problems[3,4]. It is claimed to be effective against nausea in pregnant women[4]. Decoctions of the bark are sometimes used in delayed labour, to hasten the onset of the process[3]. It is also used for chest complaints[5].

PREPARATION AND DOSAGE. Infusions or decoctions of the bark (rarely the roots)[6] are taken orally or injected as enemas, sometimes mixed with other ingredients. The powdered root may be burnt and the smoke inhaled, after which the powder is used as snuff[6]. The bark may also be chewed[3].

ACTIVE INGREDIENTS. There appears to be no published information on the chemical composition of *Dombeya* species[7]. Other members of the family (*Cola, Theobroma*) contain pharmaceutically important purine bases, such as caffeine, but these alkaloids have not yet been found in *Dombeya* species.

PHARMACOLOGICAL EFFECTS. No details about the pharmacological activity of the medicine are known.

DISTRIBUTION. The species is restricted to the northern parts of South Africa, and it is commonly found in KwaZulu-Natal, the North-West Province, Gauteng, Mpumalanga and the Northern Province[8].

Caffeine
(from *Cola* and *Theobroma*, but not reported from *Dombeya*)

---

1. **Palmer, E. & Pitman, J. 1972.** *Trees of Southern Africa.* Balkema, Cape Town.
2. **Coates Palgrave, K. 1977.** *Trees of Southern Africa.* Struik, Cape Town.
3. **Watt, J.M. & Breyer-Brandwijk, M.G. 1962.** *The Medicinal and Poisonous Plants of Southern and Eastern Africa.* 2nd edition. Livingstone, London.
4. **Pujol, J. 1990.** *Naturafrica – the Herbalist Handbook.* Jean Pujol Natural Healers' Foundation, Durban.
5. **Smith, C.A. 1966.** *Common Names of South African Plants. Memoirs of the Botanical Survey of South Africa* 35.
6. **Teichler, G.H. 1971.** *Albizia anthelmintica* (monogo) – a good worm medicine. *Botswana Notes and Records* 3: 6-7.
7. **Dictionary of Natural Products on CD-ROM, release 4:2 (1996).** Chapman & Hall, London.
8. **Von Breitenbach, F. 1986.** *National List of Indigenous Trees.* Dendrological Foundation, Pretoria.

Dombeya rotundifolia

Flowers of *Dombeya rotundifolia*

Bark of *Dombeya rotundifolia*   Leaves of *Dombeya rotundifolia*

DRIMIA ROBUSTA

Hyacinthaceae

> **indongana-zibomvana, isiklenama (Zulu); brandui (Afrikaans)**

BOTANICAL DESCRIPTION. Species of *Drimia* are geophytes with large underground bulbs, strap-shaped leaves and long, slender flowering stalks. The flowers are tubular, with the tips of the petals characteristically reflexed and the stamens fused into a narrow tube[1]. There is much confusion between *Drimia* and the closely related *Urginia*, partly because there has been an attempt to unite the two genera[1]. In *Urginia*, however, the petals and stamens are mostly free from each other and they are spreading, not folded backwards.

PLANT PARTS USED. The bulbs and leaves are used.

MEDICINAL USES. *Drimia* species have been used as expectorants and emetics[2]. *D. robusta* and *D. elata* leaves are said to be diuretic and are used to clean the bladder and to treat diseases of the uterus[3]. It is interesting to note that the closely related squill (*Urginia maritima*, sometimes called *Drimia maritima*) is used in several countries as a heart tonic, diuretic and expectorant[4,5,6]. Some *Urginea* species are important traditional medicines[7,8], such as *U. sanguinea* ("sekanama" or "skanama" in Sotho and Tswana), which is used as a "blood purifier" and as a treatment for several other ailments[7]. In KwaZulu-Natal, *U. epigea* (sometimes considered to be a form of *U. altissima*) and other species (all known as "isiklenama") are used in traditional medicine[8].

PREPARATION AND DOSAGE. Decoctions and infusions of the bulbs and leaves are taken, but these plants are highly toxic and dangerous (some have been used as arrow poisons[9]).

ACTIVE INGREDIENTS. *Drimia* species have not been studied chemically[10] but the closely related *Urginia* produces various cardiac glycosides[10], such as scillaren A. This glycoside yields, upon enzymatic hydrolysis, the medicinally important glycoside proscillaridin A. Scillaren A was also isolated from *U. sanguinea*[11].

PHARMACOLOGICAL EFFECTS. The pharmacology of *D. robusta* and *D. elata* appears to be unknown but the relationship with *Urginia* suggests similar activity (heart tonic, diuretic and expectorant). The bulbs are highly irritant when handled, but the effect is due to crystalline needles of calcium oxalate[4].

DISTRIBUTION. *D. robusta* is widely distributed over the north-eastern parts of South Africa[1].

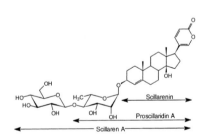

1. **Jessop, 1977.** Studies in the bulbous Liliaceae in South Africa: 7. The taxonomy of *Drimia* and certain allied genera. *Jl S. Afr. Bot.* 43: 265-319.
2. **Watt, J.M. & Breyer-Brandwijk, M.G. 1962.** *The Medicinal and Poisonous Plants of Southern and Eastern Africa.* 2nd edition. Livingstone, London.
3. **Pujol, J. 1990.** *Naturafrica – the Herbalist Handbook.* Jean Pujol Natural Healers' Foundation, Durban.
4. **Grieve, M. 1967.** *A Modern Herbal.* Hafner, London.
5. **Bruneton, J. 1995.** *Pharmacognosy, Phytochemistry, Medicinal Plants.* Intercept, Hampshire.
6. **Iwu, M.M. 1993.** *Handbook of African Medicinal Plants.* CRC Press, Boca Raton.
7. **Foukaridis, G.N.** *et al.* **1995.** The ethnopharmacology and toxicology of *Urginea sanguinea* in the Pretoria area. *J. Ethnopharmacol.* 49: 77-79.
8. **Hutchings, A. 1996.** *Zulu Medicinal Plants.* Natal University Press, Pietermaritzburg.
9. **Neuwinger, H.D. 1994.** *Afrikanische Arzneipflanzen und Jagdgifte.* Wissenschaftliche Verlagsgesellschaft, Stuttgart.
10. **Dictionary of Natural Products on CD-ROM, release 4:2 (1996).** Chapman & Hall, London.
11. **Louw, P.G.J. 1952.** Transvaalin, a cardiac glycoside isolated from *Urginea burkei*, Bkr. (Transvaal slangkop). *Onderstepoort J. Vet. Res.* 25: 123-133 [*U. burkei* is now *U. sanguinea*, see ref. 1].

Flowers of *Drimia robusta*

Drimia robusta

Bulbs of *Drimia robusta*

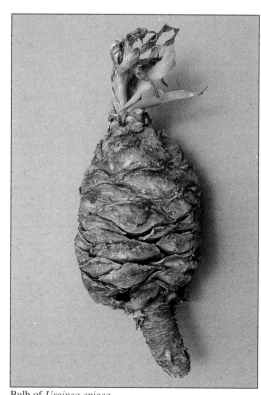

Bulb of *Urginea epigea*

EKEBERGIA CAPENSIS

Meliaceae

umnyamathi (Zulu); mmidibidibi (Northern Sotho); Cape ash (English); essenhout (Afrikaans)

BOTANICAL DESCRIPTION. It is a medium-sized tree of about 10 to 12 metres in height. The bark is grey and rough, and peels off in thick flakes. A distinctive characteristic is the thickened leaf scars on the twigs. The leaves are compound, with seven or nine broadly oblong leaflets. Small white or pinkish flowers in spring are followed by fleshy fruits in summer, which are rounded and reddish in colour[1,2].

PLANT PARTS USED. The bark is mainly used, sometimes the leaves or roots.

MEDICINAL USES. The bark is used as an emetic and for dysentery and heartburn[3,4]. The roots are also used for chronic coughs, dysentery, acute gastritis, headache and scabies[3,4,5]. A decoction of the leaves may be taken as a vermifuge[3,4]. An infusion of the powdered bark, sometimes mixed with flour, is applied externally to abscesses, boils and acne[4].

PREPARATION AND DOSAGE. To treat gastritis, equal amounts of bark and root are powdered, and an infusion of one teaspoon in half a cup of water is taken half an hour before meals[4].

ACTIVE INGREDIENTS. The chemical compounds of *Ekebergia* species are poorly known[6]. Seeds of *E. capensis* contain a limonoid – ekebergin – as the major constituent[6,7]. However, no limonoids were found in the bark or timber[7]. The medicinal value is therefore unlikely to be due to these compounds. Limonoids are insect antifeedants and have been used to treat intestinal parasites.

PHARMACOLOGICAL EFFECTS. No published information could be found.

DISTRIBUTION. The species is widely distributed in the eastern parts of South Africa[8].

Ekebergin

1. **Palmer, E. & Pitman, J. 1972.** *Trees of Southern Africa.* Balkema, Cape Town.
2. **Coates Palgrave, K. 1977.** *Trees of Southern Africa.* Struik, Cape Town.
3. **Watt, J.M. & Breyer-Brandwijk, M.G. 1962.** *The Medicinal and Poisonous Plants of Southern and Eastern Africa.* 2nd edition. Livingstone, London.
4. **Pujol, J. 1990.** *Naturafrica – the Herbalist Handbook.* Jean Pujol Natural Healers' Foundation, Durban.
5. **Hutchings, A. & Van Staden, J. 1994.** Plants used for stress-related ailments in traditional Zulu, Xhosa and Sotho medicine. Part 1: Plants used for headaches. *J. Ethnopharmacol.* 43: 89-124.
6. **Dictionary of Natural Products on CD-ROM, release 4:2 (1996).** Chapman & Hall, London.
7. **Taylor, D.A.H. 1981.** Ekebergin, a limonoid extractive from *Ekebergia capensis. Phytochemistry* 20: 2263-2265.
8. **Von Breitenbach, F. 1986.** *National List of Indigenous Trees.* Dendrological Foundation, Pretoria.

Ekebergia capensis

Leaf and flowers of *Ekebergia capensis*

Fruits of *Ekebergia capensis*

Bark of *Ekebergia capensis*, as it is sold for medicinal use

ELEPHANTORRHIZA ELEPHANTINA

Fabaceae

---

intolwane (Xhosa, Zulu); mositsane (Sotho, Tswana); mupangara (Shona);
elandsboontjie (Afrikaans); elandsbean (English)

BOTANICAL DESCRIPTION. The plant has several unbranched, annual stems of nearly one metre in height, growing from an enormous underground rhizome of up to eight metres long. The finely divided leaves have numerous small, narrow leaflets. Clusters of small, cream-coloured flowers are produced along the lower half of the aerial stem. The characteristic pods are up to 200 mm long, with the inner parts breaking free and peeling off from the persistent margins[1].

PLANT PARTS USED. The underground rhizomes, commonly referred to as roots, are used.

MEDICINAL USES. This is a traditional remedy for a wide range of ailments, including diarrhoea and dysentry, stomach disorders, haemorrhoids and perforated peptic ulcers, and as emetics[2,3,4]. It is popular for the treatment of skin diseases and acne.

PREPARATION AND DOSAGE. The grated root is steeped in water for 24 hours or more, after which it is strained and ready for external use[4]. For internal use, however, the infusion has to be boiled for 10 minutes, and small quantities are taken three times a day[4]. To treat acne, the face is held in the vapour arising from a warm infusion[4].

ACTIVE INGREDIENTS. The bright red colour of the rhizomes indicates the presence of tannins or other phenolic compounds, but there is no published information[5] on the chemistry of *Elephantorrhiza* species. The related genus *Entada* contains the pentacyclic triterpenoid entagenic acid[5], and it is possible that these or structurally related terpenoids and their saponins are present in *Elephantorrhiza*.

PHARMACOLOGICAL EFFECTS. The activity of the medicine is not clear. However, tannins are known antidiarrhoeals and antiseptics, effective in the treatment of infectious diarrhoeas[6]. As antibacterials and antifungals, they are useful to treat dermatitis and are known to form a protective layer on the skin and mucosa, thereby enhancing tissue regeneration[6].

DISTRIBUTION. *E. elephantina* occurs in grassland areas over large parts of South Africa[1].

Entagenic acid

---

1. **Ross, J.H. 1975.** Subfamily Mimosoideae. *Flora of Southern Africa* 16(1). Botanical Research Institute, Pretoria.
2. **Watt, J.M. & Breyer-Brandwijk, M.G. 1962.** *The Medicinal and Poisonous Plants of Southern and Eastern Africa.* 2nd edition. Livingstone, London.
3. **Hutchings, A. 1989.** A survey and analysis of traditional medicinal plants as used by the Zulu, Xhosa and Sotho. *Bothalia* 19: 111-123.
4. **Pujol, J. 1990.** *Naturafrica – the Herbalist Handbook.* Jean Pujol Natural Healers' Foundation, Durban.
5. **Dictionary of Natural Products on CD-ROM, release 4:2 (1996).** Chapman & Hall, London.
6. **Bruneton, J. 1995.** *Pharmacognosy, Phytochemistry, Medicinal Plants.* Intercept, Hampshire.

Elephantorrhiza elephantina

Flower clusters and dry fruits of *Elephantorrhiza elephantina*

Piece of a rhizome of
Elephantorrhiza elephantina

ELYTROPAPPUS RHINOCEROTIS

Asteraceae

renosterbos, renosterbostoppe (Afrikaans)

BOTANICAL DESCRIPTION. This exceptionally common Cape plant is an erect bushy shrub of up to one metre in height. The minute, greyish-green leaves are tightly grouped on the thin stems. The tiny flower heads are inconspicuous, with a single floret in each[1]. Renosterveld, a distinctive veld type in some parts of the Western and Eastern Cape provinces, is named after this dominant and invasive species.

PLANT PARTS USED. The young tips of the branches are used.

MEDICINAL USES. Infusions of the young branches in brandy or wine are a traditional Cape medicine for indigestion, dyspepsia, ulcers and stomach cancer[2,3,4,5]. It may also be taken as a tonic to improve a lack of appetite and as a stomachic bitter[2,3]. Some reports claim it to have been a popular remedy during the 1918 influenza epidemic and that it stimulates perspiration[2,4,5].

PREPARATION AND DOSAGE. Infusions or tinctures were traditionally used[2,3,5] – a small amount taken three times a day.

ACTIVE INGREDIENTS. Some of the activity of the medicine may be due to rhinocerotinoic acid, a labdane diterpenoid which has been isolated from *E. rhinocerotis*[6].

PHARMACOLOGICAL EFFECTS. Rhinocerotinoic acid has significant anti-inflammatory activity but tested negatively as an anti-arthritic[6].

DISTRIBUTION. The species is widely distributed in the Western, Northern and Eastern Cape[7].

Rhinocerotinoic acid

1. **Levyns, M.R. 1935.** A revision of *Elytropappus* Cass. *Jl. S. Afr. Bot.* 1: 89.
2. **Smith, C.A. 1966.** *Common Names of South African Plants. Memoirs of the Botanical Survey of South Africa* 35. 642.
3. **Cillié, A.M. 1992.** *Kruie op Witblits, Rate, Resepte en Feite.* Unpublished notes, Worcester Museum.
4. **Watt, J.M. & Breyer-Brandwijk, M.G. 1962.** *The Medicinal and Poisonous Plants of Southern and Eastern Africa.* 2nd edition. Livingstone, London.
5. **Rood, B. 1994.** *Uit die Veldapteek.* Tafelberg, Cape Town.
6. **Dekker, T.G.** *et al.* **1988.** Studies of South African medicinal plants. Part 7. Rhinocerotinoic acid: a labdane diterpene with anti-inflammatory properties from *Elytropappus rhinocerotis*. *S. Afr. J. Chem.* 41: 33-35.
7. **Koekemoer, M.,** personal communication.

Elytropappus rhinocerotis

Tincture of *Elytropappus rhinocerotis*

Stems and leaves of *Elytropappus rhinocerotis*

Elytropappus rhinocerotis, as it is sold for medicinal use

EMBELIA RUMINATA

Myrsinaceae

ibhinini (Zulu)

BOTANICAL DESCRIPTION. This plant is a climbing shrub of up to five metres in height, sometimes becoming tree-like. The dark green, shiny leaves have translucent glands dotted all over. Inconspicuous greenish flowers occur in short, elongated clusters, followed by small round pea-sized capsules[1,2].

PLANT PARTS USED. The roots are usually used, but sometimes also the bark, leaves or fruit.

MEDICINAL USES. The plant is a traditional remedy against tapeworm[3,4,5] and is also used as a general tonic. Several other African species of *Embelia* are used for the same purposes[6]. Ammonium embelate is used as an anthelmintic against cestodes[7] (see below).

PREPARATION AND DOSAGE. Alcoholic or watery infusions are used, but the plant is potentially toxic and should not be taken without proper supervision.

ACTIVE INGREDIENTS. The active ingredient is embelin, a benzoquinone which has been isolated from several *Embelia* species[8]. The diammonium salt of embelin (ammonium embelate) is used commercially as a vermifuge[7], but this product irritates mucous membranes and may cause prolonged and violent sneezing[7].

PHARMACOLOGICAL EFFECTS. Besides the proven anthelmintic properties, embelin has also been tested as an antifertility agent[9].

DISTRIBUTION. The plant has a restricted distribution along the coastal parts of the Eastern Cape and KwaZulu-Natal[1,2].

HO — OH — $(CH_2)_{10}CH_3$

Embelin

1. **Dyer, R.A. 1963.** Myrsinaceae. In: *Flora of Southern Africa* 26: 1-9. Botanical Research Institute, Pretoria.
2. **Coates Palgrave, K. 1977.** *Trees of Southern Africa.* Struik, Cape Town.
3. **Cawston, F.G. 1933.** Native medicines of Natal. *S.A. Med. J.*, 10 June 1933: 370-371.
4. **Watt, J.M. & Breyer-Brandwijk, M.G. 1962.** *The Medicinal and Poisonous Plants of Southern and Eastern Africa.* 2nd edition. Livingstone, London.
5. **Pujol, J. 1990.** *Naturafrica – the Herbalist Handbook.* Jean Pujol Natural Healers' Foundation, Durban.
6. **Iwu, M.M. 1993.** *Handbook of African Medicinal Plants.* CRC Press, Boca Raton.
7. **Merck 1989.** *The Merck Index.* 11th edition. Merck, Rahway.
8. **Dictionary of Natural Products on CD-ROM, release 4:2 (1996).** Chapman & Hall, London.
9. **Prakash, A.O. 1981.** Antifertility investigations on embelin – an oral contraceptive of plant origin. Part 1. Biological properties. *Planta Med.* 41: 259-266.

Flowers of *Embelia ruminata*

Fruits of *Embelia ruminata*

Fleshy roots of *Embelia ruminata*

ERIOCEPHALUS AFRICANUS

Asteraceae

> **kapokbos, wilde roosmaryn (Afrikaans); wild rosemary (English)**

BOTANICAL DESCRIPTION. The plant is a small, multi-branched shrub of up to a metre in height. Clusters of small silver, hairy leaves are borne along the branches. The attractive white or slightly purplish flower heads are followed by conspicuous tufts of seed hairs, giving the shrub a distinctive appearance. It is these tufts of seed hairs that resemble snow (Afrikaans: "kapok") hence the Afrikaans vernacular name[1].

PLANT PARTS USED. The leaves and twigs are used.

MEDICINAL USES. Several species of *Eriocephalus* (*E. africanus, E. ericoides, E. racemosus* and *E. umbellatus*) are traditionally used as diaphoretics and diuretics[2,3,4]. Early records show that *E. umbellatus* was used by the early Cape people and the Khoi as a diuretic to treat oedema (dropsy)[5] and for stomach ache[6]. Claims have been made that it is beneficial for heart disease, including heart failure[2,3,4].

PREPARATION AND DOSAGE. Infusions, decoctions and brandy tinctures were commonly used[2,3,4].

ACTIVE INGREDIENTS. The aboveground parts of *E. africanus* contain a mixture of sesquiterpenoid lactones[7,8] of which 4,11-eudesmanediol is the major constituent, together with smaller quantities of ivangustine and dehydrofalcarinol[7]. The last-mentioned compound is said to be characteristic of *Eriocephalus* species[7]. There are, however, no definite links between these compounds and the reported effects of the medicine.

PHARMACOLOGICAL EFFECTS. A known antispasmodic[8] which may partly contribute to the medicinal value of the plant is 4,11-eudesmanediol. The plant's reputation as a diuretic may account for its value in treating heart failure.

DISTRIBUTION. *E. africanus* occurs mainly in the Western Cape, Eastern Cape and Namaqualand.

$$H_2C=CH(CH_2)_5CH=CHCH_2C\equiv CC\equiv CCH(OH)CH=CH_2$$
Dehydrofalcarinol

4,11-Eudesmanediol

Ivangustin

1. **Smith, C.A. 1966.** *Common Names of South African Plants. Memoirs of the Botanical Survey of South Africa* 35.
2. **Watt, J.M. & Breyer-Brandwijk, M.G. 1962.** *The Medicinal and Poisonous Plants of Southern and Eastern Africa.* 2nd edition. Livingstone, London.
3. **Cillié, A.M. 1992.** *Kruie op Witblits, Rate, Resepte en Feite.* Unpublished notes, Worcester Museum.
4. **Rood, B. 1994.** *Uit die Veldapteek.* Tafelberg, Cape Town.
5. **Forbes, V.S. (ed.) 1986.** *Carl Peter Thunberg Travels at the Cape of Good Hope 1772-1775.* Van Riebeeck Society, Cape Town.
6. **Laidler, P.W. 1926.** The magic medicine of the Hottentots. *S. Afr. J. Sci.* 25: 433-447.
7. **Zdero, C. et al. 1987.** Sesquiterpene lactones and other constituents from *Eriocephalus* species. *Phytochemistry* 26: 2763-2775.
8. **Dictionary of Natural Products on CD-ROM, release 4:2 (1996).** Chapman & Hall, London.

Eriocephalus racemosus

Eriocephalus africanus

Flower heads of *Eriocephalus africanus*

Hairy fruits of *Eriocephalus africanus*

ERYTHRINA LYSISTEMON

Fabaceae

umsinsi (Zulu); nsisimbane (Tsonga); muvale (Tswana);
gewone koraalboom (Afrikaans); common coral tree (English)

BOTANICAL DESCRIPTION. This well-known tree reaches a height of about six to eight metres and can easily be recognised by the thick, thorny branches and bright red flowers[1,2,3]. The leaves are divided into three large pointed leaflets. Small, hooked thorns are present on the branches and leaf stalks. The bright red flowers are grouped in characteristic elongated clusters. The fruit is a black, cylindrical pod which is strongly constricted between the seeds. Like in most species of *Erythrina*, the seeds (commonly known as lucky beans) are bright red with a contrasting black spot. *E. lysistemon* is sometimes confused with *E. caffra*, the coastal coral tree. In the latter, the upper flower petal is longer, broader and curves upwards, so that the stamens are visible.

PLANT PARTS USED. The bark is mainly used, and sometimes the leaves or roots.

MEDICINAL USES. The main use of the bark (rarely also the crushed leaves) is to treat sores, wounds, abscesses and arthritis[3,4,5]. Open wounds may be treated with the powdered, burnt bark; infusions of the leaves are used as ear drops to relieve earache;

and decoctions of the roots are applied to sprains[3]. The Vhavenda use the bark for toothache[5]. Similar uses have been recorded for *E. caffra*[5].

PREPARATION AND DOSAGE. To treat sores, wounds and swellings, the bark is applied as a poultice, sometimes mixed with other ingredients[4,5].

ACTIVE INGREDIENTS. A large number of tetracyclic isoquinoline alkaloids (the so-called *Erythrina* alkaloids) are known from several *Erythrina* species[6]. Typical examples also reported from *E. lysistemon* and *E. caffra* include erysovine and erythraline[6,7].

PHARMACOLOGICAL EFFECTS. *Erythrina* alkaloids are known to be highly toxic[8] but the traditional uses strongly suggest antibacterial, anti-inflammatory and analgesic effects. A wide range of biological activities have been reported for extracts from various *Erythrina* species[5,9].

DISTRIBUTION. *E. lysistemon* is a common tree from the eastern and northern parts of South Africa[10] and is widely cultivated in gardens and parks.

CH₃O

HO

CH₃O''''

Erysovine

Erythraline

1. **Hennesy, E. 1991.** A revision of the genus *Erythrina. Bothalia* 21(1): 1-25.
2. **Palmer, E. & Pitman, J. 1972.** *Trees of Southern Africa.* Balkema, Cape Town.
3. **Coates Palgrave, K. 1977.** *Trees of Southern Africa.* Struik, Cape Town.
4. **Pujol, J. 1990.** *Naturafrica – the Herbalist Handbook.* Jean Pujol Natural Healers' Foundation, Durban.
5. **Hutchings, A. 1996.** *Zulu Medicinal Plants.* University of Natal Press, Pietermaritzburg (and references cited therein).
6. **Dictionary of Natural Products on CD-ROM, release 4:2 (1996).** Chapman & Hall, London.
7. **Games, D.E. et al. 1974.** Alkaloids of some African, Asian, Polynesian and Australian species of *Erythrina. Lloydia* 37: 581-585.
8. **Bruneton, J. 1995.** *Pharmacognosy, Phytochemistry, Medicinal Plants.* Intercept, Hampshire.
9. **Iwu, M.M. 1993.** *Handbook of African Medicinal Plants.* CRC Press, Boca Raton (and references cited therein).
10. **Von Breitenbach, F. 1986.** *National List of Indigenous Trees.* Dendrological Foundation, Pretoria.

Erythrina lysistemon

Flowers of *Erythrina lysistemon*

Flowers and seeds of *Erythrina caffra*

Bark or stems of both species are
sold for medicinal use

ERYTHROPHLEUM LASIANTHUM

Fabaceae

umbhemise, umkhwangu (Zulu); Swazi ordeal tree (English);
Swazi-oordeelboom (Afrikaans)

BOTANICAL DESCRIPTION. It is a tree of up to 14 metres in height, with a more or less rounded crown and greyish-brown, rough bark[1,2,3]. The leaves are twice divided into numerous leaflets, each about 40 mm long. The leaflets are hairless on the upper surface but may have some hairs on the lower surface along the midrib. Numerous small cream or greenish-yellow flowers are arranged in oblong, bottlebrush-like clusters. These are followed by thin, slightly woody pods of about 120 mm long and 35 mm wide. The plant may be distinguished from other species by the narrow, drawn out tips of the leaflets and the hairy stamens[1,3].

PLANT PARTS USED. The pounded or powdered bark is used.

MEDICINAL USES. The powdered bark is a traditional Zulu remedy for headaches, migraine, general pains in the body, intestinal spasms[4,5,6,7] and fever. The snuff, known as "mbhemiso", is sold in traditional herbal shops in KwaZulu-Natal[6]. *Erythrophleum* species have been widely used in various parts of Africa as ordeal poisons[4,8].

PREPARATION AND DOSAGE. The powdered bark is used as snuff or it may be licked from the hand ("khotha")[5,6]. Decoctions may be used in small amounts for intestinal spasms[5]. Great care should be taken, as all parts of the plant are highly toxic.

ACTIVE INGREDIENTS. Large numbers of diterpenoid alkaloids have been isolated from *Erythrophleum* species[9,10] of which cassaine and erythrophleine are well known[11].

PHARMACOLOGICAL EFFECTS. Erythrophleine and cassaine have a cardiotonic activity similar to digitalis and are highly toxic[10,12]. Erythrophleine is also said to be an analgesic and powerful vasoconstrictor[7].

DISTRIBUTION. The species has a rather limited distribution in the north-eastern part of KwaZulu-Natal, Swaziland and southern Mozambique[1,3].

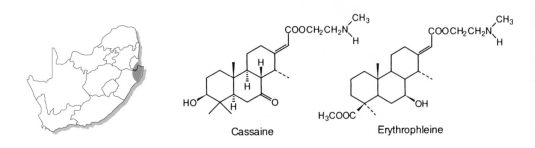

Cassaine   Erythrophleine

1. **Ross, J.H. 1977.** Subfamily Caesalpinioideae. *Flora of Southern Africa* 16(2). Botanical Research Institute, Pretoria.
2. **Palmer, E. & Pitman, J. 1972.** *Trees of Southern Africa.* Balkema, Cape Town.
3. **Coates Palgrave, K. 1977.** *Trees of Southern Africa.* Struik, Cape Town.
4. **Watt, J.M. & Breyer-Brandwijk, M.G. 1962.** *The Medicinal and Poisonous Plants of Southern and Eastern Africa.* 2nd edition. Livingstone, London.
5. **Pujol, J. 1990.** *Naturafrica – the Herbalist Handbook.* Jean Pujol Natural Healers' Foundation, Durban.
6. **Hutchings, A. & Van Staden, J. 1994.** Plants used for stress-related ailments in traditional Zulu, Xhosa and Sotho medicine. Part 1: Plants used for headaches. *J. Ethnopharmacol.* 43: 89-124.
7. **Hutchings, A. 1996.** *Zulu Medicinal Plants.* University of Natal Press, Pietermaritzburg.
8. **Iwu, M.M. 1993.** *Handbook of African Medicinal Plants.* CRC Press, Boca Raton.
9. **Dictionary of Natural Products on CD-ROM, release 4:2 (1996).** Chapman & Hall, London.
10. **Verotta, L. *et al.* 1995.** Chemical and pharmacological characterization of *Erythrophleum lasianthum* alkaloids. *Planta Med.* 61: 271-274.
11. **Merck 1989.** *The Merck Index.* 11th edition. Merck, Rahway.
12. **Bruneton, J. 1995.** *Pharmacognosy, Phytochemistry, Medicinal Plants.* Intercept, Hampshire.

Foliage of *Erythrophleum lasianthum*

Fruit of *Erythrophleum lasianthum*

Flower clusters of *Erythrophleum lasianthum*

Bark of *Erythrophleum lasianthum*

EUCLEA UNDULATA

Ebenaceae

> guarrie (Khoi); gewone ghwarrie (Afrikaans); common guarri (English); umgwali (Xhosa); mokwere kwere (Sotho); inkunzane, gwanxe (Zulu); chizuzu (Shona)

BOTANICAL DESCRIPTION. This common and widely distributed plant is a shrub or small rounded tree of about four metres in height, rarely reaching seven metres. The leaves are small, about 30 mm long and 10 mm wide, usually yellowish-green with markedly wavy margins. Small, whitish flowers are followed by round, berry-like fruit of about five mm in diameter. These thinly fleshy, edible fruits are initially brownish-red, but turn black at maturity[1,2].

PLANT PARTS USED. The roots are used, but rarely also the bark and fruits of other species.

MEDICINAL USES. Infusions of the roots have traditionally been used in the Cape for heart diseases[3,4,5] and elsewhere it is known as a remedy for headache and toothache[6]. Decoctions of the roots of other species have numerous medicinal applications[7], suggesting purgative, analgesic and anti-inflammatory properties.

PREPARATION AND DOSAGE. Infusions of the dried and powdered roots are generally used[3,4,5].

ACTIVE INGREDIENTS. *E. undulata* roots contain two naphthoquinones, diospyrin and 7-methyl-juglone as major constituents[8,9].

PHARMACOLOGICAL EFFECTS. Naphthoquinones have a wide range of activities, including antispasmodic, antibacterial, emollient and antipruritic effects but they are nonetheless of limited pharmaceutical interest[10].

DISTRIBUTION. This well-known tree is locally dominant over large parts of South Africa. Two varieties have been described: the typical variety, var. *undulata* (common guarri), which has a coastal distribution and var. *myrtina* (small-leaved guarri), which occurs mainly in the Northern Cape, North-West and Northern Province[11].

Diospyrin   7-Methyl juglone

1. **Coates Palgrave, K. 1977.** *Trees of Southern Africa.* Struik, Cape Town.
2. **Whyte, F. 1983.** *Flora Zambesiaca* 7(1): 289-295.
3. **Watt, J.M. & Breyer-Brandwijk, M.G. 1962.** *The Medicinal and Poisonous Plants of Southern and Eastern Africa.* 2nd edition. Livingstone, London.
4. **Smith, C.A. 1966.** *Common Names of South African Plants. Memoirs of the Botanical Survey of South Africa* 35.
5. **Pujol, J. 1990.** *Naturafrica – the Herbalist Handbook.* Jean Pujol Natural Healers' Foundation, Durban.
6. **Hutchings, A. & Van Staden, J. 1994.** Plants used for stress-related ailments in traditional Zulu, Xhosa and Sotho medicine. Part 1: Plants used for headaches. *J. Ethnopharmacol.* 43: 89-124.
7. **Hutchings, A. 1996.** *Zulu Medicinal Plants.* University of Natal Press, Pietermaritzburg.
8. **Van der Vijver, L.M. & Gerritsma, K.W. 1974.** Naphthoquinones of *Euclea* and *Diospyros* species. *Phytochemistry* 13: 2322-2323.
9. **Dictionary of Natural Products on CD-ROM, release 4:2 (1996).** Chapman & Hall, London.
10. **Bruneton, J. 1995.** *Pharmacognosy, Phytochemistry, Medicinal Plants.* Intercept, Hampshire.
11. **Von Breitenbach, F. 1986.** *National List of Indigenous Trees.* Dendrological Foundation, Pretoria.

Euclea undulata

Flowers of *Euclea undulata*

Berries of *Euclea undulata*

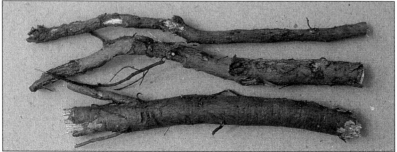

Roots of *Euclea undulata*

EUCOMIS AUTUMNALIS

Hyacinthaceae

umathunga (Zulu); pineapple flower (English); wilde pynappel (Afrikaans)

BOTANICAL DESCRIPTION. This bulbous plant has long, broad, soft-textured leaves with wavy margins. Numerous small, yellowish-green flowers are borne on a thick central stalk. Above the flowers is a rosette of green leaves, a characteristic feature which gives the flower cluster the appearance of a pineapple. The Afrikaans and English common names refer to this superficial resemblance. *E. autumnalis* has been divided into three subspecies[1], two of which are recorded as medicinal plants[2]: *E. autumnalis* subsp. *autumnalis* and *E. autumnalis* subsp. *clavata*. They differ in the flowering stalks; those of the former being cylindrical, while they become wider towards the tip in subsp. *clavata*[1].

PLANT PARTS USED. The bulb is used.

MEDICINAL USES. An enema of a bulb decoction is commonly used for low backache, to assist in postoperative recovery and to aid in the healing of fractures. A decoction of the bulbs is also used for a wide variety of other ailments, including urinary diseases, stomach ache, fevers, colic, flatulence, hangovers and syphilis, and to facilitate childbirth[2,3]. The subspecies *clavata* is also used for coughs and respiratory ailments, biliousness, lumbago, blood disorders, diarrhoea, venereal diseases and to prevent premature childbirth[2,3].

PREPARATION AND DOSAGE. Decoctions of the bulb in water or milk are usually administered as enemas[2,3].

ACTIVE INGREDIENTS. Several homoisoflavones are known from *E. autumnalis*, such as eucomnalin and 3,9-dihydroeucomnalin[4]. Other constituents of this species include the benzopyrones autumnariol and autumnariniol[5], as well as some steroidal triterpenoids such as eucosterol[6].

PHARMACOLOGICAL EFFECTS. Flavonoids are known for their anti-inflammatory and antispasmodic action[7], so that some of the beneficial effects of *Eucomis* may be linked to the presence of homoisoflavonoids. Triterpenoids are known to be beneficial in wound therapy[7] (see *Centella*).

DISTRIBUTION. *E. autumnalis* occurs along the eastern parts of South Africa. The two subspecies are geographically separated[1].

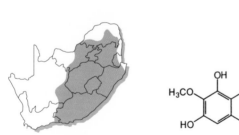

Autumnariol

Eucomnalin

Eucosterol

1. **Reyneke, W.F. 1980.** Three subspecies of *Eucomis autumnalis*. *Bothalia* 13: 140-142.
2. **Watt, J.M. & Breyer-Brandwijk, M.G. 1962.** *The Medicinal and Poisonous Plants of Southern and Eastern Africa*. 2nd edition. Livingstone, London.
3. **Hutchings, A. 1996.** *Zulu Medicinal Plants*. University of Natal Press, Pietermaritzburg.
4. **Tamm, C. 1972.** Die Homo-isoflavone, eine neue Klasse von Naturstoffen. *Arzneim.-Forsch.* 22: 1776-1784, and references cited therein.
5. **Dictionary of Natural Products on CD-ROM, release 4:2 (1996).** Chapman & Hall, London.
6. **Ziegler, R. & Tamm, C. 1976.** Isolation and structure of eucosterol and 16ß-hydroxyeucosterol, two novel spirocyclic nortriterpenes, and of a new 24-nor-5α-chola-8, 16-diene-23-oic acid from bulbs of several *Eucomis* species. *Helv. Chim. Acta* 59: 1997-2011.
7. **Bruneton, J. 1995.** *Pharmacognosy, Phytochemistry, Medicinal Plants*. Intercept, Hampshire.

Eucomis autumnalis

Flower cluster of *Eucomis autumnalis*

Bulb of *Eucomis autumnalis*

FOENICULUM VULGARE

Apiaceae

fennel (English); vinkel (Afrikaans); imboziso (Zulu)

BOTANICAL DESCRIPTION. It is an erect multi-branched robust perennial herb of up to 1,5 metres in height. The leaf stalks form sheaths around the thick stems and the leaves are finely divided into numerous needle-shaped segments, giving them a feathery appearance. Small yellow flowers are borne in a distinctive umbel, i.e. with all the flower stalks of equal length and radiating from one point. The small, yellowish-brown fruits are divided into two segments (mericarps), as in most other members of the carrot family.

PLANT PARTS USED. The small dry fruits (sometimes wrongly referred to as seeds) are mainly used, rarely the leaves or roots.

MEDICINAL USES. Due to its aromatic and carminative properties, fennel has been used since early times to treat flatulence and to reduce the griping effect of laxatives[1,2]. Syrup made from the juice has been used for chronic coughs[1]. Fennel seeds are traditionally used to prepare a domestic gripe water to treat flatulence in infants[1] and the roots are traditionally used as a diuretic to enhance the renal excretion of water[2]. Numerous uses have been recorded in the Western Cape, most commonly for the treatment of poor appetite and indigestion[3,4]. Fennel oil is still used medicinally in Europe for the symptomatic relief of digestive disturbances[2].

PREPARATION AND DOSAGE. Infusions (25 to 40 g of dry fruit in one litre of boiling water) or tinctures (60 to 80 g soaked for several days in one litre of wine)[4] are used as domestic remedies. The essential oil should be used only with proper medical supervision.

ACTIVE INGREDIENTS. Fennel fruit produces an aniseed-flavoured essential oil dominated by phenylpropanoids, mainly anethole. The quality of the medicine depends on the chemical composition of the essential oil. Two types of oil are distinguished, depending on the variety of fennel: bitter fennel oil, which should not contain less than 60% anethole and 15% fenchone and sweet fennel oil, which should have more than 80% anethole[2]. Fennel is an industrial source of *E*-anethone, used as a flavouring agent in the cosmetic and liquor industries[5]. Fennel fruits also contain various flavonoids and furanocoumarins[6].

PHARMACOLOGICAL EFFECTS. Anethole is toxic in high concentration but it has been used as a carminative in fennel water[2,5]. The oil is thought to have antispasmodic and carminative properties[2].

DISTRIBUTION. Fennel is an early introduction from Europe and has become a common roadside weed in South Africa[7].

E-Anethole
(trans-Anethole)

(+)-Fenchone

1. **Grieve, M. 1967.** *A Modern Herbal.* Hafner, London.
2. **Bruneton, J. 1995.** *Pharmacognosy, Phytochemistry, Medicinal Plants.* Intercept, Hampshire.
3. **Watt, J.M. & Breyer-Brandwijk, M.G. 1962.** *The Medicinal and Poisonous Plants of Southern and Eastern Africa.* 2nd edition. Livingstone, London.
4. **Rood, B. 1994.** *Uit die Veldapteek.* Tafelberg, Cape Town.
5. **Merck 1989.** *The Merck Index.* 11th edition. Merck, Rahway.
6. **Dictionary of Natural Products on CD-ROM, release 4:2 (1996).** Chapman & Hall, London.
7. **Smith, C.A. 1966.** *Common Names of South African Plants. Memoirs of the Botanical Survey of South Africa* 35.

Foeniculum vulgare

Flowers and fruits of *Foeniculum vulgare*

Small, dry fruits of *Foeniculum vulgare*

GERANIUM INCANUM

Geraniaceae

---

vrouebossie, bergtee, amarabossie (Afrikaans); ngope-sethsoha, tlako (Sotho)

BOTANICAL DESCRIPTION. This plant is an attractive, sprawling perennial shrublet with finely divided, silvery leaves. The white, pale pink, violet or magenta flowers are borne on long, slender stalks, followed by a characteristically elongated fruit resembling a stork's bill. The hairs on the exterior of the flowers and flower stalks lie flat and are not spreading as in related species[1]. Species of *Geranium* are all very similar and have been much confused in the past[1]. It is therefore possible that some medicinal records apply to species other than true *G. incanum* and *G. canescens*. *G. incanum* has been divided into two varieties: var. *incanum*, with small, white or pale pink flowers, and var. *multifidum*, with larger, light violet to magenta pink flowers[1].

PLANT PARTS USED. The leaves (rarely the roots or fruits) are used.

MEDICINAL USES. The leaves have been used as a tea substitute[2,3], said to be useful for treating bladder infections, venereal diseases and menstruation-related ailments, hence the common name vrouebossie ("vroue" = women; "bossie" = small bush)[4]. *G. canescens* has been used for colic, diarrhoea, fever

and bronchitis[2]. It is interesting to note that other *Geranium* species such as *G. robertianum* (Robert herb) are traditionally used in Europe and America to treat diarrhoea[5,6].

PREPARATION AND DOSAGE. An infusion of the leaves in boiling water is used as a herbal tea[3].

ACTIVE INGREDIENTS. The leaves of *Geranium* species are known to contain tannins, of which geraniin is the best known compound[6,7]. Several flavonoids have also been found in *Geranium* species but there appears to be no published information on the chemistry of *G. incanum*[7].

PHARMACOLOGICAL EFFECTS. The indication common to all tannin-containing drugs is the symptomatic treatment of mild diarrhoea[6]. Severe or persistent diarrhoea should not be treated without medical supervision because of possible dehydration.

DISTRIBUTION. *G. incanum* occurs along the southern coastal areas of the Western and Eastern Cape provinces[1]. The map shows the combined distribution areas of both varieties[1].

Geraniin

---

1. **Hilliard, O.M. & Burtt, B.L. 1985.** A revision of *Geranium* in Africa south of the Limpopo. Notes RBG Edinb. 42: 171-225.
2. **Watt, J.M. & Breyer-Brandwijk, M.G. 1962.** *The Medicinal and Poisonous Plants of Southern and Eastern Africa*. 2nd edition. Livingstone, London.
3. **Rood, B. 1994.** *Uit die Veldapteek*. Tafelberg, Cape Town.
4. **Smith, C.A. 1966.** *Common Names of South African Plants. Memoirs of the Botanical Survey of South Africa* 35.
5. **Grieve, M. 1967.** *A Modern Herbal*. Hafner, London.
6. **Bruneton, J. 1995.** *Pharmacognosy, Phytochemistry, Medicinal Plants*. Intercept, Hampshire.
7. **Dictionary of Natural Products on CD-ROM, release 4:2 (1996).** Chapman & Hall, London.

Geranium incanum

Leaves and flowers of *Geranium incanum*

Single flower of *Geranium incanum*

Dried leaves (and some fruits) of *Geranium incanum*

GETHYLLIS SPECIES

Amaryllidaceae

> ## koekemakranka (Khoi, Afrikaans); kukumakranka (English)

BOTANICAL DESCRIPTION. These interesting plants all have an underground bulb of which the scales form a distinctive neck at ground level. The long, thin leaves are usually spirally twisted or coiled. The attractive flowers appear in summer when the leaves have already died. They have a narrow tube which extends below the ground, where the fruit will eventually develop. In mid-winter, the long, club-shaped berry emerges from the ground. It has a fragrant pulp in which numerous seeds are embedded. There are about 32 *Gethyllis* species, of which *G. afra* (also called "bramakranka"[3]) and *G. spiralis* are perhaps the most fragrant and commonly used ones[1,2].

PLANT PARTS USED. The ripe fleshy fruits are gathered. They are highly aromatic and have a powerful sweet, fruity odour.

MEDICINAL USES. Koekemakranka brandy is one of the early Cape remedies for colic and indigestion[2,3,4,5,6,7]. The edible fruit was highly valued to perfume rooms and linen[4,5]. For children, the gathering of the inconspicuous fruit (which they refer to as "koekemakrankies") is a special occasion, and success depends to a large extent on a good sense of smell. Koekemakranka is one of only a few Khoi words still in use today[3] and is an interesting example of the contribution which the Khoi people have made to the cultural wealth of the Western Cape Province.

PREPARATION AND DOSAGE. Traditionally, an alcoholic infusion or tincture is made from a few ripe fruits in a bottle of brandy or "witblits" – a homemade raw spirit. Directly translated, "witblits" means "white lightning" ("wit" = white; "blits" = flash of lightning).

ACTIVE INGREDIENTS. No published information on the chemistry of *Gethyllis* species could be found[8]. The fruit probably contains palmitate esters of low molecular weight alcohols[5], but no details are available.

PHARMACOLOGICAL EFFECTS. Preliminary tests have indicated slight analgesic effects[9].

DISTRIBUTION. *Gethyllis* species are found only in southern Africa and they are most numerous in the Western and Northern Cape[1,2]. The map shows the distribution area of *G. afra*.

1. **Müller-Doblies, 1986.** Enumeration. *Willdenowia* 15: 465-471.
2. **Du Plessis, N. & Duncan, G. 1989.** *Bulbous Plants of Southern Africa.* Tafelberg, Cape Town.
3. **Smith, C.A. 1966.** *Common Names of South African Plants. Memoirs of the Botanical Survey of South Africa* 35.
4. **Forbes, V.S. (ed.) 1986.** *Carl Peter Thunberg Travels at the Cape of Good Hope 1772-1775.* Van Riebeeck Society, Cape Town.
5. **Watt, J.M. & Breyer-Brandwijk, M.G. 1962.** *The Medicinal and Poisonous Plants of Southern and Eastern Africa.* 2nd edition. Livingstone, London.
6. **Cillié, A.M. 1992.** *Kruie op Witblits, Rate, Resepte en Feite.* Unpublished notes, Worcester Museum.
7. **Rood, B. 1994.** *Uit die Veldapteek.* Tafelberg, Cape Town.
8. **Dictionary of Natural Products on CD-ROM, release 4:2 (1996).** Chapman & Hall, London.
9. **Du Plessis, N.,** personal communication.

Leaves of *Gethyllis namaquensis*

The traditional tincture – note the long, thin berries

Flowers of *Gethyllis villosa*

Flowers of *Gethyllis lanuginosa*

GLYCYRRHIZA GLABRA

Fabaceae

liquorice root (English); soethoutwortel (Afrikaans); mlomo-mnandi (Zulu)

BOTANICAL DESCRIPTION. Liquorice is a robust perennial herb of up to one metre in height, with multi-branched, underground rhizomes and erect, woody stems. The leaves are divided into numerous small, bright green, sparsely hairy leaflets, each about 35 mm long and 20 mm wide. Above the leaves are short clusters of pale purple or white flowers. The small brown pods have about three or four seeds[1].

PLANT PARTS USED. The rhizomes (underground stems), mostly referred to as roots, are harvested.

The rhizomes are dull brown on the surface but bright yellow inside. "Crude extract of liquorice" is a decoction of the washed rhizomes and roots which is filtered and concentrated. Liquorice extracts are widely used as sweeteners and flavour enhancers in beverages (ingredient of dark beers), confectionery (liquorice candy, known in South Africa as "drop") and in tobacco.

MEDICINAL USES. Since ancient times the dried rhizomes or extracts thereof have been used to treat ulcers and coughs and for its sweetening power[2,3,4]. In the Western Cape it has been an early remedy for appendicitis and tuberculosis[5,6]. The crude drug is still popular in modern medicine and is used in laxative teas as an antispasmodic[4]. It is also used in preparations to treat the symptoms of digestive ailments such as epigastric bloating and flatulence and for the symptomatic relief of coughs[4]. The main value of the rhizome is for the extraction of one of the active ingredients, glycyrrhetic acid, which is used externally for its anti-inflammatory properties, especially in pruritis, piles, sunburn and insect bites[4].

PREPARATION AND DOSAGE. Half a cup of boiling water is poured over a teaspoon of coarsely powdered root, and strained after 15 minutes. It should not be used for longer than four weeks without consulting a doctor because of mineralocorticoid side effects[4].

ACTIVE INGREDIENTS. Liquorice root contains numerous flavonoids, isoflavonoids, chalcones and saponins, to which the pharmacological activity is attributed[3,4,7]. The main flavonoids in the fresh root are liquiritin and isoliquiritin[4]. The main saponin, glycyrrhizin, is present in concentrations of 2 to 6%. One of its derivatives, 24-hydroxyglycyrrhizin, is 50 to 100 times sweeter than sugar.

PHARMACOLOGICAL EFFECTS. Glycyrrhizin (the glucoside of glycyrrhetic acid) is a proven anti-inflammatory and also shows weak antiviral, antibacterial, antihepatotoxic, immunostimulating and healing activity[4].

DISTRIBUTION. Liquorice is indigenous to the Mediterranean region of Europe, but is now cultivated in many parts of the world and has become a weed in parts of the Karoo[1].

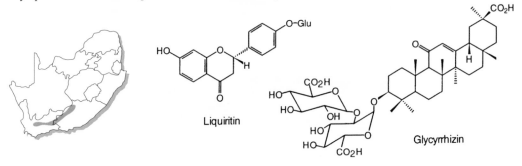

Liquiritin

Glycyrrhizin

1. Henderson, M. & Anderson, J.G. 1966. *Common weeds in South Africa. Memoirs of the Botanical Survey of South Africa* 37.
2. Grieve, M. 1967. *A Modern Herbal.* Hafner, London.
3. Gibson, M.R. 1978. *Glycyrrhiza in old and new perspectives. J. Nat. Prod. (Lloydia)* 41: 348-354.
4. Bruneton, J. 1995. *Pharmacognosy, Phytochemistry, Medicinal Plants.* Intercept, Hampshire.
5. Watt, J.M. & Breyer-Brandwijk, M.G. 1962. *The Medicinal and Poisonous Plants of Southern and Eastern Africa.* 2nd edition. Livingstone, London.
6. Rood, B. 1994. *Uit die Veldapteek.* Tafelberg, Cape Town.
7. Dictionary of Natural Products on CD-ROM, release 4:2 (1996). Chapman & Hall, London.

Glycyrrhiza glabra

Leaves and flowers of *Glycyrrhiza glabra*

Glycyrrhiza glabra product – the dried rhizomes

GNIDIA KRAUSSIANA

Thymelaeaceae

> isidikili, imfuzane, umsilawengwe (Zulu); harige gifbossie (Afrikaans);
> yellow heads (English)

BOTANICAL DESCRIPTION. This is a dense shrublet of up to 0,3 metres in height with numerous erect, hairy stems arising from a woody base. The small, oblong leaves are about 30 mm long and 10 mm wide and usually have silky hairs on the upper and especially the lower surfaces. They are borne on very short (one to two mm long) stalks. Dense, rounded heads of small, yellow, tubular flowers are produced in spring. *G. kraussiana* is very similar to other species but may be distinguished by the hairy stems, silky leaves and the elongated, leafless flower stalks[1].

PLANT PARTS USED. The rootstock and roots are used.

MEDICINAL USES. There are many medicinal uses for this highly toxic plant, ranging from the topical treatment of burns and snake bites to enemas for stomach complaints and decoctions used to ensure an easy childbirth[2,3,4]. Several other species of *Gnidia* are also used medicinally. Amongst these are *G. polycephala*, the roots of which are used in Botswana for a variety of ailments[5] and also *G. capitata* and *G. gymnostachya*, of which the leaves are ground to a snuff, smoked or used as a poultice to treat stomach ache, earache or toothache[6,7].

PREPARATION AND DOSAGE. Decoctions of the roots are mostly used, but there appears to be a wide variety of regional uses, each having a different method of application.

ACTIVE INGREDIENTS. Various toxic daphnane type esters have been identified from *G. kraussiana*[8,9], of which kraussianin is a typical example. *Gnidia* species also contain alkaloids, flavonoids and highly irritant resins[9].

PHARMACOLOGICAL EFFECTS. Diterpenoid esters of the daphnane type are highly toxic and are responsible for the use of *G. kraussiana* as fish and arrow poison[10]. These compounds cause strong inflammatory reactions, are potent inducers of skin tumours and show numerous other biological activities[11].

DISTRIBUTION. *G. kraussiana* is widely distributed in Africa[10]. In South Africa, it occurs in grassland areas in the eastern and northern parts of the country.

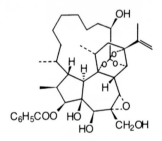

Kraussianin

1. **Van Wyk, A.E. & Malan, S. 1988.** *Field Guide to the Wild Flowers of the Witwatersrand and Pretoria Region*. Struik, Cape Town.
2. **Watt, J.M. & Breyer-Brandwijk, M.G. 1962.** *The Medicinal and Poisonous Plants of Southern and Eastern Africa*. 2nd edition. Livingstone, London.
3. **Hutchings, A. 1996.** *Zulu Medicinal Plants*. University of Natal Press, Pietermaritzburg.
4. **Veale, D.J.H.** *et al.* **1992.** South African traditional herbal medicines used during pregnancy and childbirth. *J. Ethnopharmacol.* 36: 185-191.
5. **Hedberg, I. & Staugård, F. 1989.** *Traditional Medicinal Plants – Traditional Medicine in Botswana*. Ipelegeng publishers, Gabarone.
6. **Gelfand, M.** *et al.* **1985.** *The Traditional Medical Practitioner in Zimbabwe*. Mambo press, Harare.
7. **Hutchings, A. & Van Staden, J. 1994.** Plants used for stress-related ailments in traditional Zulu, Xhosa and Sotho medicine. Part 1: Plants used for headaches. *J. Ethnopharmacol.* 43: 89-124.
8. **Borris, R.P. & Cordell, G.A. 1984.** Studies of the Thymelaeaceae. II. Antineoplastic principles of *Gnidia kraussiana*. *J. Nat. Prod.* 47: 270-278.
9. **Dictionary of Natural Products on CD-ROM, release 4:2 (1996).** Chapman & Hall, London.
10. **Neuwinger, H.D. 1994.** *Afrikanische Arzneipflanzen und Jagdgifte*. Wissenschaftliche Verlagsgesellschaft, Stuttgart.
11. **Bruneton, J. 1995.** *Pharmacognosy, Phytochemistry, Medicinal Plants*. Intercept, Hampshire.

Gnidia kraussiana

Hairy stems and leaves of *Gnidia kraussiana*

Tuberous rhizomes and roots of *Gnidia kraussiana*

GUNNERA PERPENSA

Haloragaceae (or Gunneraceae)

> **ugobho (Zulu); qobo (Sotho); rambola-vhadzimu (Venda);
> river pumpkin (English); rivierpampoen (Afrikaans)**

BOTANICAL DESCRIPTION. This vigorous perennial herb grows in marshy areas and along stream banks. Large round leaves on long, thick stalks arise from the thick, tuberous rhizomes below the ground. They superficially resemble pumpkin leaves, hence the common names. The tiny, reddish-brown flowers are borne in dense groups on a long, thick, flowering stem. Male and female flowers occur in separate parts of the flower cluster: the male ones in the upper part and the females below[1].

PLANT PARTS USED. The thick, fleshy rhizomes, which are dark brown or blackish on the outside but yellow or pinkish-red inside, are used.

MEDICINAL USES. The main medicinal use of the plant is to induce or augment labour and as an antenatal medication to tone the uterus. It is also used to assist in the expulsion of the placenta[2,3,4,5]. It may be taken to treat stomach trouble, rheumatic fever, swellings, menstrual pain and stomach bleeding[2,3,4] or applied externally for the dressing of wounds and for psoriasis[2].

PREPARATION AND DOSAGE. An infusion or decoction of the rhizome (sometimes mixed with other plants) is taken orally or sometimes used as an injection enema known as "chatha"[3].

ACTIVE INGREDIENTS. Nothing appears to be known about the chemistry of *Gunnera* species[6]. An early report mentions the presence of a bitter principle, celastrin[2].

PHARMACOLOGICAL EFFECTS. In preliminary tests, crude decoctions of the rhizome showed definite uterotonic activity[5].

DISTRIBUTION. The plant is restricted to moist habitats but has a wide distribution in the southern, eastern and northern parts of South Africa and northwards into tropical Africa[1].

1. **Mendes, E.J. 1978.** Haloragaceae. *Flora Zambesiaca* 4: 74-81.
2. **Watt, J.M. & Breyer-Brandwijk, M.G. 1962.** *The Medicinal and Poisonous Plants of Southern and Eastern Africa.* 2nd edition. Livingstone, London.
3. **Pujol, J. 1990.** *Naturafrica – the Herbalist Handbook.* Jean Pujol Natural Healers' Foundation, Durban.
4. **Hutchings, A. 1996.** *Zulu Medicinal Plants.* University of Natal Press, Pietermaritzburg.
5. **Kaido, T.L., Veale, D.J.H. & Havlik, I. 1994.** *The Preliminary Screening of Plants Used as Traditional Herbal Remedies During Pregnancy and Labour.* South African Pharmacological Society, 28th annual Congress, Cape Town, 22-24 September 1994.
6. **Dictionary of Natural Products on CD-ROM, release 4:2 (1996).** Chapman & Hall, London.

Gunnera perpensa

Flower cluster of *Gunnera perpensa*

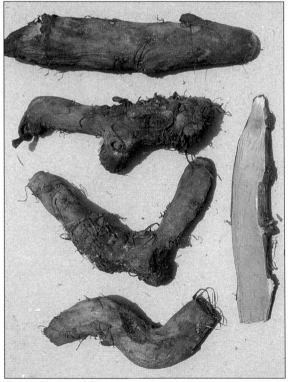

Fleshy rhizomes of *Gunnera perpensa*

HARPAGOPHYTUM PROCUMBENS

Pedaliaceae

---

devil's claw (English); duiwelsklou (Afrikaans)

BOTANICAL DESCRIPTION. This is a weedy, perennial plant[1] with creeping stems spreading from a tuberous fleshy rootstock. The leaves are greyish-green and are usually irregularly divided into several lobes. The tubular flowers are either yellow and violet or uniformly dark violet. The characteristic fruits have numerous long arms with sharp, hooked thorns, as well as two straight thorns on the upper surface. The common name of the plant is derived from the fruit, which may cling tenaciously to the foot of an animal and is dispersed in this way. Two species occur in South Africa. In *H. procumbens*, the arms on the fruit are longer than the width of the fruit, while they are as long as or shorter than the width of the fruit in the other species, *H. zeyheri*[2]. The latter can also be accepted for medicinal use, because it is chemically similar to *H. procumbens*[3].

PLANT PARTS USED. The thick, fleshy secondary roots are sliced and dried.

For conservation purposes, it is important to collect only the secondary roots without damaging the primary root.

MEDICINAL USES. The plant is commonly used to treat rheumatism and arthritis, and as a general health tonic. Infusions of the dried root are used as a cure for digestive disorders and as a tonic in lack of appetite[4]. It is also taken as an analgesic, especially during pregnancy, and the treatment continued after labour[4]. An ointment is made from the root material which is applied to sores, ulcers and boils[4].

PREPARATION AND DOSAGE. An infusion of 1,5 g of powdered material in a cup of boiling water and strained, can be taken daily. Standardised extracts are available in the form of capsules, tablets, tinctures and ointments.

ACTIVE INGREDIENTS. The roots are rich in sugars and also contain phytosterols, triterpenoids and flavonoids[5]. The following iridoids are considered to be the active ingredients: a cinnamic acid ester called harpagoside (the main compound in the fresh and dried root), harpagide (possibly a degradation product of harpagoside) and procumbide[3,5,6,7].

PHARMACOLOGICAL EFFECTS. Very few pharmacological studies have been reported. Animal studies indicate that slight analgesic and anti-arthritic effects can be expected[8]. In Germany[9], it is used in supportive therapy for degenerative disorders of the locomotor system and for lack of appetite and dyspeptic problems. No side effects have been reported. A recent clinical study indicated effectiveness in acute low backache[10].

DISTRIBUTION. *H. procumbens* is found in sandy places in the north-western parts of South Africa.

Harpagoside   Harpagide   Procumbide

1. Henderson, M. & Anderson, J.G. 1966. *Common Weeds in South Africa. Memoirs of the Botanical Survey of South Africa* 37.
2. Ihlenfeldt, H.-D. & Hartmann, H. 1970. Die Gattung *Harpagophytum* (Burch.) DC. ex Meissn. *Mitt. Staatsinst. Allg. Bot. Hamburg* 13: 15-69.
3. Czygan, F.-C. & Krüger, A. 1977. Pharmazeutisch-biologische Untersuchungen der Gattung *Harpagophytum. Planta Med.* 31: 305-307.
4. Watt, J.M. & Breyer-Brandwijk, M.G. 1962. *The Medicinal and Poisonous Plants of Southern and Eastern Africa.* 2nd edition. Livingstone, London.
5. Dictionary of Natural Products on CD-ROM, release 4:2 (1996). Chapman & Hall, London.
6. Pourrat, H. *et al.* 1986. Study on the stability of *Harpagophytum procumbens* DC. iridoids during the preparation of drug powders and atomized extracts. *Ann. Pharm. Fr.* 43: 601-606.
7. Wagner, H. & Bladt, S. 1996. *Plant Drug Analysis, a Thin Layer Chromatographic Atlas,* 2nd edition. Springer-Verlag, Berlin.
8. Bruneton, J. 1995. *Pharmacognosy, Phytochemistry, Medicinal Plants.* Intercept, Hampshire.
9. German Commission E monograph allows the stated indication.
10. Chrubasik, S. *et al.* 1996. Effectiveness of *Harpagophytum procumbens* in treatment of acute low back pain. *Phytomedicine* 3: 1-10.

Harpagophytum procumbens

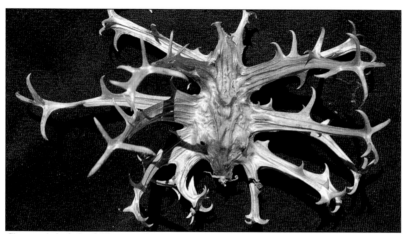

Characteristic fruit of *Harpagophytum procumbens*

Examples of *Harpagophytum procumbens* products

Sliced and dried roots of *Harpagophytum procumbens*

HARPEPHYLLUM CAFFRUM

Anacardiaceae

> **umgwenya (Xhosa, Zulu); mothêkêlê (Northern Sotho);
> wild plum (English); wildepruim (Afrikaans)**

BOTANICAL DESCRIPTION. This is a large ever-green tree reaching a height of up to 15 metres[1,2]. The bark in old specimens is rough and dark brown. The dark green, shiny leaves are divided into several leaflets, each of which is distinctly asymmetrical (the midrib is not exactly in the middle). Male and female flowers occur on separate trees. The flowers are very small, whitish or yellowish and rather inconspicuous. The sour, but edible fruits are bright red and plum-like[1,2].

PLANT PARTS USED. The stem bark is used.

MEDICINAL USES. Decoctions of the bark are used as blood purifiers or emetics[3,4]. It may also be used for facial saunas and skin washes, and to treat skin problems such as acne and eczema[4]. To treat sprains and fractures, powdered burnt bark is applied to scarifications[5].

PREPARATION AND DOSAGE. Powdered bark is boiled in water and one or two small wine glasses of the preparation are taken daily (larger doses will induce vomiting)[4].

ACTIVE INGREDIENTS. The chemical constituents of *Harpephyllum* are poorly known[6], but the presence of polyphenolic compounds and flavonoids have been reported[7]. These include organic acids, such as protocatechuic acid, and flavonols, such as kaempferol[7].

PHARMACOLOGICAL EFFECTS. The benefits derived from the use of this traditional medicine may be related to the phenolic compounds[7].

DISTRIBUTION. The natural distribution is restricted to southern Africa[1,8]. The wild plum has become a popular garden tree and is now found in most parts of South Africa.

Protocatechuic acid

Kaempferol

1. **Palmer, E. & Pitman, J. 1972.** *Trees of Southern Africa.* Balkema, Cape Town.
2. **Coates Palgrave, K. 1977.** *Trees of Southern Africa.* Struik, Cape Town.
3. **Watt, J.M. & Breyer-Brandwijk, M.G. 1962.** *The Medicinal and Poisonous Plants of Southern and Eastern Africa.* 2nd edition. Livingstone, London.
4. **Pujol, J. 1990.** *Naturafrica – the Herbalist Handbook.* Jean Pujol Natural Healers' Foundation, Durban.
5. **Hutchings, A. 1996.** *Zulu Medicinal Plants.* Natal University Press, Pietermaritzburg.
6. **Dictionary of Natural Products on CD-ROM, release 4:2 (1996).** Chapman & Hall, London.
7. **El Sherbeiny, A.E.A. & El Ansari, M.A. 1976.** The polyphenolics and flavonoids of *Harpephyllum caffrum*. *Planta Med.* 29: 129-132.
8. **Von Breitenbach, F. 1986.** *National List of Indigenous Trees.* Dendrological Foundation, Pretoria.

Harpephyllum caffrum

Plum-like fruits of *Harpephyllum caffrum*

Pounded bark of *Harpephyllum caffrum*

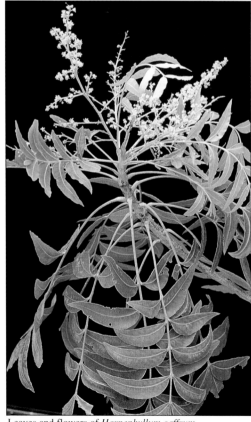

Leaves and flowers of *Harpephyllum caffrum*

HELICHRYSUM SPECIES

Asteraceae

imphepho (Xhosa, Zulu); everlastings (English); kooigoed (Afrikaans)

BOTANICAL DESCRIPTION. Species of *Helichrysum* are aromatic perennial herbs or shrublets with densely hairy or woolly leaves and persistent flower heads. The shape and size of the leaves and flower heads are characteristics which differentiate the species[1]. About 245 species occur in South Africa[1], of which the best known and commonly used medicinal plants are *H. cymosum*, *H. odoratissimum*, *H. petiolare* and *H. nudifolium*. The smoke of many *Helichrysum* species (and also of *Achyrocline stenoptera*, which is often confused with the latter) is a ritual incense, called "imphepho".

PLANT PARTS USED. The leaves and twigs are mainly used, and sometimes the roots[2,3,4].

MEDICINAL USES. Many ailments are treated with these popular medicinal plants, including coughs, colds, fever, infections, headache and menstrual pain[2,3,4,5,6,7]. It is a popular ingredient for wound dressings[3,7,8].

PREPARATION AND DOSAGE. There are several different ways of administering these traditional medicines. For coughs and colds, a tea is prepared or the leaves are boiled in milk[3,4,5]. For pain relief, smoke from burning leaves is inhaled[6,7]. Leaves are widely used on wounds to prevent infection[3,7,8].

ACTIVE INGREDIENTS. *Helichrysum* species contain flavonoids, sesquiterpenoids and acylated phloroglucinols[9,10,11]. Examples are the antimicrobial flavonoid (chalcone) helichrysetin, isolated from *H. odoratissimum*[11] and caespitin, a phloroglucinol derivative from *H. caespititium*[12]. The former species is rich in essential oil, with α-pinene and α-humulene as main compounds[13,14].

PHARMACOLOGICAL EFFECTS. Pain-relieving, anti-infective and anti-inflammatory activity have been reported for several *Helichrysum* species[12]. Proven antimicrobial activity[11] provides scientific evidence for the traditional use in wound dressing.

DISTRIBUTION. *Helichrysum* species are distributed all over South Africa and their medicinal use often depends on local availability rather than a preference for particular species. The map shows the recorded distribution[1] of *H. nudifolium*, one of the most widely known medicinal species.

Caespitin   Helichrysetin

1. **Hilliard, O.M. 1983.** Asteraceae. Inuleae. Gnaphaliinae. *Flora of Southern Africa* 33(7,2). Botanical Research Institute, Pretoria.
2. **Pujol, J. 1990.** *Naturafrica – the Herbalist Handbook.* Jean Pujol Natural Healers' Foundation, Durban.
3. **Watt, J.M. & Breyer-Brandwijk, M.G. 1962.** *The Medicinal and Poisonous Plants of Southern and Eastern Africa.* 2nd edition. Livingstone, London.
4. **Smith, C.A. 1966.** *Common Names of South African Plants. Memoirs of the Botanical Survey of South Africa* 35.
5. **Rood, B. 1994.** *Uit die Veldapteek.* Tafelberg, Cape Town.
6. **Hutchings, A. & Van Staden, J. 1994.** Plants used for stress-related ailments in traditional Zulu, Xhosa and Sotho medicine. Part 1: Plants used for headaches. *J. Ethnopharmacol.* 43: 89-124.
7. **Hutchings, A. 1996.** *Zulu Medicinal Plants.* Natal University Press, Pietermaritzburg.
8. **Bhat, R.B. & Jacobs, T.V. 1995.** Traditional herbal medicine in Transkei. *J. Ethnopharmacol.* 48: 7-12.
9. **Dictionary of Natural Products on CD-ROM, release 4:2 (1996).** Chapman & Hall, London.
10. **Jakupovic, J. et al. 1986.** Phloroglucinol derivatives and other constituents from South African *Helichrysum* species. *Phytochemistry* 25: 1133-1142.
11. **Van Puyvelde, L. et al. 1989.** Isolation of flavonoids and a chalcone from *Helichrysum odoratissimum* and synthesis of helichrysin. *J. Nat. Prod.* 52: 629-633.
12. **Dekker, T.G. et al. 1983.** Studies of South African medicinal plants. Part 2. Caespitin, a new phloroglucinol derivative with antimicrobial properties from *Helichrysum caespitosum*. *S. Afr. J. Chem.* 114: 14-17.
13. **Lwande, W. et al. 1993.** Constituents of the essential oil of *Helichrysum odoratissimum* (L.) Less. *J. Essent. Oil Res.* 5: 93-95.
14. **Gundidza, M. & Zwaving, J.H. 1993.** The chemical composition of the essential leaf oil of *Helichrysum odoratissimum* from Zimbabwe. *J. Essent. Oil Res.* 5: 341-343.

Helichrysum nudifolium

Helichrysum petiolare

Helichrysum cymosum

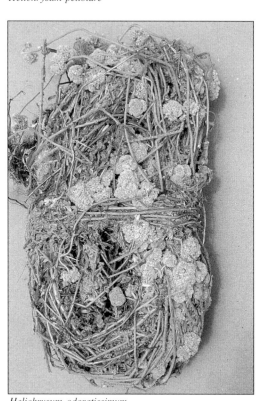

Helichrysum odoratissimum

HETEROMORPHA ARBORESCENS

Apiaceae

---

umbangandlala (Xhosa, Zulu); mkatlala (Sotho);
wildepietersielie (Afrikaans); parsley tree (English)

BOTANICAL DESCRIPTION. This is a woody shrub or small tree of up to 15 metres in height, with a characteristic smooth, shiny bark which peels off in horizontal flakes[1,2]. In common with many members of the carrot family, the roots are thick and fleshy. The leaves are very variable in size and shape, and may have one, three or several smaller leaflets[1]. The yellow, inconspicuous flowers are characteristically arranged in umbels, i.e. all the stalks arise from the same point. The small winged fruits have two wings on the one side and three wings on the other side – a unique feature referred to in the genus name ("hetero-morphous" = "of two different forms").

PLANT PARTS USED. The roots are mainly used, but sometimes also the stem bark and leaves.

MEDICINAL USES. The main use of the plant is to treat scrofula, abdominal pains and colic[3,4,5]. It is also widely used to treat nervous and mental disorders[3,4,6,7], headaches, fever, shortness of breath, asthma, coughs, dysentry, infertility, weakness and intestinal worms, and for purifying the blood, stomach or kidneys[3,4,5,6].

PREPARATION AND DOSAGE. Decoctions or infusions of the leaves or roots may be used. Smoke from the burning plant is inhaled to treat headaches[6].

ACTIVE INGREDIENTS. Two antifungal compounds have been isolated from the plant, namely falcarindiol and asaricin[8]. Falcarindiol also has analgesic effects[9] which may account for the treatment of abdominal pain and headaches. The volatile oil is known to contain α-pinene, germacrene D and sabinene as major constituents[10].

PHARMACOLOGICAL EFFECTS. The activity of the medicine may be linked to the presence of the two known antifungal compounds mentioned above[8,9], one of which has analgesic effects. The volatile oil has shown definite antibacterial and antifungal activity[11].

DISTRIBUTION. *H. arborescens* is widely distributed in South Africa and further north along the eastern parts of the African continent[1]. There are several distinct forms which are now considered to be varieties of a single variable species[1].

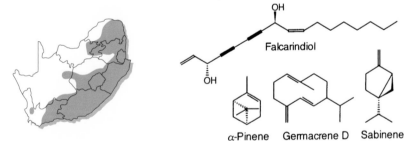

Falcarindiol

α-Pinene   Germacrene D   Sabinene   Asaricin

1. **Winter, P.J.D. & Van Wyk, B-E. 1996.** A revision of the genus *Heteromorpha* (Apiaceae). *Kew Bull.* 51: 225-265.
2. **Coates Palgrave, K. 1977.** *Trees of Southern Africa.* Struik, Cape Town.
3. **Watt, J.M. & Breyer-Brandwijk, M.G. 1962.** *The Medicinal and Poisonous Plants of Southern and Eastern Africa.* 2nd edition. Livingstone, London.
4. **Pujol, J. 1990.** *Naturafrica - the Herbalist Handbook.* Jean Pujol Natural Healers' Foundation, Durban.
5. **Hutchings, A. & Van Staden, J. 1994.** Plants used for stress-related ailments in traditional Zulu, Xhosa and Sotho medicine. Part 1: Plants used for headaches. *J. Ethnopharmacol.* 43: 89-124.
6. **Hutchings, A. 1996.** *Zulu Medicinal Plants.* Natal University Press, Pietermaritzburg.
7. **Watt, J.M. 1967.** African plants potentially useful in mental health. *Lloydia* 30: 1-22.
8. **Villegas, M. *et al.* 1988.** Isolation of the antifungal compounds falcarindiol and sarisan from *Heteromorpha trifoliata. Planta Med.* 54: 36.
9. **Dictionary of Natural Products on CD-ROM, release 4:2 (1996).** Chapman & Hall, London.
10. **Mwangi, J.W. *et al.* 1994.** Volatile components of *Heteromorpha trifoliata* (Wendl.) Eckl. & Zeyh. *Flavour Fragrance J.* 9: 241-243.
11. **Deans, S.G. *et al.* 1994.** Antimicrobial activities of the volatile oil of *Heteromorpha trifoliata* (Wendl.) Eckl. & Zeyh. (Apiaceae). *Flavour Fragrance J.* 9: 245-248.

Flowers of *Heteromorpha arborescens*

Fruits of *Heteromorpha arborescens*

Stems of *Heteromorpha arborescens* as they are sold for medicinal use

Characteristic bark of *Heteromorpha arborescens*

HETEROPYXIS NATALENSIS

Myrtaceae

---

inkunzi, uhuzu, umkhuswa (Zulu); laventelboom (Afrikaans); lavender tree (English)

BOTANICAL DESCRIPTION. This is a small tree of up to 10 metres in height[1,2], with a branched trunk, densely leafy branches and strongly aromatic foliage. As a result of regular flaking, the bark has a distinctive mottled appearance. The leaves are simple, oblong and shiny green at maturity, but often tinged red when young. The inconspicuous yellowish flowers are followed by small dry capsules.

PLANT PARTS USED. The leaves are mainly used, but sometimes also the roots.

MEDICINAL USES. Leaf infusions are used for treating colds. Nose bleeding and bleeding gums are treated with steam from root decoctions[3,4]. The roots are also reported to be of use against menorrhagia (excessive menstrual flow) and the fresh leaves for weaning[4]. A traditional medicinal tea may be prepared from the leaves[3,4].

PREPARATION AND DOSAGE. Decoctions of the roots or infusions of the leaves are reported to be used[3,4]. Powdered leaves form part of traditional veterinary medicine[3], probably as a vermifuge[5].

ACTIVE INGREDIENTS. The essential oil of *H. natalensis* contains a wide range of monoterpenoids, mainly ß-ocimene, 1,8-cineole, limonene, linalool and myrcene[6,7]. Distinct seasonal variation in the relative importance of these compounds has been reported[6].

PHARMACOLOGICAL EFFECTS. The essential oil is highly aromatic and has shown clear antimicrobial activity against both bacteria and fungi[7]. The chemical basis for the reported haemostatic effects is not known.

DISTRIBUTION. *H. natalensis* is a common tree of the north-eastern parts of South Africa[8].

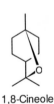
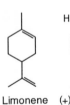
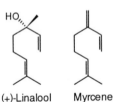

ß-Ocimene   1,8-Cineole   Limonene   (+)-Linalool   Myrcene

---

1. **Palmer, E. & Pitman, J. 1972.** *Trees of Southern Africa.* Balkema, Cape Town.
2. **Coates Palgrave, K. 1977.** *Trees of Southern Africa.* Struik, Cape Town.
3. **Watt, J.M. & Breyer-Brandwijk, M.G. 1962.** *The Medicinal and Poisonous Plants of Southern and Eastern Africa.* 2nd edition. Livingstone, London.
4. **Hutchings, A. 1996.** *Zulu Medicinal Plants.* Natal University Press, Pietermaritzburg.
5. **Smith, C.A. 1966.** *Common Names of South African Plants. Memoirs of the Botanical Survey of South Africa* 35.
6. **Weyerstahl, P. et al. 1992.** Constituents of the essential oil of *Heteropyxis natalensis. J. Essent. Oil Res.* 4: 439-445.
7. **Gundidza, M. et al. 1993.** The essential oil from *Heteropyxis natalensis* Harv.: Its antimicrobial activities and phytoconstituents. *J. Sci. Food Agric.* 63: 361-364.
8. **Von Breitenbach, F. 1986.** *National List of Indigenous Trees.* Dendrological Foundation, Pretoria.

Heteropyxis natalensis

Characteristic bark of *Heteropyxis natalensis*

Flowers of *Heteropyxis natalensis*

Foliage of *Heteropyxis natalensis*

HYPERICUM PERFORATUM

Clusiaceae

Saint John's wort (English); Johanneskruid (Afrikaans)

BOTANICAL DESCRIPTION. The plant is a perennial shrublet of up to one metre in height, with creeping rhizomes and erect, flowering branches[1,2]. The opposite leaves are without hairs but have small translucent oil glands. The characteristic yellow flowers occur in groups on the branch tips, followed by small, dry capsules of about 10 mm long, filled with numerous dark brown, shiny seeds[1,2].

PLANT PARTS USED. Above-ground parts are harvested.

MEDICINAL USES. The powdered drug or extracts of the drug are used as an antidiarrhoeal, for rheumatism and gout, as anti-depressant and as a diuretic[3,4,5]. An oily extract of the plant is used in the treatment of wounds and first degree burns[4]. In Germany[6], the drug is allowed for the supportive treatment of nervous excitement and sleep disturbances. An indigenous species, *H. aethiopicum*, has been used for treating backache and loin pain[7], as well as for fevers and the treatment of wounds[8].

PREPARATION AND DOSAGE. Half a cup of boiling water must be poured over two teaspoons of the coarsely powdered drug and strained after 10 minutes. Photosensitivity may arise in fair-skinned people, especially of those parts exposed to fairly strong sunshine.

ACTIVE INGREDIENTS. The naphthodianthrone hypericin and hypericin-like substances occur in several species of *Hypericum*[9]. The flavonoids rutin, hyperin, isoquercetrin and biflavonoids are also present, together with up to 3% of a known antibacterial substance called hyperforin[9].

PHARMACOLOGICAL EFFECTS. Extensive clinical trials have shown that the drug has antidepressant effects in milder forms of neurodepression which could be linked to MAO inhibition[5,10]. It was previously thought that one of the constituents, hypericin, was responsible for this action. It is, however, now known that the effect is due to xanthones yet unidentified[5]. Recent studies have shown substantial antiviral activity[11,12].

DISTRIBUTION. *H. perforatum* is indigenous to Europe but has become a troublesome weed in the Western Cape[1,2].

Hypericin

Hyperforin

1. Henderson, M. & Anderson, J.G. 1966. *Common weeds in South Africa. Memoirs of the Botanical Survey of South Africa 37*.
2. Stirton, C.H. (ed.) 1978. *Indringerplante, Mooi Maar Gevaarlik*. Department of Nature- and Environmental Conservation, Cape Town.
3. Grieve, M. 1967. *A Modern Herbal*. Hafner, London.
4. Bruneton, J. 1995. *Pharmacognosy, Phytochemistry, Medicinal Plants*. Intercept, Hampshire.
5. Ernst, E. 1995. St John's Wort, an anti-depressant? A systematic, criteria-based review. *Phytomedicine* 2: 67-71.
6. The German Standard Licence allows the supportive treatment of the stated indication.
7. Watt, J.M. & Breyer-Brandwijk, M.G. 1962. *The Medicinal and Poisonous Plants of Southern and Eastern Africa*. 2nd edition. Livingstone, London.
8. Rood, B. 1994. *Uit die Veldapteek*. Tafelberg, Cape Town.
9. Dictionary of Natural Products on CD-ROM, release 4:2 (1996). Chapman & Hall, London.
10. Hölzl, J. *et al.* 1989. Investigations about antidepressive and mood changing effects of *Hypericum perforatum. Planta Med.* 55: 643.
11. Hamburger, M. & Hostettmann, K. 1991. Bioactivity in plants: the link between phytochemistry and medicine. *Phytochemistry* 30: 3864-3874.
12. Hudson, J.B. *et al.* 1994. Antiviral assays on phytochemicals: the influence of reaction parameters. *Planta Med.* 60: 329-332.

Hypericum perforatum

Flowers of *Hypericum perforatum*

Hypericum aethiopicum   Dried leaves and stems of *Hypericum perforatum*

HYPOXIS HEMEROCALLIDEA

Hypoxidaceae

inkomfe (Zulu)

BOTANICAL DESCRIPTION. *Hypoxis* species are tuberous perennials with long, strap-shaped leaves and yellow, star-shaped flowers. The species can be distinguished by the size, shape and orientation of the leaves and the size and shape of the flowers. *H. hemerocallidea* (previously also known by the name *H. rooperi*) has broad, slightly hairy leaves which are arranged one above the other to form three distinct groups spreading outwards from the centre of the plant. Bright yellow, star-shaped flowers are borne on long, slender stalks.

PLANT PARTS USED. The tuberous rootstock (corm), which is dark brown or black on the outside and yellow within when freshly cut, is used.

MEDICINAL USES. Infusions of the corm are used as emetics to treat dizziness, bladder disorders and insanity[1,2]. Decoctions have been given to weak children as a tonic and the juice is reported to be applied to burns[3]. The stems and leaves are mixed with other ingredients to treat prostate problems[1]. Traditional uses are also said to include testicular tumours, prostate hypertrophy and urinary infections[4].

PREPARATION AND DOSAGE. Infusions of the corms and/or leaves are used.

ACTIVE INGREDIENTS. The activity of the drug against prostatic adenoma is ascribed to phytosterol glycosides, mainly ß-sitosterol[5]. It is interesting to note that pumpkin oil, which contains high levels of phytosterols, is marketed in Europe for the treatment of benign prostate hypertrophy[6]. Anti-cancer, anti-HIV and anti-inflammatory activity is ascribed to rooperol (the aglycone of hypoxoside, which is the 4,4'-diglucoside)[7] and the compound has showed promising results in clinical trials[4].

PHARMACOLOGICAL EFFECTS. The activity of sitosterols is ascribed to enzymatic effects (inhibition of 5α-reductase) or to decreased binding of dihydrotestosterone within the prostate[6]. Rooperol was shown to have several biological activities. It is markedly antimutagenic and cytotoxic to cancer cells[4].

DISTRIBUTION. *H. hemerocallidea* is widely distributed in the grassland areas of South Africa.

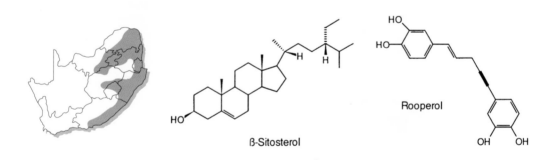

β-Sitosterol

Rooperol

1. **Pujol, J. 1990.** *Naturafrica – the Herbalist Handbook.* Jean Pujol Natural Healers' Foundation, Durban.
2. **Hutchings, A. 1996.** *Zulu Medicinal Plants.* Natal University Press, Pietermaritzburg.
3. **Watt, J.M. & Breyer-Brandwijk, M.G. 1962.** *The Medicinal and Poisonous Plants of Southern and Eastern Africa.* 2nd edition. Livingstone, London.
4. **Albrecht, C.F. 1996.** Hypoxoside as a putative non-toxic, multi-functional prodrug for the treatment of certain cancers, HIV-infection and inflammatory conditions. Lecture presented at the IOCD International Symposium, 25 to 28 February 1996, Victoria Falls, Zimbabwe.
5. **Merck 1989.** *The Merck Index.* 11th edition. Merck, Rahway.
6. **Bruneton, J. 1995.** *Pharmacognosy, Phytochemistry, Medicinal Plants.* Intercept, Hampshire.
7. **Drewes, S.E. et al. 1984.** Isolation of hypoxoside from *Hypoxis rooperi* and synthesis of (*E*)-1,5-*bis*(3',4'-dimethoxyphenyl)pent-4-en-1-yne. *Phytochemistry* 23: 1313-1316.

Hypoxis hemerocallidea

Flowers of *Hypoxis hemerocallidea*

Tuberous rootstock of *Hypoxis hemerocallidea*

Corms of *Hypoxis hemerocallidea* as they are sold for medicinal use

JATROPHA CURCAS

Euphorbiaceae

> mathlapametse (Tswana); inhlakuva (Zulu); mafuredonga (Venda);
> mbono (Swahili); purging nut (English); purgeerboontjie (Afrikaans)

BOTANICAL DESCRIPTION. This plant is a shrub or small tree of up to six metres in height[1]. The hairless leaves are heart-shaped, usually with five large lobes (sometimes three-lobed or up to seven-lobed). Both the male and female flowers are small, greenish-yellow and hairy. The fruits are egg-shaped capsules, initially green but eventually turning dark brown or black. They split into three parts at maturity, releasing the three large black seeds (nuts), each about 20 mm long and 10 mm in diameter. The indigenous *J. zeyheri* (Zulu: "ugodide"; Afrikaans: "verfbol") is also used medicinally. This species is a small, perennial herb with characteristically multi-lobed leaves and a thick underground rhizome.

PLANT PARTS USED. The seeds of *J. curcas* and the rhizomes of *J. zeyheri* are used[2,3,4,5].

MEDICINAL USES. Nuts of *J. curcas* are taken in a small quantity as a purgative[2,3] but the leaves and bark have the same effect[2,4]. The rhizomes of *J. zeyheri* may be used as blood purifiers[2,3] or applied externally in fresh form to treat wounds and boils[5].

PREPARATION AND DOSAGE. In Tswana traditional medicine, the leaves, seeds or bark are boiled and the watery extract is taken as a purgative[4]. Two

seeds are said to be strongly purgative[2], while larger numbers may cause severe diarrhoea, abdominal pain and vomiting[2,4,6]. The nuts are tasty and acute poisoning in children is often reported[6], but patients usually recover rapidly after treatment.

ACTIVE INGREDIENTS. The seed oil contains irritant diterpenoids[7] of the tiglian (phorbol) type, such as curcuson A and curcuson C. Curcuson C appears to be identical to jaherin, an active antimicrobial which was isolated from *J. zeyheri*[8]. The activity of the seed oil is also partly ascribed to curcanoleic acid, which is similar to ricinoleic acid (from castor oil) and crotonoleic acid (from croton oil)[4,6]. The seeds also contain a toxic protein (lectin) named curcin[2,4,6].

PHARMACOLOGICAL EFFECTS. The toxicity and gastro-intestinal irritation is ascribed to partially identified diterpenoid esters[9], but the numerous diterpenoids (many with reported antimicrobial[8], antitumour[10] and even tumour-promoting activity[11]) and the toxalbumin curcin should also be considered.

DISTRIBUTION. The plant originates from tropical America, but has become naturalised in the northern parts of the country and in KwaZulu-Natal[1].

Curcuson A   Curcuson C

1. **Coates Palgrave, K. 1977.** *Trees of Southern Africa.* Struik, Cape Town.
2. **Watt, J.M. & Breyer-Brandwijk, M.G. 1962.** *The Medicinal and Poisonous Plants of Southern and Eastern Africa.* 2nd edition. Livingstone, London.
3. **Hutchings, A. 1996.** *Zulu Medicinal Plants.* Natal University Press, Pietermaritzburg.
4. **Mampane, K.J. et al. 1987.** *Jatropha curcas*: use as a traditional Tswana medicine and its role as a cause of acute poisoning. *Phytother. Res.* 1: 50-51.
5. **Pujol, J. 1990.** *Naturafrica – the Herbalist Handbook.* Jean Pujol Natural Healers' Foundation, Durban.
6. **Joubert, P.H. et al. 1984.** Acute poisoning with *Jatropha curcas* (purging nut tree) in children. *S. Afr. Med. J.* 65: 729-730.
7. **Adolf, W. et al. 1984.** Irritant phorbol derivatives from four *Jatropha* species. *Phytochemistry* 23: 129-132.
8. **Dekker, T.G. et al. 1987.** Studies of South African medicinal plants. Part 4. Jaherin, a new daphnane diterpene with antimicrobial properties from *Jatropha zeyheri*. *S. Afr. J. Chem.* 40: 74-76.
9. **Neuwinger, H.D. 1994.** *Afrikanische Arzneipflanzen und Jagdgifte.* Wissenschaftliche Verlagsgesellschaft, Stuttgart.
10. **Dictionary of Natural Products on CD-ROM, release 4:2 (1996).** Chapman & Hall, London.
11. **Hirota, M. et al. 1988.** A new tumour promotor from the seed oil from *Jatropha curcas* L. *Cancer Res.* 48: 5800-5804.

Green fruits of *Jatropha curcas*

Flowers of *Jatropha curcas*

Seeds (nuts) of *Jatropha curcas*

KIGELIA AFRICANA

Bignoniaceae

---

muvevha (Venda); modukguhlu (Northern Sotho); umfongothi (Zulu);
worsboom (Afrikaans); sausage tree (English)

BOTANICAL DESCRIPTION. This is a large, rounded tree with a thick trunk and smooth grey bark[1,2]. The leaves have seven to 11 large leaflets of which the terminal one is usually bigger than the others. The very large, dark maroon flowers are borne on pendulous stalks. The flowers are very attractive but have an unpleasant smell. They are followed by enormous greyish-brown, sausage-shaped fruits of up to a metre in length, which contain a fibrous pulp with numerous seeds embedded in them.

PLANT PARTS USED. The fruit is mainly used, sometimes also the bark[3,4].

MEDICINAL USES. The dried fruit is powdered and used as a dressing for ulcers, sores, syphilis and is also applied locally for rheumatism[1,2,3,4]. Bark decoctions are used for dysentery[5].

PREPARATION AND DOSAGE. In addition to the external use, decoctions of the fruit and bark may also be taken orally or as an enema for stomach ailments in children[4]. The fruit is reported to be purgative[3].

ACTIVE INGREDIENTS. The roots and bark have the naphthoquinone lapachol and the dihydroisocoumarin kigelin as major compounds[6,7]. Several other compounds, including kigelinone, pinnatal, isopinnatal, stigmasterol and ß-sitosterol (see *Prunus africana*) have been isolated from the bark[6], but the beneficial effect of external use may be due to the dihydroisocoumarins and their glycosides[6,7,8].

PHARMACOLOGICAL EFFECTS. Antimicrobial activity has been demonstrated[8], using watery extracts of the bark. It is likely that kigelin and related compounds (the suggested active ingredients) are also present in the fruit.

DISTRIBUTION. *K. africana* occurs in the northern and north-eastern parts of South Africa[9] and it is widely distributed further north in tropical Africa.

Lapachol

Kigelin

1. **Palmer, E. & Pitman, J. 1972.** *Trees of Southern Africa.* Balkema, Cape Town.
2. **Coates Palgrave, K. 1977.** *Trees of Southern Africa.* Struik, Cape Town.
3. **Watt, J.M. & Breyer-Brandwijk, M.G. 1962.** *The Medicinal and Poisonous Plants of Southern and Eastern Africa.* 2nd edition. Livingstone, London.
4. **Hutchings, A. 1996.** *Zulu Medicinal Plants.* Natal University Press, Pietermaritzburg.
5. **Von Koenen, E. 1996.** *Heil-, Gift- u Essbare Pflanzen in Namibia.* Klauss Hess Verlag, Göttingen.
6. **Dictionary of Natural Products on CD-ROM, release 4:2 (1996).** Chapman & Hall, London.
7. **Govindachari, T.R. *et al.* 1971.** Isolation and structure of two new dihydroisocoumarins from *Kigelia pinnata.* *Phytochemistry* 10: 1603-1606.
8. **Akunyili, D.N. *et al.* 1991.** Anti-microbial activities of the stem bark of *Kigelia africana. J. Ethnopharmacol.* 35: 173-178.
9. **Von Breitenbach, F. 1986.** *National List of Indigenous Trees.* Dendrological Foundation, Pretoria.

Kigelia africana

Fruit of *Kigelia africana*

Flower of *Kigelia africana*

Fruits of *Kigelia africana* as they are sold for medicinal use

KNOWLTONIA VESICATORIA

Ranunculaceae

brandblare, katjiedrieblaar (Afrikaans)

BOTANICAL DESCRIPTION. The plant is a perennial herb with a short rhizome and fleshy roots, usually growing on shady slopes and in forests. The leaves are firm-textured, dark green and divided into three leaflets. The leaf stalks are purplish-red towards their bases. White or yellowish flowers are produced in the winter and early spring, followed by small black fleshy fruits. Several other species of *Knowltonia*, including *K. anemonoides* (Zulu: "uxaphusa"), *K. bracteata* (Zulu: "umvuthuza") and *K. capensis* (Afrikaans: "katjiedrieblaar") are known to be used medicinally[1,2].

PLANT PARTS USED. The fresh leaves are mainly used, sometimes also the roots.

MEDICINAL USES. The plant is an old Cape remedy for lumbago and rheumatism[3,4,5]. Decoctions of the roots, mixed with *Pelargonium* roots, have also been used to treat colds and influenza[1,5]. Numerous other uses are known. The fresh roots and leaves of some species, for example, are sniffed for headaches[2] or may be directly applied to alleviate toothache[5].

PREPARATION AND DOSAGE. Fresh leaves or roots are bruised and applied to the skin, producing blisters (hence the names "vesicatoria" and "brandblaar")[1,4]. Infusions may be used for the same purpose[5]. Smoke from burning leaves[2] or the fumes from crushed leaves[1] may be inhaled for headaches.

ACTIVE INGREDIENTS. Many species of the Ranunculaceae family are known to contain an irritant, toxic yellow oil known as protoanemonin[6]. When the leaves or roots are dried, protoanemonin is rapidly dimerised to form non-toxic anemonin[6]. A structurally related glucoside, ranunculin, is known from several members of the family[7].

PHARMACOLOGICAL EFFECTS. Protoanemonin produces a strong allergic reaction on the skin, resulting in blistering[6]. This has an effect similar to mustard oil, which is a powerful irritant and has been used as a counter-irritant and rubefacient[8].

DISTRIBUTION. *K. vesicatoria* is widely distributed in the western and southern parts of South Africa, mainly in the Western Cape.

Protoanemonin   Anemonin

1. Watt, J.M. & Breyer-Brandwijk, M.G. 1962. *The Medicinal and Poisonous Plants of Southern and Eastern Africa*. 2nd edition. Livingstone, London.
2. Hutchings, A. 1996. *Zulu Medicinal Plants*. Natal University Press, Pietermaritzburg.
3. Forbes, V.S. (ed.) 1986. *Carl Peter Thunberg Travels at the Cape of Good Hope 1772-1775*. Van Riebeeck Society, Cape Town.
4. Smith, C.A. 1966. *Common Names of South African Plants. Memoirs of the Botanical Survey of South Africa* 35.
5. Rood, B. 1994. *Uit die Veldapteek*. Tafelberg, Cape Town.
6. Bruneton, J. 1995. *Pharmacognosy, Phytochemistry, Medicinal Plants*. Intercept, Hampshire.
7. Dictionary of Natural Products on CD-ROM, release 4:2 (1996). Chapman & Hall, London.
8. Martindale 1993. *The Extra Pharmacopoeia*. 30th edition. Pharmaceutical Press, London.

Leaves and fruits of *Knowltonia vesicatoria*

Leaves of *Knowltonia bracteata*

Flower of *Knowltonia bracteata*

Roots of *Knowltonia bracteata*

Roots of *Knowltonia vesicatoria*

LANNEA EDULIS

Anacardiaceae

**wild grape (English); wildedruif (Afrikaans);
pheho (Tswana); muporotso (Venda)**

BOTANICAL DESCRIPTION. This plant is a small shrublet of up to a metre in height, with short, leafy branches developing from an enormous woody, underground rootstock. The leaves are divided into two to four pairs of leaflets, each about 100 mm long and densely hairy, particularly on the lower side (the strong contrast between the upper and lower surfaces is a useful distinguishing characteristic). Small yellowish flowers are borne in erect clusters, followed by numerous small red to purplish-black fleshy berries of about 5 mm in diameter[1].

PLANT PARTS USED. The bark of the thick and woody underground rootstock, which has a bright red underbark, is used.

MEDICINAL USES. Decoctions or infusions of the root bark are used to treat diarrhoea[2]. Stem or root bark of other *Lannea* species, such as *L. discolor* and *L. schweinfurthii* are used for the same purpose[2,3]. Leaf poultices or leaf infusions of *L. edulis* and *L.*

discolor are sometimes applied externally to treat sore eyes, boils and abscesses[2,3].

PREPARATION AND DOSAGE. Cold infusions of the bark are said to be used for the treatment of diarrhoea[2].

ACTIVE INGREDIENTS. Nothing appears to be known about the chemistry of *L. edulis*[4] but the bark is likely to be rich in phenolic compounds and tannins. The only phenolic compound thus far reported from the genus as a whole is a flavanone, 2',4',5',7-tetrahydroxyflavanone, isolated from *L. acida*[4].

PHARMACOLOGICAL EFFECTS. No published information appears to be available. Tannins, flavonoids and other phenolic compounds are probably responsible for the reported activity of the medicine.

DISTRIBUTION. *L. edulis* is widely distributed in the grassland areas of the summer rainfall region.

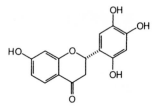

2',4',5',7 - Tetrahydroxyflavanone

---

1. **Van Wyk, A.E. & Malan, S. 1988.** *Field Guide to the Wild Flowers of the Witwatersrand and Pretoria Region.* Struik, Cape Town.
2. **Watt, J.M. & Breyer-Brandwijk, M.G. 1962.** *The Medicinal and Poisonous Plants of Southern and Eastern Africa.* 2nd edition. Livingstone, London.
3. **Hutchings, A. 1996.** *Zulu Medicinal Plants.* Natal University Press, Pietermaritzburg.
4. **Dictionary of Natural Products on CD-ROM, release 4:2 (1996).** Chapman & Hall, London.

Lannea edulis

Fruits of *Lannea edulis*

Thick, woody rhizome of *Lannea edulis*

LEONOTIS LEONURUS

Lamiaceae

---

wilde dagga (Afrikaans); wild dagga (English); umunyane (Zulu);
lebake (Sotho); umfincafincane (Xhosa); umhlahlampetu (Shona)

BOTANICAL DESCRIPTION. This attractive plant is a shrub of two to five metres in height, with a thick, woody base and pale brown branches[1]. All parts of the plant have a strong smell. The leaves are opposite each other on the stems, long and narrow, toothed in the upper half and distinctly hairy. Bright orange, tubular flowers are borne in characteristic rounded groups, which are neatly arranged along the branch ends. The hairy flowers resemble lion's ears, hence the name "leonurus" (which means lion's ears).

PLANT PARTS USED. The leaves and stems are mainly used, sometimes also the roots.

MEDICINAL USES. Numerous traditional uses have been recorded[2,3,4,5,6,7]. There is some doubt about early reports[2,3] of the plant being smoked as a substitute for dagga, because it is only mildly narcotic[4]. However, it has been smoked for the relief of epilepsy[7]. The leaves or roots are widely used as a remedy for snake bite[4,5] and also to treat other bites and stings. Externally, decoctions have been applied to treat boils, eczema, skin diseases, itching and muscular cramps[4,6]. Internally, decoctions are used for coughs, colds and influenza, and also for bronchitis, high blood pressure and headaches[4,5,6]. Leaf infusions have been used for asthma and viral hepatitis.

PREPARATION AND DOSAGE. Early reports claim that the Nama people smoked the leaves[2,3] and used the powdered leaf to make small cakes, which were then chewed or eaten[4,6]. Decoctions are used externally for skin problems and internally, either by mouth or as an enema, to treat coughs, colds, fever, headaches and high blood pressure[4,5,6].

ACTIVE INGREDIENTS. In addition to volatile oil, *Leonotis* species contain several unusual diterpenoids (labdane type lactones). A typical example is marrubiin, which has been isolated from *L. leonurus*[8]. There is evidence that premarrubiin actually occurs in the plant and that marrubiin may be an artefact derived from premarrubiin[9,10].

PHARMACOLOGICAL EFFECTS. It is interesting to note that marrubiin is the main diterpenoid lactone in white horehound (*Marrubium vulgare*)[8,9,10]. This traditional European phytomedicine is used for the symptomatic treatment of coughs in acute bronchial disease[10,11]. The actual pharmacological effect is not known[10,11].

DISTRIBUTION. *L. leonurus* has a wide natural distribution over large parts of South Africa[1] and has become a popular garden plant.

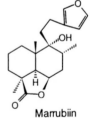

Premarrubiin   Marrubiin

1. **Codd, L.E. 1985.** Lamiaceae. *Flora of Southern Africa* 28(4). Botanical Research Institute, Pretoria.
2. **Forbes, V.S. (ed.) 1986.** *Carl Peter Thunberg Travels at the Cape of Good Hope 1772-1775.* Van Riebeeck Society, Cape Town.
3. **Smith, C.A. 1966.** *Common Names of South African Plants. Memoirs of the Botanical Survey of South Africa* 35.
4. **Watt, J.M. & Breyer-Brandwijk, M.G. 1962.** *The Medicinal and Poisonous Plants of Southern and Eastern Africa.* 2nd edition. Livingstone, London.
5. **Hutchings, A. 1996.** *Zulu Medicinal Plants.* Natal University Press, Pietermaritzburg.
6. **Rood, B. 1994.** *Uit die Veldapteek.* Tafelberg, Cape Town.
7. **Watt, J.M. 1967.** African plants potentially useful in mental health. *Lloydia* 30: 1-22.
8. **Dictionary of Natural Products on CD-ROM, release 4:2 (1996).** Chapman & Hall, London.
9. **Merck 1989.** *The Merck Index.* 11th edition. Merck, Rahway.
10. **Bruneton, J. 1995.** *Pharmacognosy, Phytochemistry, Medicinal Plants.* Intercept, Hampshire.
11. **Martindale 1993.** *The Extra Pharmacopoeia.* 30th edition. Pharmaceutical Press, London.

Leonotis leonurus

Flowers of *Leonotis leonurus*

Dried leaves and stems of *Leonotis leonurus*

LIPPIA JAVANICA

Verbenaceae

> musukudu, bokhukhwane (Tswana); inzinziniba (Xhosa); umsuzwane (Zulu);
> mumara (Shona); fever tea (English); koorsbossie (Afrikaans)

BOTANICAL DESCRIPTION. This species is an erect, woody shrub of up to two metres in height. The hairy leaves have conspicuous veins and are highly aromatic, with a strong lemon smell. Small yellowish-white flowers are produced in dense rounded heads. It is very similar to *L. rehmannii* but the latter is a smaller plant, up to 0,5 metres high, with many stems arising from ground level. *L. scaberrima* (Tswana: "musukujane"), a species which is easily recognised by the large bracts below the flowers, is also used medicinally.

PLANT PARTS USED. Leaves and twigs are used, less often also the roots.

MEDICINAL USES. Infusions are used as a tea, mainly to treat coughs, colds, fever[1,2,3] and bronchitis. It is also used for various chest ailments, influenza, measles, rashes, malaria, stomach problems and headaches[1,2,3,4]. Weak infusions are taken as a general health tea and strong infusions are used topically for scabies and lice.

PREPARATION AND DOSAGE. Hot leaf infusions (usually with water but sometimes with milk) are taken[1].

ACTIVE INGREDIENTS. *L. javanica* is rich in volatile oil and numerous monoterpenoids have been identified, including myrcene, caryophyllene, linalool, *p*-cymene and ipsdienone[5,6]. Various organic acids and alcohols occur in the plant[7,8]. Iridoid glycosides[9] and toxic triterpenoids (icterogenins)[10] have been detected in some *Lippia* species.

PHARMACOLOGICAL EFFECTS. Volatile oils have decongestant and antiseptic effects[11] but the fever-reducing and possible pain-relieving activities need further study. *Aloysia triphylla* (previously known as *L. citriodora*) is used in Europe in preparations for the treatment of nervous disorders, hyperactivity and pain[12]. Animal poisoning and photosensitisation have been ascribed to the icterogenins[2,13].

DISTRIBUTION. *L. javanica* occurs over large parts of South Africa and the distribution extends northwards into tropical Africa.

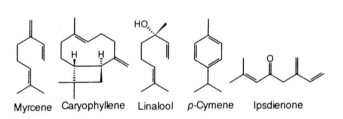

Myrcene   Caryophyllene   Linalool   *p*-Cymene   Ipsdienone

1. **Smith, C.A. 1966.** *Common Names of South African Plants. Memoirs of the Botanical Survey of South Africa* 35.
2. **Watt, J.M. & Breyer-Brandwijk, M.G. 1962.** *The Medicinal and Poisonous Plants of Southern and Eastern Africa.* 2nd edition. Livingstone, London.
3. **Hutchings, A. 1996.** *Zulu Medicinal Plants.* Natal University Press, Pietermaritzburg.
4. **Hutchings, A. & Van Staden, J. 1994.** Plants used for stress-related ailments in traditional Zulu, Xhosa and Sotho medicine. Part 1: Plants used for headaches. *J. Ethnopharmacol.* 43: 89-124.
5. **Neidlein, R. & Staehle, R. 1974.** Constituents of *Lippia javanica.* III. *Deut. Apoth. Ztg.* 114(40): 1588-1592; 114(49): 1941.
6. **Mwangi, J.W. *et al.* 1991.** Essential oils of Kenyan *Lippia* species. Part III. *Flavour Fragrance J.* 6(3): 221-224.
7. **Neidlein, R. & Staehle, R. 1973.** Constituents of *Lippia javanica.* *Deut. Apoth. Ztg.* 113(26): 993-997.
8. **Neidlein, R. & Staehle, R. 1973.** Constituents of *Lippia javanica.* II. *Deut. Apoth. Ztg.* 113(32): 1219-1222.
9. **Rimpler, H. & Sauerbier, H. 1986.** Iridoid glucosides as taxonomic markers in the genera *Lantana, Lippia, Aloysia* and *Phyla.* *Biochem. Syst. Ecol.* 14(3): 307-310.
10. **Dictionary of Natural Products on CD-ROM, release 4:2 (1996).** Chapman & Hall, London.
11. **Bruneton, J. 1995.** *Pharmacognosy, Phytochemistry, Medicinal Plants.* Intercept, Hampshire.
12. **Martindale 1993.** *The Extra Pharmacopoeia.* 30th edition. Pharmaceutical Press, London.
13. **Vahrmeijer, J. 1981.** *Poisonous Plants of Southern Africa That Cause Stock Losses.* Tafelberg, Cape Town.

Lippia javanica

Dried leaves and stems of *Lippia javanica*

Leaves and flowers of *Lippia javanica*

Example of a product from *Lippia scaberrima*

LOBOSTEMON FRUTICOSUS

Boraginaceae

agdaegeneesbos, douwurmbos (Afrikaans)

BOTANICAL DESCRIPTION. The plant is a small, woody shrublet of up to a metre in height with densely hairy branches. The leaves are silver-green and covered with a mixture of coarse and soft hairs[1]. The attractive trumpet-shaped flowers are different shades of blue and pink (or rarely white), varying in colour even in the same plant[1].

PLANT PARTS USED. The fresh leaves and twigs are used.

MEDICINAL USES. Decoctions of the plant are an old Cape remedy for wounds, skin diseases and ring-worm[2,3,4]. The vernacular name "agdaegeneesbos" refers to the ability of the plant to heal ("genees") a wound within eight days ("ag dae")[2]. The treatment against ringworm is reflected in the name "douwurmbos" ("douwurm" = ringworm, "bos" = bush or shrub). Infusions have also been used as a tea to treat internal problems and to purify the blood[2,3,4].

PREPARATION AND DOSAGE. The fresh leaves and branch tips are ground to a paste (often mixed with other plants such as *Melianthus*) and applied to wounds[2,3]. For internal use, leaves are brewed as a tea[3]. The crushed leaves may be fried in sweet oil or fat for use as a wound-healing ointment.

ACTIVE INGREDIENTS. The plant is closely related to comfrey (*Symphytum officinale*) and borage (*Borago officinalis*) and it is possible that it has similar chemical compounds. The roots of comfrey contain appreciable amounts of allantoin, a compound well known for its wound healing properties[5]. Pyrrolizidine alkaloids such as symphytine and structurally related alkaloids occur in several members of the family[5,6].

PHARMACOLOGICAL EFFECTS. The wound healing properties of the plant may perhaps be due to allantoin but its presence in *Lobostemon* needs confirmation. *Symphytum officinale* was used as an application to wounds and ulcers to stimulate healing and was also given internally for gastric ulcers[7]. Most pyrrolizidine alkaloids are cumulative liver toxins so that the internal use of medicines containing these compounds should best be avoided[5].

DISTRIBUTION. The plant is widely distributed in the fynbos region of South Africa[1].

Allantoin   Symphytine

1. Levyns, M.R. 1934. A revision of *Lobostemon* Lehm., and a discussion of the species problem. *J. Linn. Soc. Bot.* 49: 393-445.
2. Smith, C.A. 1966. *Common Names of South African Plants. Memoirs of the Botanical Survey of South Africa* 35.
3. Watt, J.M. & Breyer-Brandwijk, M.G. 1962. *The Medicinal and Poisonous Plants of Southern and Eastern Africa.* 2nd edition. Livingstone, London.
4. Rood, B. 1994. *Uit die Veldapteek.* Tafelberg, Cape Town.
5. Bruneton, J. 1995. *Pharmacognosy, Phytochemistry, Medicinal Plants.* Intercept, Hampshire.
6. Dictionary of Natural Products on CD-ROM, release 4:2 (1996). Chapman & Hall, London.
7. Martindale 1993. *The Extra Pharmacopoeia.* 30th edition. Pharmaceutical Press, London.

Lobostemon fruticosus

Leaves and flowers of comfrey (*Symphytum officinale*)

Leaves and flowers of *Lobostemon fruticosus*

Flowers of *Lobostemon fruticosus*

MELIANTHUS COMOSUS

Melianthaceae

---

kruidjie-roer-my-nie (Afrikaans); ibonya (Zulu)

BOTANICAL DESCRIPTION. The plant is a multi-branched shrub of up to three metres in height. All parts of the plant produce a strong, unpleasant smell when touched or bruised. This distinctive feature is referred to in the Afrikaans vernacular name. The leaves are clustered towards the tips of the branches. They are divided into about five pairs of leaflets which are oblong in shape, with prominently toothed margins. Small, green flowers with small, bright red petals are borne in a short cluster, followed by a four-winged bladdery capsule[1,2]. Another species, *M. major*, is also used medicinally in the same way as *M. comosus*. This is a more robust plant with larger, greyish-green leaves and large clusters of dark purplish-red flowers at the branch ends. The whole flower cluster, including the stalk, is purple-coloured in this species, which makes it easy to distinguish from *M. comosus*.

PLANT PARTS USED. Fresh leaves or roots are used.

MEDICINAL USES. Leaf poultices and leaf decoctions of both species are widely used to treat septic wounds, sores, bruises, backache and rheumatic joints[3,4,5,6]. *M. comosus* is a traditional remedy for snake bite[6,7]. The ability to treat snake bite was an integral part of the Khoi healing culture[8]. Root infusions are used for treating cancer and strong leaf decoctions are applied topically for ringworm.

PREPARATION AND DOSAGE. Leaf poultices or leaf decoctions were applied externally, or added to bath water in the case of rheumatism and backache[3,4,5]. These plants are toxic and there are cases where internal use has led to fatalities[3,4].

ACTIVE INGREDIENTS. *M. comosus* contains several highly toxic bufadienolides, of which melianthusigenin is a typical example[9]. A triterpenoid, oleanolic acid, as well as a cinnamic acid derivative thereof, has been isolated from the root bark[10].

PHARMACOLOGICAL EFFECTS. *Melianthus* bufadienolides are known to be highly toxic and have caused human death[3,4]. Nothing appears to be known about the wound-healing properties of the plant. Some triterpenoids are used in wound therapy (see *Centella*, for example) and it is possible that the medicinal value of *Melianthus* is partly due to triterpenoids in the leaves and roots.

DISTRIBUTION. The genus *Melianthus* is restricted to Southern Africa. *M. comosus* has a wide distribution, mainly in the dry interior of South Africa[1,2], while *M. major* occurs only in the Western Cape.

Melianthusigenin   Oleanolic acid

1. **Phillips, E.P. & Hofmeyr, J. 1927.** The genus *Melianthus*. *Bothalia* 2: 351-355.
2. **Vahrmeijer, J. 1981.** *Poisonous Plants of Southern Africa That Cause Stock Losses.* Tafelberg, Cape Town.
3. **Watt, J.M. & Breyer-Brandwijk, M.G. 1962.** *The Medicinal and Poisonous Plants of Southern and Eastern Africa.* 2nd edition. Livingstone, London.
4. **Smith, C.A. 1966.** *Common Names of South African Plants. Memoirs of the Botanical Survey of South Africa* 35.
5. **Rood, B. 1994.** *Uit die Veldapteek.* Tafelberg, Cape Town.
6. **Cillié, A.M. 1992.** *Kruie op Witblits, Rate, Resepte en Feite.* Unpublished notes, Worcester Museum.
7. **Dykman, E.J. 1891.** *Kook-, Koek- en Resepte Boek.* Paarlse Drukpers Maatskappy, Paarl.
8. **Laidler, P.W. 1926.** The magic medicine of the hottentots. *S. Afr. J. Sci.* 25: 433-447.
9. **Anderson, L.A.P. & Koekemoer, J.M. 1969.** Toxic bufadienolides from *Melianthus comosus. J. S. Afr. Chem. Inst.* 22: S119-S124.
10. **Koekemoer, J.M.** *et al.* **1974.** Chemistry of *Melianthus comosus*. VI. Structure of a new triterpenoid acid from the root bark. *J. S. Afr. Chem. Inst.* 27: 131-136, and references cited therein.

Melianthus comosus

Leaves, flowers and fruits of *Melianthus comosus*

Melianthus major

Flower cluster of *Melianthus major*

MENTHA LONGIFOLIA

Lamiaceae

ballerja, kruisement (Afrikaans); wild mint (English); ufuthane lomhlange (Zulu); koena-ya-thaba (Sotho); inixina (Xhosa)

BOTANICAL DESCRIPTION. The plant is a perennial herb with creeping rhizomes below the ground and erect flowering stems of up to 0,8 metres in height[1]. All parts are highly aromatic with a strong typical mint smell. The leaves appear opposite each other in pairs along the stems, which are square in cross-section. Small white or pale purple flowers are borne in elongated clusters on the tips of the stems. Several different subspecies of *M. longifolia* are known, of which the best known one in South Africa is subsp. *capensis*[1].

PLANT PARTS USED. The leaves are mostly used, sometimes also the stems and rhizomes.

MEDICINAL USES. Wild mint is used for many different ailments. The main use is for coughs, colds, asthma and other respiratory ailments[2,3]. It has also been used to treat headaches, fevers, indigestion, flatulence, hysteria, painful menstruation, delayed pregnancy[2,3,4,5,6] and for urinary tract infections. It is believed to be a diaphoretic and antispasmodic[3,5]. Externally, it has been used to treat wounds and swollen glands[2,3,4,6].

PREPARATION AND DOSAGE. Infusions or decoctions of the leaves are drunk or administered as enemas[2,3,6]. Crushed leaves may be inserted in the nostrils for the relief of headache[3,5] or placed under the bedding of someone suffering from breathing problems[3].

ACTIVE INGREDIENTS. The volatile oil of *Mentha* species contains numerous monoterpenoids, amongst others, carvone, limonene, menthone and menthol[7]. The composition is known to vary considerably at different localities but no information appears to be available on South African plants. The species also contains hesperidin and several other flavonoids[8,9].

PHARMACOLOGICAL EFFECTS. Volatile oils are known for their decongestant and antiseptic effects[7]. Bioflavonoids such as hesperidin are thought to improve capillary function. They have been given to relieve capillary impairment and venous insufficiency of the lower limbs[10].

DISTRIBUTION. *M. longifolia* is widely distributed in South Africa and is found only in wet places[1].

(-) - Menthone   (-) - Menthol   Hesperidin

1. **Codd, L.E. 1985.** Lamiaceae. *Flora of Southern Africa* 28(4). Botanical Research Institute, Pretoria.
2. **Smith, C.A. 1966.** *Common Names of South African Plants. Memoirs of the Botanical Survey of South Africa* 35.
3. **Watt, J.M. & Breyer-Brandwijk, M.G. 1962.** *The Medicinal and Poisonous Plants of Southern and Eastern Africa.* 2nd edition. Livingstone, London.
4. **Rood, B. 1994.** *Uit die Veldapteek.* Tafelberg, Cape Town.
5. **Hutchings, A. & Van Staden, J. 1994.** Plants used for stress-related ailments in traditional Zulu, Xhosa and Sotho medicine. Part 1: Plants used for headaches. *J. Ethnopharmacol.* 43: 89-124.
6. **Hutchings, A. 1996.** *Zulu Medicinal Plants.* Natal University Press, Pietermaritzburg.
7. **Bruneton, J. 1995.** *Pharmacognosy, Phytochemistry, Medicinal Plants.* Intercept, Hampshire.
8. **Bourwieg, D. & Pohl, R. 1973.** Flavonoids from *Mentha longifolia. Planta Med.* 24: 304-314.
9. **Dictionary of Natural Products on CD-ROM, release 4:2 (1996).** Chapman & Hall, London.
10. **Martindale 1993.** *The Extra Pharmacopoeia.* 30th edition. Pharmaceutical Press, London.

Mentha longifolia

Flower cluster of *Mentha longifolia*

Leaves of *Mentha longifolia*

MYROTHAMNUS FLABELLIFOLIUS

Myrothamnaceae

---

resurrection plant (English); bergboegoe (Afrikaans); uvukwabafile (Zulu)

BOTANICAL DESCRIPTION. This interesting plant is a small, rigid, woody shrub of up to 0,4 metres in height, with tough branches[1]. The leaves are fan-shaped, folded lengthwise and toothed along the upper edges. The inconspicuous flowers are produced in summer, with male and female flowers on separate plants. A distinctive feature of the plant is the ability of the seemingly dead, dormant leaves to unfold and turn bright green when placed in water. It is this remarkable property to which the English and Zulu vernacular names refer.

PLANT PARTS USED. Leaves and twigs are used, rarely also the roots.

MEDICINAL USES. Numerous traditional uses have been reported[2,3,4,5]. Infusions are drunk for colds and respiratory ailments. Decoctions are taken to alleviate pain and for backache, kidney problems, haemorrhoids and painful menstruation. It may also be used externally to treat abrasions. Smoke from burning leaves is inhaled for chest pains and asthma[2,4].

Dried, powdered leaves are used to dress burns and wounds[6].

PREPARATION AND DOSAGE. The medicine is taken orally as infusions or decoctions, or smoke from burning leaves is inhaled[2,3,4,5].

ACTIVE INGREDIENTS. *Myrothamnus* contains volatile oil, but there appears to be no reliable publication in which the main compounds have been reported[7]. Our studies have shown that camphor is the major ingredient of the oil, with small amounts of α-pinene and 1,8-cineole.

PHARMACOLOGICAL EFFECTS. Camphor and other monoterpenoids are known to be decongestant and antiseptic[8] and it is likely that the reported pain-relieving activity is also related to these compounds.

DISTRIBUTION. The plant occurs in the northern part of South Africa, where it is always found in exposed rocky places on dry mountain slopes[1].

Camphor

α-Pinene

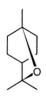
1,8-Cineole
(Eucalyptol)

1. **Weimarck, H. 1936.** *Myrothamnus flabellifolia* Welw., eine polymorphe Pflanzenart. *Bot. Notiser* 26: 451-462.
2. **Watt, J.M. & Breyer-Brandwijk, M.G. 1962.** *The Medicinal and Poisonous Plants of Southern and Eastern Africa.* 2nd edition. Livingstone, London.
3. **Smith, C.A. 1966.** *Common Names of South African Plants. Memoirs of the Botanical Survey of South Africa* 35.
4. **Hutchings, A. 1996.** *Zulu Medicinal Plants.* Natal University Press, Pietermaritzburg.
5. **Rood, B. 1994.** *Uit die Veldapteek.* Tafelberg, Cape Town.
6. **Von Koenen, E. 1996.** *Heil-, Gift- u Essbare Pflanzen in Namibia.* Klauss Hess Verlag, Göttingen.
7. **Dictionary of Natural Products on CD-ROM, release 4:2 (1996).** Chapman & Hall, London.
8. **Bruneton, J. 1995.** *Pharmacognosy, Phytochemistry, Medicinal Plants.* Intercept, Hampshire.

Myrothamnus flabellifolius in the dormant state

Myrothamnus flabellifolius in the growing season

Dry leaves and twigs of *Myrothamnus flabellifolius*

Dormant leaves (left) rapidly expand and turn green when placed in water

OCOTEA BULLATA

Lauraceae

---

unukani (Zulu, Xhosa); black stinkwood (English); stinkhout (Afrikaans)

BOTANICAL DESCRIPTION. Stinkwood is a large evergreen tree of up to 20 or 30 metres[1,2]. The bark is pale brown and has a beautiful, mottled appearance, but may become dark brown and flaky in old trees. The leaves are large, glossy green in appearance, with characteristic swollen pits ('bullae') in the axils of the main veins. The small greenish-yellow flowers appear in summer (mainly December and January). Small acorn-like fruits appear from March to June. The timber is finely textured with a beautiful glossy sheen, which has made it one of the most popular indigenous timbers for high quality furniture.

PLANT PARTS USED. The stem bark is used. It has become expensive as a result of its popularity and shortage of supply.

MEDICINAL USES. Finely ground, the bark is used as a snuff or the smoke is inhaled to relieve headaches[3,4,5]. It is also used as a local application to the area of the bladder in urinary disorders[3,6] and is claimed to be beneficial for stomach trouble and as an emetic for emotional and nervous disorders[6].

Cryptocarya species are sometimes used as substitutes[7]. An infusion of the powdered bark is said to be an effective remedy for infantile diarrhoea.

PREPARATION AND DOSAGE. Ground bark is used as a snuff or the smoke is inhaled[3,4].

ACTIVE INGREDIENTS. The bark contains several neolignans[8,9], of which ocobullenone is the major compound[9]. The bark and leaves are rich in unidentified volatile compounds, presumably monoterpenoids.

PHARMACOLOGICAL EFFECTS. Numerous biological activities have been ascribed to neolignans[10] but the pharmacological effects (possible pain-relieving activity) of the *Ocotea* compounds have not yet been studied.

DISTRIBUTION. The tree is widely distributed in the afromontane forests along the southern and eastern parts of South Africa, from the Cape Peninsula eastwards to the Southern Cape, Eastern Cape, KwaZulu-Natal, Mpumalanga and the Northern Province[11].

Ocobullenone

---

1. **Palmer, E. & Pitman, J. 1972.** *Trees of Southern Africa.* Balkema, Cape Town.
2. **Coates Palgrave, K. 1977.** *Trees of Southern Africa.* Struik, Cape Town.
3. **Watt, J.M. & Breyer-Brandwijk, M.G. 1962.** *The Medicinal and Poisonous Plants of Southern and Eastern Africa.* 2nd edition. Livingstone, London.
4. **Hutchings, A. & Van Staden, J. 1994.** Plants used for stress-related ailments in traditional Zulu, Xhosa and Sotho medicine. Part 1: Plants used for headaches. *J. Ethnopharmacol.* 43: 89-124.
5. **Hutchings, A. 1996.** *Zulu Medicinal Plants.* Natal University Press, Pietermaritzburg.
6. **Pujol, J. 1990.** *Naturafrica – the Herbalist Handbook.* Jean Pujol Natural Healers' Foundation, Durban.
7. **Drewes S.E. et al. 1997.** *Cryptocarya liebertiana* and *Ocotea bullata* – their phytochemical relationship. *Phytochemistry* 44(3): 437-440.
8. **Sehlapelo, B.M. et al. 1993.** Ocobullenone, a bicyclo[3.2.1.]octanoid neolignan from *Ocotea bullata. Phytochemistry* 32(5): 1352-1353.
9. **Drewes, S.E. et al. 1995.** Iso-ocobullenone and a neolignan ketone from *Ocotea bullata* bark. *Phytochemistry* 38(6): 1505-1508.
10. **Bruneton, J. 1995.** *Pharmacognosy, Phytochemistry, Medicinal Plants.* Intercept, Hampshire.
11. **Von Breitenbach, F. 1986.** *National List of Indigenous Trees.* Dendrological Foundation, Pretoria.

Flowers and fruits of *Ocotea bullata*

Leaves of *Ocotea bullata*, showing the characteristic small swellings along the midribs

Bark of *Ocotea bullata*

OLEA EUROPAEA

Oleaceae

---

motholoari (Sotho); umquma (Xhosa, Zulu);
wild olive (English); olienhout (Afrikaans)

BOTANICAL DESCRIPTION. The wild olive is a small to medium-sized tree, usually about five metres in height but sometimes up to 18 metres[1,2,3]. The branchlets are dotted with numerous small, white spots (lenticels). The narrow leaves are dark glossy green above and yellowish-grey below. They occur in opposite pairs. Small white or cream-coloured flowers are followed by egg-shaped, 10 mm long, thinly fleshy fruits, which become black when they ripen. The plant occuring in South Africa was previously known as *Olea africana* but it is now regarded as a small-fruited subspecies (subsp. *africana*) of the commercial olive.

PLANT PARTS USED. The dried leaves are mainly used, sometimes the roots or stem bark.

MEDICINAL USES. The main use of the plant is as a hypotensive to lower blood pressure[4] and to enhance renal function. Several other traditional uses have been recorded[5,6,7]. An infusion of the fresh bark is taken to relieve colic, while infusions of the leaves are widely used as eye lotions. Decoctions are taken as diuretics, tonics, antidiarrhoeals and gargled to treat sore throats.

PREPARATION AND DOSAGE. Infusions and decoctions are used.

ACTIVE INGREDIENTS. The main active compounds in the leaves are two secoiridoids – oleuropein[4] and oleacein[8]. The leaves also contain numerous other secoiridoids, triterpenoids and flavonoids[4,9]. A number of lignans have been isolated from the bark of both subspecies of *O. europaea*, including africanol, 8-hydroxypinoresinol derivatives and olivil[9].

PHARMACOLOGICAL EFFECTS. Oleuropein lowers blood pressure by increasing coronary flow, while a recent study has shown that oleacein inhibits the angiotensin converting enzyme (ACE)[8]. The two compounds work in combination[8]. Oleuropein has significant antispasmodic and anti-oxidant activity[4]. European tradition also attributes fever-relieving and hypoglycaemic properties to the leaves[4]. The contribution of lignans, terpenoids and flavonoids to the pharmacological activities are poorly known.

DISTRIBUTION. The wild olive grows in many different habitats and is widely distributed in South Africa[10].

Oleuropein

Oleacein

1. **Verdoorn, I.C. 1963.** Oleaceae. *Flora of Southern Africa* 28: 100-128. Botanical Research Institute, Pretoria.
2. **Palmer, E. & Pitman, J. 1972.** *Trees of Southern Africa.* Balkema, Cape Town.
3. **Coates Palgrave, K. 1977.** *Trees of Southern Africa.* Struik, Cape Town.
4. **Bruneton, J. 1995.** *Pharmacognosy, Phytochemistry, Medicinal Plants.* Intercept, Hampshire.
5. **Watt, J.M. & Breyer-Brandwijk, M.G. 1962.** *The Medicinal and Poisonous Plants of Southern and Eastern Africa.* 2nd edition. Livingstone, London.
6. **Hutchings, A. 1996.** *Zulu Medicinal Plants.* Natal University Press, Pietermaritzburg.
7. **Iwu, M.M. 1993.** *Handbook of African Medicinal Plants.* CRC Press, Boca Raton.
8. **Hansen, K. et al. 1996.** Isolation of an Angiotensin Converting Enzyme (ACE) inhibitor from *Olea europaea* and *Olea lancea*. *Phytomedicine* 2(4): 319-325.
9. **Dictionary of Natural Products on CD-ROM, release 4:2 (1996).** Chapman & Hall, London.
10. **Von Breitenbach, F. 1986.** *National List of Indigenous Trees.* Dendrological Foundation, Pretoria.

Olea europaea

Dried leaves of *Olea europaea*

Leaves, flowers and berries of *Olea europaea*

OSMITOPSIS ASTERISCOIDES

Asteraceae

bels, belskruie (Afrikaans)

BOTANICAL DESCRIPTION. This is a sparse, erect shrub of up to two metres in height, with long, bare stems and leaves crowded on the branch ends. The leaves are aromatic, with a strong camphor smell. They are oblong, without stalks and somewhat glandular as a result of numerous small glands on the surface. The attractive large white flower heads are arranged in groups on the branch tips. When not in flower, the plant may be confused with *Leucadendron* species (tolbosse) and other members of the *Protea* family. It can be distinguished from other species by its large size, the hairy bracts around the flower heads and the large leaves (more than 15 mm long)[1].

PLANT PARTS USED. The leaves are used.

MEDICINAL USES. Bels is a traditional Cape Dutch remedy for numerous ailments and there are several records of its early popularity in the Cape[2,3,4]. Brandy tinctures are used mainly for chest complaints (coughs and hoarseness) and externally for inflammation, cuts and swellings and colic. It is also used for stomach problems, fever, influenza, body pains and even paralysis[2,3,4,5,6,7].

PREPARATION AND DOSAGE. A brandy tincture (Afrikaans: "belsbrandewyn") is traditionally used or the dried herb is placed in small bags for external application[2,3].

ACTIVE INGREDIENTS. The leaves contain a volatile oil rich in 1,8-cineole (eucalyptol) and camphor as the two main ingredients. Three sesquiterpenoid lactones have been isolated from leaves, namely osmitopsin and two different epoxides thereof[8,9].

PHARMACOLOGICAL EFFECTS. Preparations containing eucalyptol (cineole) have been taken by mouth for catarrh and coughs. It has been used as an inhalant and a rubefacient[10,11]. Camphor is well known for its external use as counter-irritant in fibrositis and neuralgia and internally as a carminative[11]. Sesquiterpenoid lactones have a wide range of biological activities, mainly through their action on enzymes[10] and they may also be partly responsible for the beneficial effects of the medicine.

DISTRIBUTION. The plant is restricted to the Western Cape[1].

CH₃

1,8-Cineole
(Eucalyptol)

Camphor

Osmitopsin

1. **Bremer, K. 1972.** The genus *Osmitopsis* (Compositae). *Bot. Notiser* 125: 9-48.
2. **Forbes, V.S. (ed.) 1986.** *Carl Peter Thunberg Travels at the Cape of Good Hope 1772-1775.* Van Riebeeck Society, Cape Town.
3. **Smith, C.A. 1966.** *Common Names of South African Plants. Memoirs of the Botanical Survey of South Africa* 35.
4. **Cillié, A.M. 1992.** *Kruie op Witblits, Rate, Resepte en Feite.* Unpublished notes, Worcester Museum.
5. **Dykman, E.J. 1891.** *Kook-, Koek- en Resepte Boek.* Paarlse Drukpers Maatskappy, Paarl.
6. **Watt, J.M. & Breyer-Brandwijk, M.G. 1962.** *The Medicinal and Poisonous Plants of Southern and Eastern Africa.* 2nd edition. Livingstone, London.
7. **Rood, B. 1994.** *Uit die Veldapteek.* Tafelberg, Cape Town.
8. **Dictionary of Natural Products on CD-ROM, release 4:2 (1996).** Chapman & Hall, London.
9. **Bohlmann, F. & Zdero, C. 1974.** Neue Sesquiterpenlactone aus *Osmitopsis asteriscoides* (L.) Cass. *Chemische Berichte* 107: 1409-1415.
10. **Bruneton, J. 1995.** *Pharmacognosy, Phytochemistry, Medicinal Plants.* Intercept, Hampshire.
11. **Martindale 1993.** *The Extra Pharmacopoeia.* 30th edition. Pharmaceutical Press, London.

Leaves and flower heads of *Osmitopsis asteriscoides*

Dried leaves and stems of *Osmitopsis asteriscoides*

Typical growth form and habitat of *Osmitopsis asteriscoides*

PELARGONIUM LURIDUM

Geraniaceae

ishaqa (Zulu)

BOTANICAL DESCRIPTION. This herbaceous perennial has a tuberous rootstock from which a rosette of leaves develops in the growing season. The leaves are exceptionally variable, with the first formed ones shallowly lobed but those developing later strongly divided into numerous narrow lobes. The flower heads are borne on tall slender stalks of up to a metre in height. The flowers are usually pink but may occasionally be white or greenish-yellow[1].

PLANT PARTS USED. The tuberous, fleshy rootstock, which is bright red inside, is harvested.

MEDICINAL USES. Infusions of the tubers are used to treat diarrhoea and dysentery[2,3,4,5,6]. Several other species have similar fleshy underground structures that are also antidiarrhoetic. The Afrikaans names "rabassam", "rabas" or "rooirabas" are often used for these species, which include *P. antidysentericum*, *P. rapaceum*, *P. reniforme*, *P. sidoides* and *P. triste*. The pink-flowered *P. reniforme* and the closely similar (but black-flowered) *P. sidoides* are ingredients of a German medicinal remedy called "Umckaloabo", which is used mainly to treat bronchitis in children.

PREPARATION AND DOSAGE. Infusions and decoctions of the fleshy tubers are taken[2,3,4,5,6]. The traditional Nama method of using *P. antidysentericum* is to boil the tuber in milk[3,4,5]. The roots may also be directly chewed or powdered and mixed with food[4,5,6].

ACTIVE INGREDIENTS. The tubers contain tannins and possibly other phenolic compounds but details are not available. The activity of the medicine prepared from *P. reniforme* tubers may partly be due to the presence of umckalin and structurally related coumarins[7]. The traditional use of species such as *P. betulinum* and *P. cucullatum* for coughs and chest trouble[3] (and as wound-healing emollients)[2] may be explained by the presence of essential oils. *Pelargonium* oils contain various monoterpenoids such as (+)-isomenthone and are widely used in the perfume industry[8].

PHARMACOLOGICAL EFFECTS. Antidiarrhoeal effects may be attributed to the presence of highly astringent tannins[9]. There are, however, various other medicinal properties of *Pelargonium* species requiring further study, such as wound-healing, antispasmodic and analgesic effects[4]. Geranium oil, obtained from different African *Pelargonium* species, was still official in the British Pharmaceutical Codex[10] of 1949.

DISTRIBUTION. *P. luridum* occurs over large parts of the interior of southern Africa[1].

(+)-Isomenthone   Umckalin

1. **Van der Walt, J.J.A. 1977.** *Pelargoniums of Southern Africa.* Purnell, Cape Town.
2. **Forbes, V.S. (ed.) 1986.** *Carl Peter Thunberg Travels at the Cape of Good Hope 1772-1775.* Van Riebeeck Society, Cape Town.
3. **Smith, C.A. 1966.** *Common Names of South African Plants. Memoirs of the Botanical Survey of South Africa* 35.
4. **Watt, J.M. & Breyer-Brandwijk, M.G. 1962.** *The Medicinal and Poisonous Plants of Southern and Eastern Africa.* 2nd edition. Livingstone, London.
5. **Rood, B. 1994.** *Uit die Veldapteek.* Tafelberg, Cape Town.
6. **Hutchings, A. 1996.** *Zulu Medicinal Plants.* Natal University Press, Pietermaritzburg.
7. **Wagner, H. *et al.* 1975.** Cumarine aus Südafrikanischen *Pelargonium*-arten. *Phytochemistry* 14: 2061-2064.
8. **Dictionary of Natural Products on CD-ROM, release 4:2 (1996).** Chapman & Hall, London.
9. **Bruneton, J. 1995.** *Pharmacognosy, Phytochemistry, Medicinal Plants.* Intercept, Hampshire.
10. **Martindale 1958.** *The Extra Pharmacopoeia.* 24th edition. Pharmaceutical Press, London.

Pelargonium reniforme

Pelargonium luridum

Example of a medicinal product from *Pelargonium* tubers

Tubers of *Pelargonium luridum*

PELLAEA CALOMELANOS

Adiantaceae

lehorometso (Sotho); inkomankomo (Zulu); hard fern (English)

BOTANICAL DESCRIPTION. This distinctive and common fern has an underground rootstock of about six mm in diameter, covered with small brown scales. The firm-textured leaves are composed of numerous blue-green leaflets which are broadly triangular in shape, with a distinct line of brown spore-producing bodies (sori) along the edges[1,2].

PLANT PARTS USED. The leaves and rhizomes are used.

MEDICINAL USES. The leaves are smoked for head colds, chest colds and asthma[3,4,5]. Decoctions of rhizomes are traditionally used to treat boils and abscesses, and for intestinal parasites[6]. The leaves of several other species of ferns are also smoked to relieve head and chest colds[4]. These include *Adiantum aethiopicum, A. capillus-veneris, Cheilanthes hirta, C. eckloniana, C. involuta* and *Mohria caffrorum*. It is interesting to note that the maidenhair fern, *Adiantum capillus-veneris*, is a traditional European remedy[7] for coughs, asthma and kidney problems (it is believed to be mildly diuretic). Tea made from this species was an early Cape remedy for colds and chest ailments[8].

PREPARATION AND DOSAGE. Leaves are smoked or smoke from burning leaves is inhaled (many ferns are used in this way)[4]. Decoctions or infusions of the rhizomes are taken or applied externally[3,5].

ACTIVE INGREDIENTS. Nothing appears to be known about the chemistry of *Pellaea* species[9]. However, many ferns contain triterpenoids of the hopane type, such as adiantone and related compounds[9], as well as a wide range of flavonoids[10]. Adiantone is known from *Adiantum* species, including *A. capillus-veneris*[9].

PHARMACOLOGICAL EFFECTS. There appears to be no clear link between the chemistry of fern leaves and their reported therapeutic value but it is possible that triterpenoid saponins are at least partly responsible. Some saponin-containing medicines have potential as analgesics and anti-inflammatory agents[11].

DISTRIBUTION. *P. calomelanos* occurs over large parts of southern Africa[1,2]. It can withstand seasonal droughts remarkably well and is therefore found even in exceptionally dry places.

Adiantone

1. **Schelpe, E.A.C.L.E. & Anthony, N.C. 1986.** Pteridophyta. *Flora of Southern Africa.* Botanical Research Institute, Pretoria.
2. **Jacobsen, W.B.G. 1983.** *The Ferns and Fern Allies of Southern Africa.* Butterworths, Durban.
3. **Watt, J.M. & Breyer-Brandwijk, M.G. 1962.** *The Medicinal and Poisonous Plants of Southern and Eastern Africa.* 2nd edition. Livingstone, London.
4. **Hutchings, A. & Van Staden, J. 1994.** Plants used for stress-related ailments in traditional Zulu, Xhosa and Sotho medicine. Part 1: Plants used for headaches. *J. Ethnopharmacol.* 43: 89-124.
5. **Hutchings, A. 1996.** *Zulu Medicinal Plants.* Natal University Press, Pietermaritzburg.
6. **Pujol, J. 1990.** *Naturafrica – the Herbalist Handbook.* Jean Pujol Natural Healers' Foundation, Durban.
7. **Grieve, M. 1967.** *A Modern Herbal.* Hafner, London.
8. **Forbes, V.S. (ed.) 1986.** *Carl Peter Thunberg Travels at the Cape of Good Hope 1772-1775.* Van Riebeeck Society, Cape Town.
9. **Dictionary of Natural Products on CD-ROM, release 4:2 (1996).** Chapman & Hall, London.
10. **Markham, K.R. 1988.** Distribution of flavonoids in the lower plants and its evolutionary significance. Chapter 12 in Harborne, J.B. (ed.), *The Flavonoids – Advances in Research Since 1980.* Chapman & Hall, London.
11. **Bruneton, J. 1995.** *Pharmacognosy, Phytochemistry, Medicinal Plants.* Intercept, Hampshire.

Typical growth form of *Pellaea calomelanos*

Leaves of *Pellaea calomelanos*

Cheilanthes hirta

Adiantum capillus-veneris

PENTANISIA PRUNELLOIDES

Rubiaceae

> icimamlilo (Zulu); wild verbena (English); sooibrandbossie (Afrikaans)

BOTANICAL DESCRIPTION. The plant is a perennial herb of about 0,3 metres in height and 0,6 metres wide, with leafy branches spreading from a thick, tuberous root. The leaves are oblong and usually somewhat hairy, and are borne in pairs. Small pale purple flowers occur in dense groups on the branch ends[1].

PLANT PARTS USED. The fleshy, tuberous root is mainly used, but sometimes also the leaves.

MEDICINAL USES. A wide range of uses has been recorded for this important traditional medicine[2,3,4,5,6,7]. Decoctions are often used for burns, swellings, sore joints and rheumatism. The plant is also used to treat heartburn, vomiting, fever, chest pain, toothache, tuberculosis, blood impurities, haemorrhoids and snakebite. It is taken regularly by pregnant women to ensure an easy childbirth. A leaf poultice is applied for a retained placenta.

PREPARATION AND DOSAGE. Root decoctions may be taken orally, used externally or as enemas. The fresh root may be chewed and swallowed to relieve heartburn[2]. The use of leaf poultices has also been recorded[2].

ACTIVE INGREDIENTS. Nothing appears to be known about the chemical compounds of *Pentanisia* species[8]. The chemistry of the related genus *Pentas* is equally poorly known but a naphthoquinone – pentalongin – has been found in one species[8].

PHARMACOLOGICAL EFFECTS. Antibiotic activity has been reported[5] but no details are available. The Zulu vernacular name means "putting out the fire", suggesting the relief of heartburn.

DISTRIBUTION. The plant is an important component of grasslands in the eastern parts of South Africa.

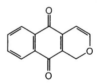

Pentalongin

1. **Verdcourt, B. 1952.** A revision of certain African genera of herbaceous Rubiaceae. I. The genus *Pentanisia* Harvey. *Bull. Jard. Bot. Brux.* 22: 233-286.
2. **Watt, J.M. & Breyer-Brandwijk, M.G. 1962.** *The Medicinal and Poisonous Plants of Southern and Eastern Africa.* 2nd edition. Livingstone, London.
3. **Rood, B. 1994.** *Uit die Veldapteek.* Tafelberg, Cape Town.
4. **Hutchings, A. 1989.** A survey and analysis of traditional medicinal plants as used by the Zulu, Xhosa and Sotho. *Bothalia* 19: 111-123.
5. **Hutchings, A. 1989.** Observations on plant usage in Xhosa and Zulu medicine. *Bothalia* 19: 225-235.
6. **Pujol, J. 1990.** *Naturafrica – the Herbalist Handbook.* Jean Pujol Natural Healers' Foundation, Durban.
7. **Hutchings, A. 1996.** *Zulu Medicinal Plants.* Natal University Press, Pietermaritzburg.
8. **Dictionary of Natural Products on CD-ROM, release 4:2 (1996).** Chapman & Hall, London.

Pentanisia prunelloides

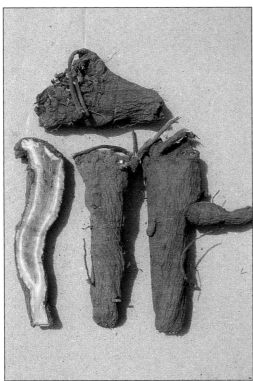

Tuberous roots of *Pentanisia prunelloides*

Leaves and flowers of *Pentanisia prunelloides*

PEUCEDANUM GALBANUM

Apiaceae

---

bergseldery (Afrikaans); blister bush (English)

BOTANICAL DESCRIPTION. This is a robust, erect shrub of about two metres in height with a strong resinous smell. The large leaves are divided into numerous diamond-shaped leaflets with serrated edges. The small yellow flowers are arranged in characteristic groups (umbels) and are followed by dry, flat, winged fruit. The large size and distinctive shape of the leaflets makes it easy to distinguish this species from other members of the family. Contact with the skin, followed by exposure to sunlight, may cause severe blistering of the skin, hence the English common name.

PLANT PARTS USED. The leaves are used.

MEDICINAL USES. The main use of the plant is to treat kidney and bladder ailments[1,2]. Other traditional uses include treatment of rheumatism, water retention, glandular swelling and high blood pressure[1,2,3]. A brandy tincture of the leaves is an early Cape remedy for obesity in men[4].

PREPARATION AND DOSAGE. Infusions of the leaves are taken, but the plant is potentially toxic and should be used with caution. For rheumatism, an infusion of *Peucedanum* is often used in combination with *Chironia*.

ACTIVE INGREDIENTS. The volatile oil of *P. galbanum* contains *p*-cymene as major monoterpenoid, but it also has several furanocoumarins, mainly xanthotoxin, psoralen and bergapten[5,6,7].

PHARMACOLOGICAL EFFECTS. Furanocoumarin-containing medicines are commonly used as diuretics even though there is rarely scientific evidence to support their therapeutic value[8]. Linear furanocoumarins such as xanthotoxin are phototoxic and skin contact may result in acute dermatitis after exposure to sunlight[8]. The compounds are potentially carcinogenic but have been used medicinally in a technique known as photochemotherapy to treat skin diseases[8] such as psoriasis. Preparations containing bergapten (5-methoxypsoralen) is commercially available for this indication[9].

DISTRIBUTION. *P. galbanum* is restricted to fynbos areas of the Western Cape, where it grows at medium to high altitudes, usually in partially shaded, moist places.

Psoralen

p-Cymene   Xanthotoxin   OCH3

Bergapten

OCH3

---

1. **Watt, J.M. & Breyer-Brandwijk, M.G. 1962.** *The Medicinal and Poisonous Plants of Southern and Eastern Africa*. 2nd edition. Livingstone, London.
2. **Cillié, A.M. 1992.** *Kruie op Witblits, Rate, Resepte en Feite*. Unpublished notes, Worcester Museum.
3. **Rood, B. 1994.** *Uit die Veldapteek*. Tafelberg, Cape Town.
4. **Dykman, E.J. 1891.** *Kook-, Koek- en Resepte Boek*. Paarlse Drukpers Maatskappy, Paarl.
5. **Finkelstein, N. *et al.* 1993.** Isolation and structure elucidation of xanthotoxin, a phototoxic furanocoumarin from *Peucedanum galbanum*. *S. Afr. J. Bot.* 59: 81-84.
6. **Campbell, W.E., Mathee, S. & Wewers, F. 1993.** Phytochemical studies on the blister bush, *Peucedanum galbanum*. *Extended Abstracts of the Fifth NAPRECA Symposium on Natural Products, 19-23 September 1993, Antananarivo, Madagascar*, p. 27-28.
7. **Campbell, W.E. *et al.* 1994.** Phytochemical studies on the blister bush, *Peucedanum galbanum*. *Planta Med.* 60: 586-587.
8. **Bruneton, J. 1995.** *Pharmacognosy, Phytochemistry, Medicinal Plants*. Intercept, Hampshire.
9. **Martindale 1993.** *The Extra Pharmacopoeia*. 30th edition. Pharmaceutical Press, London.

Peucedanum galbanum

Foliage of *Peucedanum galbanum*

Leaves of *Peucedanum galbanum* as they are sold for medicinal use

PITTOSPORUM VIRIDIFLORUM

Pittosporaceae

umkhwenkhwe (Xhosa, Zulu), umfusamvu (Zulu); kgalagangwe
(Northern Sotho); kasuur (Afrikaans); cheesewood (English)

BOTANICAL DESCRIPTION. The plant varies in size from a shrub of about four metres in height to a large forest tree of up to 30 metres[1,2]. The bark is pale brown to greyish with distinctive white dots (lenticels). The leaves are usually wider above the middle, dark green and glossy, with conspicuous net-veining on the lower surfaces. Small greenish-white flowers with a sweet smell are produced in early summer, followed by small brown capsules. These split open to release numerous small orange seeds which are covered in a sticky resinous exudate[1,2].

PLANT PARTS USED. The stem bark, which has a bitter taste and strong resinous smell, is used.

MEDICINAL USES. Decoctions or infusions are widely used to treat stomach complaints, biliousness, abdominal pain and fever[3,4]. It is said to ease pain and have a calming effect[3].

PREPARATION AND DOSAGE. Decoctions and infusions are used as emetics and enemas[3,4].

ACTIVE INGREDIENTS. Nothing appears to be known about the chemical constituents of *P. viridiflorum*[5]. However, saponins with barrigenol A_1 and structurally related triterpenoids as the sapogenins and various polyacetylenes have been isolated from other *Pittosporum* species[5]. The medicinal properties of *P. viridiflorum* may possibly be due to these or similar compounds.

PHARMACOLOGICAL EFFECTS. Anti-inflammatory, analgesic, antibiotic and immunoregulating effects have been ascribed to saponin-containing drugs[6] and it is possible that the beneficial effects of *P. viridiflorum* bark are due to terpenoids or their saponins.

DISTRIBUTION. The natural distribution of *P. viridiflorum* stretches over much of the southern and eastern parts of South Africa[7] and further north into tropical Africa. The plant is very attractive, tolerant of drought and frost and as a result, has become a popular garden tree.

Barrigenol A_1

1. **Palmer, E. & Pitman, J. 1972.** *Trees of Southern Africa.* Balkema, Cape Town.
2. **Coates Palgrave, K. 1977.** *Trees of Southern Africa.* Struik, Cape Town.
3. **Watt, J.M. & Breyer-Brandwijk, M.G. 1962.** *The Medicinal and Poisonous Plants of Southern and Eastern Africa.* 2nd edition. Livingstone, London.
4. **Hutchings, A. 1996.** *Zulu Medicinal Plants.* Natal University Press, Pietermaritzburg.
5. **Dictionary of Natural Products on CD-ROM, release 4:2 (1996).** Chapman & Hall, London.
6. **Bruneton, J. 1995.** *Pharmacognosy, Phytochemistry, Medicinal Plants.* Intercept, Hampshire.
7. **Von Breitenbach, F. 1986.** *National List of Indigenous Trees.* Dendrological Foundation, Pretoria.

Leaves, flowers and fruits of *Pittosporum viridiflorum*

Bark of *Pittosporum viridiflorum*

Growth form of *Pittosporum viridiflorum*

PLUMBAGO AURICULATA

Plumbaginaceae

umabophe (Xhosa); utshilitshili (Zulu), syselbos (Afrikaans)

BOTANICAL DESCRIPTION. *P. auriculata* (previously known as *P. capensis*) is an attractive shrub or scrambler with a height of up to two metres or more[1]. The leaves are oblong, thin in texture and often minutely gland-dotted. A characteristic feature is the leaf stalk, which is winged at the base, partly clasping the stem. The sticky, glandular flowers are pale blue or rarely white and occur in short clusters at the branch tips[1].

PLANT PARTS USED. The roots and leaves are used.

MEDICINAL USES. The powdered roots or leaves are snuffed to relieve headache[2,3,4]. Various other uses have been recorded, such as the removal of warts and the treatment of fractures[2].

PREPARATION AND DOSAGE. Powdered roots and leaves are both used for snuff[2,3,4]. Powdered roots

are applied to warts, or rubbed into scarifications (in the latter case, roasted root is used)[2].

ACTIVE INGREDIENTS. *Plumbago* species contain naphthoquinones, of which plumbagin is one of the major compounds[5].

PHARMACOLOGICAL EFFECTS. Experiments with animals show that a plumbagin-containing tincture is an antispasmodic[6,7]. It is interesting to note that plumbagin-containing *Drosera* species are traditionally used in Europe to treat spasmodic coughs[6]. Plumbagin also shows antibacterial and antifungal activity but is toxic at high doses[6].

DISTRIBUTION. The plant occurs in the northern and eastern parts of South Africa, as far south as George and Knysna[1]. It has become a popular ornamental shrub and is now widely cultivated in gardens.

Plumbagin

1. **Dyer, R.A. 1963.** Plumbaginaceae. In: *Flora of Southern Africa* 26, pp. 15-31. Botanical Research Institute, Pretoria.
2. **Watt, J.M. & Breyer-Brandwijk, M.G. 1962.** *The Medicinal and Poisonous Plants of Southern and Eastern Africa.* 2nd edition. Livingstone, London.
3. **Hutchings, A. & Van Staden, J. 1994.** Plants used for stress-related ailments in traditional Zulu, Xhosa and Sotho medicine. Part 1: Plants used for headaches. *J. Ethnopharmacol.* 43: 89-124.
4. **Hutchings, A. 1996.** *Zulu Medicinal Plants.* Natal University Press, Pietermaritzburg.
5. **Dictionary of Natural Products on CD-ROM, release 4:2 (1996).** Chapman & Hall, London.
6. **Bruneton, J. 1995.** *Pharmacognosy, Phytochemistry, Medicinal Plants.* Intercept, Hampshire.
7. **Martindale 1993.** *The Extra Pharmacopoeia.* 30th edition. Pharmaceutical Press, London.

Plumbago auriculata

Flowers of *Plumbago auriculata*

Leaves, roots and underground stems of *Plumbago auriculata*

POLYGALA FRUTICOSA

Polygalaceae

ithethe (Zulu)

BOTANICAL DESCRIPTION. The plant is a shrublet of up to 0,5 metres in height. In the growing season, numerous erect branches grow from the persistent woody rootstock. The leaves occur opposite each other on the stems, are rounded in shape and somewhat greyish-green in colour. Attractive purple flowers, similar to other species of *Polygala*, are produced in summer. The flowers are superficially similar to those of the legume family but may easily be distinguished by a tufted outgrowth near the tip of the bottom petal. *P. fruticosa* can easily be distinguished from all other South African species by the leaves, which are in opposite pairs and not alternating each other on the stems[1].

PLANT PARTS USED. The whole plant is used.

MEDICINAL USES. A large number of different traditional uses have been recorded[2,3,4,5]. The roots form part of blood purifying decoctions and are also used to treat poor circulation, intestinal sores, tuberculosis, gonorrhoea and as snuff to improve sinusitis. Leaves and stems of several other species of *Polygala* (including *P. virgata*, also known as "ithethe" in Zulu) are used as traditional medicine[6] but the exact purpose is not clear[5,6].

PREPARATION AND DOSAGE. Root decoctions are used on their own or the roots may also form an ingredient of various medicines. Decoctions of the chopped leaves and stems may be used.

ACTIVE INGREDIENTS. Three unusual coumarins, frutinones A, B and C, have been isolated from *P. fruticosa*[7]. Other *Polygala* species are known to contain saponins of presenegenin (so-called bidesmosides), as well as methyl salicylate and organic acids[8,9]. The best known example is *P. senega* (snakeroot) – a traditional European cough medicine[9].

PHARMACOLOGICAL EFFECTS. Frutinone A shows antifungal activity[7] but the pharmacological effects of *P. fruticosa* are not known and may be due to a combination of active ingredients.

DISTRIBUTION. The plant occurs along the coastal parts of the Western Cape, Eastern Cape and KwaZulu-Natal[1].

Frutinone A

1. **Levyns, M.R. 1955.** The species of *Polygala* in the South-Western Cape Province. *Jl S. Afr. Bot.* 21: 9-50.
2. **Watt, J.M. & Breyer-Brandwijk, M.G. 1962.** *The Medicinal and Poisonous Plants of Southern and Eastern Africa.* 2nd edition. Livingstone, London.
3. **Hutchings, A. 1989.** A survey and analysis of traditional medicinal plants as used by the Zulu, Xhosa and Sotho. *Bothalia* 19: 111-123.
4. **Pujol, J. 1990.** *Naturafrica – the Herbalist Handbook.* Jean Pujol Natural Healers' Foundation, Durban.
5. **Hutchings, A. 1996.** *Zulu Medicinal Plants.* Natal University Press, Pietermaritzburg.
6. **Cunningham, A.B. 1988.** *An Investigation of the Herbal Medicine Trade in Natal/KwaZulu.* Investigational report no 29, Institute of Natural Resources, University of Natal.
7. **Di Paolo, E.R. et al. 1989.** New chromonocoumarin derivatives from *Polygala fruticosa* Berg. *Helv. Chim. Acta* 72: 1455-1462.
8. **Dictionary of Natural Products on CD-ROM, release 4:2 (1996).** Chapman & Hall, London.
9. **Bruneton, J. 1995.** *Pharmacognosy, Phytochemistry, Medicinal Plants.* Intercept, Hampshire.

Polygala fruticosa

Flowering stems of *Polygala fruticosa*

Leaves and flowers of *Polygala fruticosa*

Chopped leaves and stems of *Polygala virgata*

PROTEA REPENS

Proteaceae

---

suikerbos (Afrikaans), sugarbush (English)

BOTANICAL DESCRIPTION. This is an erect shrub of about three metres in height, with narrow, hairless leaves. The flower heads are cream-coloured, pink or red, with a shiny sticky exudate on the outer surface. *P. repens* can also be recognised by the characteristic dry flower heads which are retained on the plant. *P. caffra* (Zulu: "isiqalaba") is used medicinally in the eastern and north-eastern parts of South Africa. It is a robust shrub or small tree with silvery leaves and short, funnel-shaped flower heads[1].

PLANT PARTS USED. The nectar is boiled to a syrup (*P. repens*) and in the case of *P. caffra*, the stem bark or root bark is used.

MEDICINAL USES. The syrup produced from the nectar, known as "bossiestroop", was an important early Cape remedy for chest disorders[2] and formed an ingredient of cough mixtures[3]. It was also used to treat diabetes[4]. The bark of *P. caffra* is used to treat bleeding stomach ulcers and diarrhoea[4,5,6]. It is interesting to note that the closely related *P. nitida* was an early Cape remedy for diarrhoea[2].

PREPARATION AND DOSAGE. Nectar is collected from the flower heads by shaking them into a bucket, after which it is boiled to a syrup (Afrikaans: "bossiestroop"). The syrup was mixed with other ingredients[2], or two teaspoons several times a day was prescribed for diabetes[4]. Warm infusions of the bark or root bark of *P. caffra* are taken orally or in the form of enemas[4,5,6].

ACTIVE INGREDIENTS. *P. repens* nectar contains mainly glucose and fructose, with small amounts (about 5%) xylose, but practically no sucrose[7]. The antidiarrhoeal effects of bark may be ascribed to tannins[8] but no details are available on the actual chemical compounds[9].

PHARMACOLOGICAL EFFECTS. Monosaccharides and their syrups are important sweeteners in liquid preparations and in the food industry. Simple Linctus (British Pharmaceutical Codex) is still prescribed as an antitussive and demulcent. It contains a viscous concentrated sugar solution with an aniseed flavour and amaranth as colourant[10,11].

DISTRIBUTION. *P. repens* is one of the most widely distributed fynbos proteas and is often locally dominant, forming large dense stands. *P. caffra* occurs over large parts of the grasslands of South Africa[1].

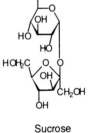

Glucose   Fructose   Sucrose

---

1. **Rebelo, T. 1995.** *Sasol Proteas: a Field Guide to the Proteas of Southern Africa.* Fernwood Press, Cape Town.
2. **Forbes, V.S. (ed.) 1986.** *Carl Peter Thunberg Travels at the Cape of Good Hope 1772-1775.* Van Riebeeck Society, Cape Town.
3. **Dykman, E.J. 1891.** *Kook-, Koek- en Resepte Boek.* Paarlse Drukpers Maatskappy, Paarl.
4. **Watt, J.M. & Breyer-Brandwijk, M.G. 1962.** *The Medicinal and Poisonous Plants of Southern and Eastern Africa.* 2nd edition. Livingstone, London.
5. **Hutchings, A. 1996.** *Zulu Medicinal Plants.* Natal University Press, Pietermaritzburg.
6. **Pujol, J. 1990.** *Naturafrica – the Herbalist Handbook.* Jean Pujol Natural Healers' Foundation, Durban.
7. **Van Wyk, B-E. & Nicolson, S.W. 1995.** Xylose is a major nectar sugar in *Protea* and *Faurea.* *S. Afr. J. Sci.* 91: 151-153.
8. **Bruneton, J. 1995.** *Pharmacognosy, Phytochemistry, Medicinal Plants.* Intercept, Hampshire.
9. **Dictionary of Natural Products on CD-ROM, release 4:2 (1996).** Chapman & Hall, London.
10. **British Pharmaceutical Codex, 1959.** The Pharmaceutical Press, London.
11. **Martindale 1977.** *The Extra Pharmacopoeia.* 27th edition. Pharmaceutical Press, London.

Protea repens

Traditional cough syrup known as "bossiestroop",
prepared from *Protea repens* nectar

Red colour form of *Protea repens*

PRUNUS AFRICANA

Rosaceae

> **inyazangoma-elimnyana (Zulu); umkakase (Xhosa);
> rooistinkhout (Afrikaans); red stinkwood (English)**

BOTANICAL DESCRIPTION. This tall forest tree may reach a height of more than 30 metres. Buttress roots are often present and the bark is coarse, with a dark brown and black colour. The dark green, glossy leaves have minute serrations along the edges and smell of almonds when crushed. Small white flowers in elongated clusters are followed by reddish-brown berries of about 10 mm in diameter[1,2].

PLANT PARTS USED. The stem bark is used.

MEDICINAL USES. The bark is reported to be of value in treating chest pain[3]. Bark extracts have become popular in Europe for the treatment of benign prostate hypertrophy[4].

PREPARATION AND DOSAGE. Bark decoctions are traditionally used in Zulu medicine, while lipid and phytosterol extracts (100 mg per day in six to eight week cycles) are most commonly used in Europe for the symptomatic treatment of prostatism[4].

ACTIVE INGREDIENTS. Phytosterols (free and conjugated ß-sitosterol, campesterol) have been isolated from bark extracts[4,5]. It also contains pentacyclic triterpenoid esters and various linear aliphatic alcohols and their ferulic acid esters[4,5]. The presence of amygdalin, a cyanogenic glycoside, has been reported[6]. Wild cherry bark (*P. serotina*) contains another cyanogenic glycoside, prunasin[7].

PHARMACOLOGICAL EFFECTS. The reported activity of bark extracts against prostatic adenoma is possibly due to ß-sitosterol, which is also found in other plants that are traditionally used for the same purpose[4,8] (see *Hypoxis*). It is possible that terpenoids and various other compounds also contribute to the beneficial effects. Cherry-laurel water (produced from *P. laurocerasus*) is still used in Europe as a respiratory stimulant[4]. Wild cherry bark from *P. serotina*, in the form of a syrup (Wild Cherry Syrup, British Pharmaceutical Codex), has been used in the treatment of coughs[7].

DISTRIBUTION. *P. africana* is found mainly in afromontane forests along the mistbelt regions of South Africa[9] and it occurs further north into tropical Africa.

ß-Sitosterol   Amygdalin

1. **Palmer, E. & Pitman, J. 1972.** *Trees of Southern Africa.* Balkema, Cape Town.
2. **Coates Palgrave, K. 1977.** *Trees of Southern Africa.* Struik, Cape Town.
3. **Pujol, J. 1990.** *Naturafrica – the Herbalist Handbook.* Jean Pujol Natural Healers' Foundation, Durban.
4. **Bruneton, J. 1995.** *Pharmacognosy, Phytochemistry, Medicinal Plants.* Intercept, Hampshire.
5. **Dictionary of Natural Products on CD-ROM, release 4:2 (1996).** Chapman & Hall, London.
6. **Watt, J.M. & Breyer-Brandwijk, M.G. 1962.** *The Medicinal and Poisonous Plants of Southern and Eastern Africa.* 2nd edition. Livingstone, London.
7. **Martindale 1993.** *The Extra Pharmacopoeia.* 30th edition. Pharmaceutical Press, London.
8. **Merck 1989.** *The Merck Index.* 11th edition. Merck, Rahway.
9. **Von Breitenbach, F. 1986.** *National List of Indigenous Trees.* Dendrological Foundation, Pretoria.

Prunus africana

Berries of *Prunus africana*

Flowers of *Prunus africana*

Bark of *Prunus africana*

PSIDIUM GUAJAVA

Myrtaceae

guava (English); koejawel (Afrikaans); ugwava (Zulu)

BOTANICAL DESCRIPTION. The guava is a shrub or small tree, usually not more than four metres in height. The bark peels off in flakes, revealing the characteristically smooth trunk. The large leaves are formed opposite each other in pairs, with prominent veins, particularly on the lower side. Small white flowers of about 25 mm in diameter, with numerous stamens, are produced in early summer, followed by rounded or pear-shaped yellow, many-seeded fruit. Due to their delicious taste and high vitamin C content, guavas are an important commercial crop.

PLANT PARTS USED. The leaves are mainly used, sometimes the unripe fruit, bark or roots.

MEDICINAL USES. Guava leaves are commonly used in South Africa as a remedy for diarrhoea[1,2]. The leaves are also used for several other ailments, including diabetes, fever, cough, ulcers, boils and wounds[1,2]. The main ethnotherapeutic use in Africa is said to be for malaria[3]. Leaf infusions are used in the Cape for diabetes.

PREPARATION AND DOSAGE. Crushed leaves are boiled in water and the infusion is either taken orally as a tea or as an enema[2]. For severe diarrhoea, an infusion of one crushed leaf in a litre of water is used[2].

ACTIVE INGREDIENTS. Numerous tannins and other phenolic compounds have been identified from *P. guajava*[4], of which amritoside is of particular importance. Amritoside is a glycoside (gentiobioside) of ellagic acid. Another biologically interesting compound in the plant is guiajaverin, a glycoside (arabinopyroside) of quercetin[4]. The leaves also contain essential oils and triterpenoids[4].

PHARMACOLOGICAL EFFECTS. Ellagic acid is a known intestinal astringent and haemostatic[4,5,6] which explains the therapeutic value of the plant against diarrhoea and dysentery. The tannins are generally of value because of their vasoconstricting effects and their ability to form a protective layer on the skin and mucosas[6]. These effects, together with proven antibacterial and antifungal activity, result in effective treatment of both internal and external infections[6]. Quercetin (and its glycosides) undoubtedly also contribute to the efficacy of the medicine, because it is a known antioxidant with anticarcinogenic, anti-HIV and antibiotic effects[4]. Hypoglycemic effects have been documented[7].

DISTRIBUTION. The guava occurs naturally in central America but has become naturalised in many parts of the world, including Africa. In South Africa, it is found as a weed in the warm subtropical areas of KwaZulu-Natal, Mpumalanga and the Northern Province.

Ellagic acid

Quercetin

1. **Watt, J.M. & Breyer-Brandwijk, M.G. 1962.** *The Medicinal and Poisonous Plants of Southern and Eastern Africa.* 2nd edition. Livingstone, London.
2. **Hutchings, A. 1996.** *Zulu Medicinal Plants.* Natal University Press, Pietermaritzburg.
3. **Iwu, M.M. 1993.** *Handbook of African Medicinal Plants.* CRC Press, Boca Raton.
4. **Dictionary of Natural Products on CD-ROM, release 4:2 (1996).** Chapman & Hall, London.
5. **Merck 1989.** *The Merck Index.* 11th edition. Merck, Rahway.
6. **Bruneton, J. 1995.** *Pharmacognosy, Phytochemistry, Medicinal Plants.* Intercept, Hampshire.
7. **Ponglux, D. *et al.* (eds) 1987.** *Medicinal Plants.* The first Princess Chulabhorn Science Congress, Bangkok, Thailand.

Psidium guajava

Dried leaves of *Psidium guajava*

Flowers of *Psidium guajava*

Fruits of *Psidium guajava*

PTAEROXYLON OBLIQUUM

Ptaeroxylaceae

---

umthathe (Xhosa, Zulu); sneezewood (English); nieshout (Afrikaans)

BOTANICAL DESCRIPTION. Sneezewood varies in size from a shrub to a large tree of about 15 to 20 metres in height[1,2,3]. The bark is pale greyish-brown to dark grey and becomes rough and flaky in old specimens. The leaves have up to eight pairs of leaflets, each of which are distinctly assymetrical in shape. Male and female flowers occur on different trees. They are small, pale yellow and are borne in dense clusters, often resulting in a beautiful sight when the tree is in full flower. The fruits are oblong capsules which split in the middle when ripe, each releasing two winged seeds[1,2,3].

PLANT PARTS USED. Wood[4,5] or bark[6] is used.

MEDICINAL USES. The powdered wood is used as a snuff to relieve headache[4,5] and the bark is used for the treatment of rheumatism and arthritis[7]. Infusions of the powdered wood are taken for the treatment of rheumatism and heart disease[4].

PREPARATION AND DOSAGE. Wood is powdered and used as snuff, or decoctions and infusions of the wood or bark are taken[4,7].

ACTIVE INGREDIENTS. The wood is chemically highly complex and contains numerous unusual chromones and other phenolic compounds[8]. Typical examples are ptaeroxylone and umtatin[8,9,10]. The leaves contain perforatin A[8].

PHARMACOLOGICAL EFFECTS. Sneezing is induced by highly irritant substances (presumably the chromones) in the wood. Perforatin A has antihypertensive effects[11].

DISTRIBUTION. Sneezewood grows naturally along the eastern coastal parts of South Africa and northwards to the Northern Province[12]. The town of Umtata in the Eastern Cape Province is named after this tree.

Ptaeroxylone

Umtatin

Perforatin A

1. **Palmer, E. & Pitman, J. 1972.** *Trees of Southern Africa.* Balkema, Cape Town.
2. **Coates Palgrave, K. 1977.** *Trees of Southern Africa.* Struik, Cape Town.
3. **Van Wyk, P. 1995.** *Field Guide to the Trees of the Kruger National Park.* Struik, Cape Town.
4. **Watt, J.M. & Breyer-Brandwijk, M.G. 1962.** *The Medicinal and Poisonous Plants of Southern and Eastern Africa.* 2nd edition. Livingstone, London.
5. **Hutchings, A. & Van Staden, J. 1994.** Plants used for stress-related ailments in traditional Zulu, Xhosa and Sotho medicine. Part 1: Plants used for headaches. *J. Ethnopharmacol.* 43: 89-124.
6. **Hutchings, A. 1996.** *Zulu Medicinal Plants.* Natal University Press, Pietermaritzburg.
7. **Pujol, J. 1990.** *Naturafrica – the Herbalist Handbook.* Jean Pujol Natural Healers' Foundation, Durban.
8. **Dictionary of Natural Products on CD-ROM, release 4:2 (1996).** Chapman & Hall, London.
9. **Dean, F.M. & Taylor, D.A.H. 1966.** Extractives from East African timbers. Part II. *Ptaeroxylon obliquum. J. Chem. Soc.(C)* 1966: 114-116.
10. **Dean, F.M. et al. 1967.** Umtatin and related chromones from the heartwood of *Ptaeroxylon obliquum. Tet. Lett.* 1967: 2737-2740.
11. **Langenhoven, J.H. et al. 1988.** An antihypertensive chromone from *Ptaeroxylon obliquum. Planta Med.* 54: 373.
12. **Von Breitenbach, F. 1986.** *National List of Indigenous Trees.* Dendrological Foundation, Pretoria.

Leaves and fruit capsules of *Ptaeroxylon obliquum*

Ptaeroxylon obliquum

Flowers of *Ptaeroxylon obliquum*

Bark of *Ptaeroxylon obliquum*

PUNICA GRANATUM

Punicaceae

pomegranate (English); granaat (Afrikaans)

BOTANICAL DESCRIPTION. The pomegranate is a thorny, deciduous shrub or small tree of about three metres in height. The leaves are glossy and bright green, without hairs. Attractive orange-red flowers occur on the tips of the branches. The large fruits have a leathery rind and numerous bright red seeds inside. Each seed has a juicy, edible flesh around it.

PLANT PARTS USED. The fruit rind is used as anti-diarrhoeal; the root and stem bark as vermifuge.

MEDICINAL USES. The dried fruit rind (Afrikaans: "granaatskille") is an early Cape remedy for diarrhoea and stomach ache[1,2]. Its use in antidiarrhoeal decoctions has also been recorded in the Eastern Cape[3]. The root bark (occasionally with stem bark and leaves included) is a well known and widely used treatment for tapeworm[4,5].

PREPARATION AND DOSAGE. Infusions or tinctures of the fresh or dried fruit rind are taken, usually with honey added to counter the bitter taste[2]. Decoctions of the root bark (sometimes with stem bark, leaves or young fruit added) have been widely used as a tapeworm remedy[4,5].

ACTIVE INGREDIENTS. Punicalin and punicalagin are the two main gallotannins of the fruit rind[6,7], where they occur in concentrations[8] of up to 28%. Several piperidine alkaloids are present in the roots, bark, leaves and young fruit (but not in the rind[8]), with pelletierine as the major active compound[6,9].

PHARMACOLOGICAL EFFECTS. Tannins are well known for their beneficial effects in treating diarrhoea and dysentery[10]. Pelletierine and other alkaloids of the root bark are active against tapeworms. It was once widely used for this purpose but in modern times it is no longer recommended because of undesirable side effects[8,10]. Anthelmintic, antipyretic, diuretic, hypoglycaemic, antiviral and antibacterial activities have been demonstrated[11].

DISTRIBUTION. The pomegranate originated in the eastern Mediterranean region and was one of the first fruit crops to be cultivated in the Old World (records date back to several centuries BC)[12]. It is still a minor fruit crop in North Africa and the Middle East. The plant was introduced into South Africa before 1700 and is now commonly cultivated in most parts of the country[13].

Pelletierine   Punicalin

1. **Dykman, E.J. 1891.** *Kook-, Koek- en Resepte Boek.* Paarlse Drukpers Maatskappy, Paarl.
2. **Cillié, A.M. 1992.** *Kruie op Witblits, Rate, Resepte en Feite.* Unpublished notes, Worcester Museum.
3. **Hutchings, A. 1989.** Observations on plant usage in Xhosa and Zulu medicine. *Bothalia* 19: 225-235.
4. **Watt, J.M. & Breyer-Brandwijk, M.G. 1962.** *The Medicinal and Poisonous Plants of Southern and Eastern Africa.* 2nd edition. Livingstone, London.
5. **Iwu, M.M. 1993.** *Handbook of African Medicinal Plants.* CRC Press, Boca Raton.
6. **Dictionary of Natural Products on CD-ROM, release 4:2 (1996).** Chapman & Hall, London.
7. **Tanaka, T. *et al.* 1986.** Tannins and related compounds. XL. Revision of the structures of punicalin and punicalagin, and isolation and characterization of 2-*O*-galloylpunicalin from bark of *Punica granatum. Chem. Pharm. Bull.* 34: 650-655.
8. **Martindale 1977.** *The Extra Pharmacopoeia.* 27th edition. Pharmaceutical Press, London.
9. **Merck 1989.** *The Merck Index.* 11th edition. Merck, Rahway.
10. **Bruneton, J. 1995.** *Pharmacognosy, Phytochemistry, Medicinal Plants.* Intercept, Hampshire.
11. **Ponglux, D. *et al.* (eds) 1987.** *Medicinal Plants.* The first Princess Chulabhorn Science Congress, Bangkok, Thailand.
12. **Zohary, D. & Hopf, M. 1994**. *Domestication of plants in the Old World.* 2nd edition, p. 162. Clarendon Press, Oxford.
13. **Smith, C.A. 1966.** *Common Names of South African Plants. Memoirs of the Botanical Survey of South Africa* 35.

Punica granatum

Flowers and young fruit of *Punica granatum*

Dried fruit rind of *Punica granatum*, known as "granaatskille"

RAPANEA MELANOPHLOEOS

Myrsinaceae

**isiqalaba-sehlathi (Xhosa, Zulu); isiqwane-sehlati (Xhosa); umaphipha (Zulu);
Cape beech (English); Kaapse boekenhout (Afrikaans)**

BOTANICAL DESCRIPTION. It is usually a medium-sized tree of about five to ten metres in height, but it may reach a height of 20 metres under favourable circumstances[1,2]. The bark is grey, sometimes dotted with small diamond-shaped spots (raised areas). The leaves are rather large, about 100 mm long, oblong in shape and narrowing towards their bases. Young leaves and leaf stalks are characteristically purplish-red in colour, a helpful feature by which to recognise this tree. Small greenish flowers are borne densely clustered along the stems, followed by small, round, purple berries of about five mm in diameter.

PLANT PARTS USED. The bark is mainly used, sometimes the roots.

MEDICINAL USES. Decoctions of the bark are used by the Zulu as expectorants and emetics[3], and also against muscular pain, stomach disorders and to strengthen the heart[3,4,5].

PREPARATION AND DOSAGE. Decoctions or infusions of the bark are taken or the roots may be eaten[3,5].

ACTIVE INGREDIENTS. *Rapanea* bark is known to contain tannins[3] but no details are available[6]. Triterpenoid saponins, such as sakurasosaponin, have been isolated from the leaves[7], and it is possible that these or similar compounds occur in the bark. Several triterpenoids with a steroidal skeleton are known from other *Rapanea* species[6]. An example is 3-oxo-20,24-dammaradien-26-al.

PHARMACOLOGICAL EFFECTS. Nothing appears to be known about the pharmacological activities of *Rapanea* bark. It may be speculated that the expectorant properties are due to saponins. Snakeroot (*Polygala senega*) and primrose (*Primula veris*) are two examples of saponin-containing medicines traditionally used for the symptomatic treatment of coughs[8].

DISTRIBUTION. The tree grows naturally in the afromontane region and along the east coast of South Africa[9].

Sakurasosaponin   3-Oxo-20,24-dammaradien-26-al

---

1. **Palmer, E. & Pitman, J. 1972.** *Trees of Southern Africa.* Balkema, Cape Town.
2. **Coates Palgrave, K. 1977.** *Trees of Southern Africa.* Struik, Cape Town.
3. **Watt, J.M. & Breyer-Brandwijk, M.G. 1962.** *The Medicinal and Poisonous Plants of Southern and Eastern Africa.* 2nd edition. Livingstone, London.
4. **Pujol, J. 1990.** *Naturafrica – the Herbalist Handbook.* Jean Pujol Natural Healers' Foundation, Durban.
5. **Hutchings, A. 1996.** *Zulu Medicinal Plants.* Natal University Press, Pietermaritzburg.
6. **Dictionary of Natural Products on CD-ROM, release 4:2 (1996).** Chapman & Hall, London.
7. **Ohtani, K. et al. 1993.** Molluscicidal and antifungal triterpenoid saponins from *Rapanea melanophloeos* leaves. *Phytochemistry* 33: 83-86.
8. **Bruneton, J. 1995.** *Pharmacognosy, Phytochemistry, Medicinal Plants.* Intercept, Hampshire.
9. **Von Breitenbach, F. 1986.** *National List of Indigenous Trees.* Dendrological Foundation, Pretoria.

Bark, leaves and fruits of *Rapanea melanophloeos*

Flowers of *Rapanea melanophloeos*

Bark of *Rapanea melanophloeos*

RAUVOLFIA CAFFRA

Apocynaceae

**umhlambamase (Xhosa); umhlambamanzi (Zulu);
quinine tree (English); kinaboom (Afrikaans)**

BOTANICAL DESCRIPTION. The quinine tree varies in height from about five to 20 metres. Mature specimens have spreading crowns and pale yellowish-brown to grey bark, which is soft and corky, splitting into small rectangular blocks[1,2,3]. The oblong leaves occur in groups of three to five on the branches and are oblong in shape, bright shiny green, hairless, with a prominent main vein. Small, white, waxy flowers are followed by rounded or egg-shaped berries. They are bright green, sometimes with conspicuous white spots, but become black and wrinkled when ripe.

PLANT PARTS USED. The bark or root bark is mainly used, rarely the leaves.

MEDICINAL USES. The main use of the bark is to treat fevers and malaria, as well as insomnia and hysteria[4,5,6,7]. The milky latex is applied to rashes[4,7] – also the rash caused by measles. Numerous other traditional uses have been recorded for *R. caffra* and the closely related *R. vomitaria*[4,6,7,8,9].

PREPARATION AND DOSAGE. Decoctions of the bark are taken[4,7].

ACTIVE INGREDIENTS. A large number of indole alkaloids occur in *R. caffra*[10], of which reserpine and ajmalicine (sometimes also called raubasine) are of particular interest. Commercially, these alkaloids are obtained from *R. serpentina* (snakewood), *R. vomitaria* and *R. tetraphylla*[11,12].

PHARMACOLOGICAL EFFECTS. Reserpine is a well-known antihypertensive, widely used to reduce blood pressure, to reduce the heart rate and for its sedative effects[11,12]. Reserpine has important side effects, notably depression[8,11]. Ajmalicine increases blood flow to the brain and forms an ingredient of products used to treat psychological and behavioural problems associated with senility, as well as cerebro-vascular and cranial traumas[11,13].

DISTRIBUTION. *R. caffra* occurs in the eastern parts of South Africa and further north into east Africa.

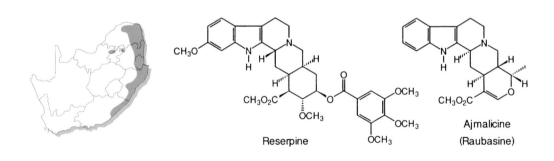

Reserpine

Ajmalicine
(Raubasine)

1. **Codd, L.E. 1963.** Apocynaceae. In: *Flora of Southern Africa* 26, pp. 244-296. Botanical Research Institute, Pretoria.
2. **Coates Palgrave, K. 1977.** *Trees of Southern Africa.* Struik, Cape Town.
3. **Van Wyk, P. 1995.** *Field Guide to the Trees of the Kruger National Park.* Struik, Cape Town.
4. **Watt, J.M. & Breyer-Brandwijk, M.G. 1962.** *The Medicinal and Poisonous Plants of Southern and Eastern Africa.* 2nd edition. Livingstone, London.
5. **Watt, J.M. 1967.** African plants potentially useful in mental health. *Lloydia* 30: 1-22.
6. **Pujol, J. 1990.** *Naturafrica - the Herbalist Handbook.* Jean Pujol Natural Healers' Foundation, Durban.
7. **Hutchings, A. 1996.** *Zulu Medicinal Plants.* Natal University Press, Pietermaritzburg.
8. **Iwu, M.M. 1993.** *Handbook of African Medicinal Plants.* CRC Press, Boca Raton.
9. **Neuwinger, H.D. 1994.** *Afrikanische Arzneipflanzen und Jagdgifte.* Wissenschaftliche Verlagsgesellschaft, Stuttgart.
10. **Dictionary of Natural Products on CD-ROM, release 4:2 (1996).** Chapman & Hall, London.
11. **Bruneton, J. 1995.** *Pharmacognosy, Phytochemistry, Medicinal Plants.* Intercept, Hampshire.
12. **Merck 1989.** *The Merck Index.* 11th edition. Merck, Rahway.
13. **Goodman, L.S. & Gilman, A. 1992.** *The Pharmacological Basis of Therapeutics.* 8th edition. Pergamon Press, New York.

Rauvolfia caffra

Flowers of *Rauvolfia caffra*

Leaves and green fruits of *Rauvolfia caffra*

Bark of *Rauvolfia caffra*

RHOICISSUS TRIDENTATA

Vitaceae

isinwazi (Zulu); wild grape (English); bobbejaantou (Afrikaans)

BOTANICAL DESCRIPTION. The plant is a shrubby creeper with the branches spreading outwards from a thick woody base[1]. The dark green, glossy leaves have three leaflets, each wedge-shaped, with a serrated margin. The inconspicuous greenish flowers are followed by small berries[1,2]. The widely distributed form of the species in South Africa is known as *R. tridentata* subsp. *cuneifolia*[2].

PLANT PARTS USED. The roots or tuberous rootstock (lignotuber) are used. They have bright red pigments in the outer layer, resembling blood when fresh.

MEDICINAL USES. The roots or tubers are used for stomach ailments, kidney and bladder complaints, infertility[3,4,5] and dysmennorhoea. It is also administered as an enema for delayed menstruation and to facilitate childbirth[3,5]. Other members of the family (*Cissus, Cyphostemma*) are widely used in Africa to relieve pain and for various other ailments[6].

PREPARATION AND DOSAGE. Decoctions and infusions of the roots or tubers are taken orally or administered as enemas[3,5].

ACTIVE INGREDIENTS. Nothing appears to be known about the chemical compounds in wild grape[7]. In other members of the family, particularly *Vitis* species (grapes), numerous phenolic compound have been isolated and identified[7]. Vine leaf is a traditional medicine in Europe, and contains various polyphenols, anthocyanins and proanthocyanidins[8]. Examples of two common anthocyanins – delphinidin and cyanidin – are shown below.

PHARMACOLOGICAL EFFECTS. Anthocyanin-containing drugs are traditionally used to treat the symptoms of capillary and venous fragility[8]. Anthocyanins and polyphenols show numerous pharmacological activities[7] and these compounds may be directly or indirectly responsible for the reported value of wild grape. The traditional Zulu uses of the plant suggest analgesic effects[9], an aspect in need of further study.

DISTRIBUTION. The plant occurs over large parts of South Africa and is found in a variety of habitats. The map shows the distribution area of both subspecies[2].

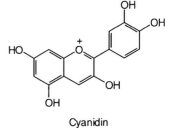

Delphinidin   Cyanidin

1. **Wild, H. & Drummond, R.B. 1963.** Vitaceae. *Flora Zambesiaca* 2(2): 439-449. Crown Agents, London.
2. **Urton, N.R. *et al.* 1986.** The taxonomy of the *Rhoicissus tridentata* (Vitaceae) complex in southern Africa. *S. Afr. J. Bot.* 52: 389-396.
3. **Watt, J.M. & Breyer-Brandwijk, M.G. 1962.** *The Medicinal and Poisonous Plants of Southern and Eastern Africa.* 2nd edition. Livingstone, London.
4. **Pujol, J. 1990.** *Naturafrica – the Herbalist Handbook.* Jean Pujol Natural Healers' Foundation, Durban.
5. **Hutchings, A. 1996.** *Zulu Medicinal Plants.* Natal University Press, Pietermaritzburg.
6. **Iwu, M.M. 1993.** *Handbook of African Medicinal Plants.* CRC Press, Boca Raton.
7. **Dictionary of Natural Products on CD-ROM, release 4:2 (1996).** Chapman & Hall, London.
8. **Bruneton, J. 1995.** *Pharmacognosy, Phytochemistry, Medicinal Plants.* Intercept, Hampshire.
9. **Watt, J.M. 1967.** African plants potentially useful in mental health. *Lloydia* 30: 1-22.

Leaves and fruit of *Rhoicissus tridentata*

Flowers of *Rhoicissus tridentata*

Thick, tuberous roots of *Rhoicissus tridentata*

RHUS UNDULATA

Anacardiaceae

---

t'kuni (Khoi); kuni-bush (English); koeniebos, garrabos (Afrikaans)

BOTANICAL DESCRIPTION. The plant is a shrub of up to three metres in height[1]. The leaves are very variable but characteristically have three leaflets arising from a narrowly winged leaf stalk. Each leaflet is variable in size and shape, with a pointed tip and a distinctly wavy margin. Young leaves are usually shiny and resinous. The inconspicuous greenish flowers are followed by small, thinly fleshy, green or slightly reddish berries. *R. undulata* is difficult to distinguish from the closely related *R. burchellii* and was previously considered to be the same species[2].

PLANT PARTS USED. The leaves, bark or roots are used.

MEDICINAL USES. Traditional uses include the chewing of leaves for chest colds by the Nama, and leaf decoctions for post partem problems[3]. The roots are claimed to be of therapeutic value in infective disorders of the gastro-intestinal tract[4]. The bark and leaves of several other species are used medicinally, including *R. burchellii, R. chirindensis, R. laevigata* and *R. viminalis*[3,5,6].

PREPARATION AND DOSAGE. Leaves are chewed or decoctions of the roots or bark are taken.

ACTIVE INGREDIENTS. A flavone from the roots of a species related to *R. undulata* has been identified as apigenin dimethylether[4]. No other chemical compounds appear to be known from *R. undulata* or any of the related species[7].

PHARMACOLOGICAL EFFECTS. Apigenin dimethylether was shown to have anti-inflammatory activity[4].

DISTRIBUTION. The kuni-bush is widely distributed along the west coast of the Cape and occurs in a range of different habitats[1].

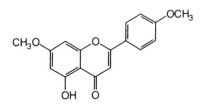

Apigenin dimethylether

---

1. **Moffett, R.O. 1993.** Anacardiaceae. *Rhus. Flora of Southern Africa* 19. Botanical Research Institute, Pretoria.
2. **Coates Palgrave, K. 1977.** *Trees of Southern Africa.* Struik, Cape Town.
3. **Watt, J.M. & Breyer-Brandwijk, M.G. 1962.** *The Medicinal and Poisonous Plants of Southern and Eastern Africa.* 2nd edition. Livingstone, London.
4. **Fourie, T.G. & Snyckers, F.O. 1984.** A flavone with antiinflammatory activity from the roots of *Rhus undulata. J. Nat. Prod.* 47: 1057-1058.
5. **Pujol, J. 1990.** *Naturafrica – the Herbalist Handbook.* Jean Pujol Natural Healers' Foundation, Durban.
6. **Hutchings, A. 1996.** *Zulu Medicinal Plants.* Natal University Press, Pietermaritzburg.
7. **Dictionary of Natural Products on CD-ROM, release 4:2 (1996).** Chapman & Hall, London.

Rhus undulata

Leaves and flowers of *Rhus chirindensis*

Leaves and fruits of *Rhus undulata*

Roots and leaves of *Rhus undulata*

RICINUS COMMUNIS

Euphorbiaceae

kasterolieboom (Afrikaans); castor oil plant (English);
mokhura (Northern Sotho); umhlakuva (Xhosa, Zulu)

BOTANICAL DESCRIPTION. This is a large shrub or small tree of up to four metres in height, with very large, hand-shaped leaves on long, stout leaf stalks[1]. The flower clusters appear near the tips of the branches. Female flowers occur above the male flowers. The fruits are three-lobed capsules, with spine-like projections on their surfaces. Each capsule has three seeds, which are about 10 mm long, conspicuously shiny, irregularly mottled with silver, brown and black. At the tip of the seed is a hard, white, fleshy aril[1]. Castor oil is grown commercially on a large scale for the oil, which is mainly an industrial product, used as a lubricant and as starting material in the manufacture of polymers and various other products.

PLANT PARTS USED. The oil, which is extracted from the seeds, is mostly used; sometimes also the fruits, seeds or leaves.

MEDICINAL USES. Castor oil is a well-known purgative medicine, commonly referred to in South Africa as "blue bottle" (Afrikaans: "bloubottel") because of the characteristic blue bottle in which it was traditionally packed and sold. This product is very effective but was much feared by children because of the disagreeable taste. The seeds are not popular as purgatives in Sotho and Zulu traditional medicine[2], but leaf infusions, administered orally or as enemas, are used for stomach ache[3,4]. Root and leaf poultices are widely applied to wounds, sores and boils[3,4]. Numerous other uses have been recorded[3,4,5].

PREPARATION AND DOSAGE. One (5 ml) to four teaspoons of the oil are taken as a laxative.

ACTIVE INGREDIENTS. Castor oil contains a fatty acid known as ricinoleic acid, which accounts for about 90% of the triglyceride fatty acids in the oil[6]. The seeds also contain two highly toxic substances, which are not present in the oil – an alkaloid: ricinine; and a lectin: ricin[6,7]. The latter is among the most toxic compounds known[6] and two seeds may cause fatal poisoning in humans[3].

PHARMACOLOGICAL EFFECTS. Like other anionic surfactants, ricinoleic acid, which is formed under the influence of lipase in the small intestine, reduces the net absorption of fluids and electrolytes and stimulates the intestinal peristalsis. During the seventeenth and eighteenth centuries, a fortnightly purging was considered necessary for good health, but the ritualised purgation of children and the excessive use of laxatives have virtually disappeared in modern times[8,9].

DISTRIBUTION. The plant is believed to be indigenous to north-east Africa and India[1], but it is now widely distributed in the tropics. It occurs throughout South Africa as a weed[1] and is also commonly cultivated.

$$CH_3(CH_2)_5CH(OH)CH_2-CH=CH(CH_2)_7COOH$$

Ricinoleic acid

Ricinine

1. **Henderson, M. & Anderson, J.G. 1966.** *Common Weeds in South Africa. Memoirs of the Botanical Survey of South Africa* 37.
2. **Cawston, F.G. 1933.** Native medicines of Natal. *S.A. Medical Journal*, 10 June 1933: 370-371.
3. **Watt, J.M. & Breyer-Brandwijk, M.G. 1962.** *The Medicinal and Poisonous Plants of Southern and Eastern Africa*. 2nd edition. Livingstone, London.
4. **Hutchings, A. 1996.** *Zulu Medicinal Plants.* Natal University Press, Pietermaritzburg.
5. **Iwu, M.M. 1993.** *Handbook of African Medicinal Plants.* CRC Press, Boca Raton.
6. **Merck 1989.** *The Merck Index.* 11th edition. Merck, Rahway.
7. **Bruneton, J. 1995.** *Pharmacognosy, Phytochemistry, Medicinal Plants*. Intercept, Hampshire.
8. **Lewis, W.H. & Elvin-Lewis, M.P.F. 1977.** *Medical Botany.* John Wiley & Sons, New York.
9. **Goodman, A.L. & Gilman, A. 1992.** *The Pharmacological Basis of Therapeutics*. 8th edition. Pergamon Press, New York.

Ricinus communis

Female flowers (top) and male flowers (below) of *Ricinus communis*

Ripe fruit capsules of *Ricinus communis*

Traditional product and seeds of *Ricinus communis*

RUMEX LANCEOLATUS

Polygonaceae

> idololenkonyane, dolonyana (Xhosa, Zulu); kxamane (Sotho);
> tongblaar (Afrikaans); common dock (English)

BOTANICAL DESCRIPTION. This herbacous perennial is 0,3 m to 0,5 metres in height, with erect, leafy branches. The bright green, hairless leaves are about 120 mm long and 25 mm wide, with slightly wavy margins and are borne on short stalks of 30 or 40 mm long. Small, yellowish flowers are produced in long, narrow clusters, followed by pale brown winged fruits, four mm long and three mm wide. Inside the fruits are dark brown seeds, two mm in length[1]. The way in which the smaller side branches also form flowers and fruits (and not just the main branches) is a useful way to distinguish this plant from its relatives[1]. Nowadays, no distinction appears to be made between *R. lanceolatus* and *R. crispus* and both are equally popular as medicinal plants. The latter is also known as "idololenkonyane" in Zulu (English: "curly dock"). This is a robust herb of up to 1,5 metres in height, with large leaves of up to 300 mm long and 60 mm wide. *Rumex* species are related to the well-known medicinal plants known as rhubarbs (*Rheum* species). The real (official) rubarb is the dried root of *R. palmatum* or *R. officinale* (or a mixture of both), while rhapontic rhubarb (*R. rhaponticum, R. compactum* and others) is sometimes used as a substitute[2].

PLANT PARTS USED. The roots are mainly used, sometimes the leaves.

MEDICINAL USES. The plant is a traditional remedy for internal parasites (tapeworm and roundworm)[3,4,5,6]. The whole plant is also said to be widely used for vascular diseases and internal bleeding[5]. Externally, it is applied to abscesses, boils and tumours[3,5,6].

PREPARATION AND DOSAGE. The roots or leaves are boiled in water (or sometimes milk) and the infusion is taken[3,4]. For topical use, a hot poultice is made from the pounded roots and leaves[5].

ACTIVE INGREDIENTS. Members of this family are well known for the presence of anthraquinones[7]. *Rumex* roots contain glycosides of chrysophanol, such as chrysophanein, while *Rheum* species have various glycosides of rhein[7]. The leaves of *Rumex* species contain large amounts of oxalic acid.

PHARMACOLOGICAL EFFECTS. The laxative effect of *Rumex* is due to chrysophanol and related glycosides. Oxalic acid is toxic in high concentrations[2], but is medically used (5% solution, together with 5% malonic acid) as haemostatic agent[8].

DISTRIBUTION. *R. lanceolatus* is widely distributed in South Africa[1] and is found along dams, rivers and other wet places (see map). The naturalised exotic weed, *R. crispus*, has become very common in most parts of South Africa.

Chrysophanein   Oxalic acid

1. **Rechinger, K.H. 1954.** Monograph of the genus *Rumex* in Africa. *Botaniska Notiser*, Supplement Volume 3.
2. **Bruneton, J. 1995.** *Pharmacognosy, Phytochemistry, Medicinal Plants*. Intercept, Hampshire.
3. **Watt, J.M. & Breyer-Brandwijk, M.G. 1962.** *The Medicinal and Poisonous Plants of Southern and Eastern Africa*. 2nd edition. Livingstone, London.
4. **Rood, B. 1994.** *Uit die Veldapteek*. Tafelberg, Cape Town.
5. **Pujol, J. 1990.** *Naturafrica – the Herbalist Handbook*. Jean Pujol Natural Healers' Foundation, Durban.
6. **Hutchings, A. 1996.** *Zulu Medicinal Plants*. Natal University Press, Pietermaritzburg.
7. **Dictionary of Natural Products on CD-ROM, release 4:2 (1996).** Chapman & Hall, London.
8. **Merck 1989.** *The Merck Index*. 11th edition. Merck, Rahway.

Rumex crispus

Rumex lanceolatus

Roots of *Rumex crispus*

RUTA GRAVEOLENS

Rutaceae

wynruit, binnewortel (Afrikaans); rue, herb of grace (English)

BOTANICAL DESCRIPTION. Rue is a woody, perennial shrub of about a metre in height. All parts of the plant are strongly aromatic. The leaves are irregularly divided into several leaflets, which are variable in size and shape, dull green and hairless, but with numerous minute, translucent glands. Clusters of small yellow flowers are borne at or near the tips of the branches. Each flower has four yellow petals, of which the margins are irregularly toothed. The fruits are small four-lobed capsules, densely covered with glands. Black wedge-shaped seeds are released from the capsules when they are ripe[1].

PLANT PARTS USED. The leaves and twigs are harvested.

MEDICINAL USES. Leaf infusions are taken for fever[2,3] and also for convulsions and fits in children, and for epilepsy and hysteria[4]. Alcoholic tinctures have been popular for respiratory problems and heart diseases[2,3]. Bruised leaves are used as a treatment against toothache and earache[2,3,4], while decoctions have been used to ease childbirth[2,4]. The plant is traditionally used in Europe for a wide range of ailments, ranging from hysteria to rheumatism[5].

PREPARATION AND DOSAGE. An infusion of 28 g of the herb in 500 ml water is recommended for rheumatism and gout, while 5 ml of chopped leaves in 500 ml of water have been used to treat high blood pressure[3]. Bruised leaves may be placed on a tooth and in the ears to alleviate pain[2,3,4].

ACTIVE INGREDIENTS. A large number of chemical compounds are known from *R. graveolens*[6]. Of interest in the identification of the drug are the coumarins (for example: rutaretin, the aglycone of rutarin), furanocoumarins (for example: bergapten), furanoquinoline alkaloids (for example: kokusaginine) and the flavonoid rutin[6,7]. Methylnonylketone (2-undecanone) is a major component of the volatile oil and is used in perfumery and flavourings[6]. Rutin is an important ingredient of various plant medicines used to treat the symptoms of venous and lymphatic vessel insufficiency and capillary fragility[7]. There is evidence of analgesic effects[4] but this is not clearly linked to any particular compound.

PHARMACOLOGICAL EFFECTS. Furanocoumarin-containing drugs are traditionally used for minor vascular disorders and other ailments[8] but the possibility that coumarins or furanoquinoline alkaloids have analgesic effects cannot be excluded. Rutin is a well-known capillary protectant[9], and is used as supplementary treatment for chronic venous diseases[10].

DISTRIBUTION. The plant is commonly grown as a herb in gardens in South Africa and has become naturalised in some parts[1]. It is particularly well known as a medicinal plant in the Calvinia district[3].

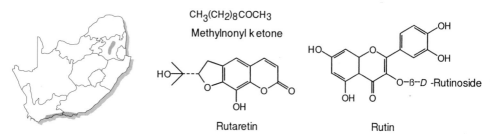

$$CH_3(CH_2)_8COCH_3$$
Methylnonyl ketone

Rutaretin

Rutin

O-β-*D*-Rutinoside

1. **Henderson, M. & Anderson, J.G. 1966.** *Common Weeds in South Africa. Memoirs of the Botanical Survey of South Africa* 37.
2. **Watt, J.M. & Breyer-Brandwijk, M.G. 1962.** *The Medicinal and Poisonous Plants of Southern and Eastern Africa.* 2nd edition. Livingstone, London.
3. **Rood, B. 1994.** *Uit die Veldapteek.* Tafelberg, Cape Town.
4. **Watt, J.M. 1967.** African plants potentially useful in mental health. *Lloydia* 30: 1-22.
5. **Grieve, M. 1967.** A Modern Herbal. Hafner, London.
6. **Dictionary of Natural Products on CD-ROM, release 4:2 (1996).** Chapman & Hall, London.
7. **Wagner, H. & Bladt, S. 1996.** *Plant Drug Analysis, a Thin Layer Chromatographic Atlas.* 2nd edition. Springer-Verlag, Berlin.
8. **Bruneton, J. 1995.** *Pharmacognosy, Phytochemistry, Medicinal Plants.* Intercept, Hampshire.
9. **Merck 1989.** *The Merck Index.* 11th edition. Merck, Rahway.
10. **Goodman, A.L. & Gilman, A. 1992.** *The Pharmacological Basis of Therapeutics*, 8th edition. Pergamon Press, New York.

Ruta graveolens

Leaves and flowers of *Ruta graveolens*

Dried leaves and stems of *Ruta graveolens*

SALIX MUCRONATA

Salicaceae

> **wilde wilger (Afrikaans); wild willow (English)**

BOTANICAL DESCRIPTION. This is a shrub or tree of up to 12 metres in height, with drooping branches when mature[1,2]. The bark is dark brown, rough and fissured. The narrow leaves are dark green above and paler below, with minute teeth along the margins. Male and female flowers occur separately on the tree. Both are small, yellowish-green and inconspicuous. The fruits are small brown capsules which split open to release the white, woolly seeds. The species are divided into several subspecies[1], of which *S. mucronata* subsp. *capensis* is most commonly used.

PLANT PARTS USED. The branch tips and leaves, known as willow tips (Afrikaans: "wilgertoppe"), are used; sometimes also the bark.

MEDICINAL USES. Willow tips are traditionally used in many parts of South Africa to treat rheumatism and fever[3,4]. Several other uses have been described[3,4,5,6].

PREPARATION AND DOSAGE. Decoctions or infusions are taken.

ACTIVE INGREDIENTS. Willows are known to contain numerous phenolic compounds[7], of which salicortin and salicin are of special medicinal interest[8].

PHARMACOLOGICAL EFFECTS. The anti-inflammatory properties of willows are ascribed to salicylic acid[8]. The compound does not occur naturally in the plant, but is formed by the intestinal hydrolysis of salicin. The latter in turn may be present in the plant or may be formed as a degradation product of salicortin[8]. The acetylated form of salicylic acid is the widely used analgesic – aspirin – which is manufactured from salicylic acid and acetic anhydride[9]. The first use of salicylic acid was as sodium salicylate in 1875 in the treatment of rheumatic fever and as an antipyretic[10].

DISTRIBUTION. The wild willow occurs over a large part of South Africa[1]. Distribution areas of the various subspecies are not shown separately on the map below.

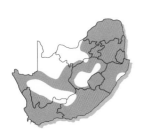

Salicortin

Salicin

Salicylic acid

Aspirin

1. **Immelman, K.L. 1987.** Synopsis of the genus *Salix* (Salicaceae) in southern Africa. *Bothalia* 17: 171-177.
2. **Coates Palgrave, K. 1977.** *Trees of Southern Africa.* Struik, Cape Town.
3. **Watt, J.M. & Breyer-Brandwijk, M.G. 1962.** *The Medicinal and Poisonous Plants of Southern and Eastern Africa.* 2nd edition. Livingstone, London.
4. **Rood, B. 1994.** *Uit die Veldapteek.* Tafelberg, Cape Town.
5. **Cillié, A.M. 1992.** *Kruie op Witblits, Rate, Resepte en Feite.* Unpublished notes, Worcester Museum.
6. **Dykman, E.J. 1891.** *Kook-, Koek- en Resepte Boek.* Paarlse Drukpers Maatskappy, Paarl.
7. **Dictionary of Natural Products on CD-ROM, release 4:2 (1996).** Chapman & Hall, London.
8. **Bruneton, J. 1995.** *Pharmacognosy, Phytochemistry, Medicinal Plants.* Intercept, Hampshire.
9. **Merck 1989.** *The Merck Index.* 11th edition. Merck, Rahway.
10. **Goodman, A.L. & Gilman, A. 1992.** *The Pharmacological Basis of Therapeutics.* 8th edition. Pergamon Press, New York.

Salix mucronata

Leaves and flowers of *Salix mucronata*

Bark of *Salix mucronata*

Fruits and seeds of *Salix mucronata*

SANSEVIERIA HYACINTHOIDES

Dracaenaceae

> isikholokotho (Xhosa, Zulu); aambeiwortel (Afrikaans);
> piles root (English); kai, ghaiwortel (Khoi)

BOTANICAL DESCRIPTION. The plant is a perennial herb with long, strap-shaped leaves arising from a horizontal, fleshy rootstock[1]. The leaves are succulent and fibrous, with a characteristically mottled appearance. An attractive elongated flower cluster appears in summer, with numerous small, white flowers. These form small berry-like fruits, which are green at first, gradually becoming yellow when they ripen. The closely related *S. aethiopica* is used in the same way as *S. hyacinthoides*. They can easily be distinguished by the leaves: *S. hyacinthoides* has only a few (two to eight) leaves per rosette and they are flat; while *S. aethiopica* has numerous leaves per rosette and they are always half folded lengthwise, making them v-shaped[1].

PLANT PARTS USED. Rhizomes or leaves are used.

MEDICINAL USES. In South Africa, the plant is a popular remedy for ear infection, earache[2,3,4,5] and sometimes toothache[2,3,4]. It is also traditionally used to treat haemorrhoids, ulcers and intestinal worms[2,3,4]. Other treatments include stomach disorders and diarrhoea[4,5]. *S. liberica* has similar uses in North Africa[6].

PREPARATION AND DOSAGE. For earache, a cut leaf is heated and the warm juice squeezed into the ear. The same procedure may be followed for toothache. For treating haemorrhoids, ulcers or intestinal parasites, the fresh or boiled rhizomes are simply chewed and the juice swallowed. Decoctions or infusions of the root may be used for the same purpose[2,3,4,5]. The juice may also be directly applied to haemorrhoids or varicose veins.

ACTIVE INGREDIENTS. The value of *Sansevieria* species in treating haemorrhoids is clearly linked to the presence of various sapogenins, of which ruscogenin is the best-known example[7]. Ruscogenin was first isolated from *Ruscus aculeatus* and the 25S-isomer of ruscogenin later also from *S. trifasciata*, together with structurally related compounds such as neoruscogenin[7].

PHARMACOLOGICAL EFFECTS. Ruscogenin is widely used for the treatment of haemorrhoids[8,9]. This sapogenin and related compounds are proven anti-inflammatory agents and venotonics.

DISTRIBUTION. *S. hyacinthoides* occurs naturally in the eastern and northern parts of South Africa[1] where it grows in shaded areas. *Sansevieria* species have become popular garden plants and are also widely used indoors as potplants due to their ability to flourish under low light conditions.

Ruscogenin (25 S) - form

1. **Bos, J.J. 1992.** Dracaenaceae. *Flora of Southern Africa* 5: 1-9. National Botanical Institute, Pretoria.
2. **Watt, J.M. & Breyer-Brandwijk, M.G. 1962.** *The Medicinal and Poisonous Plants of Southern and Eastern Africa*. 2nd edition. Livingstone, London.
3. **Rood, B. 1994.** *Uit die Veldapteek.* Tafelberg, Cape Town.
4. **Hutchings, A. 1996.** *Zulu Medicinal Plants.* Natal University Press, Pietermaritzburg.
5. **Pujol, J. 1993.** *Naturafrica – the Herbalist Handbook.* Jean Pujol Natural Healers' Foundation, Durban.
6. **Iwu, M.M. 1993.** *Handbook of African Medicinal Plants.* CRC Press, Boca Raton.
7. **Dictionary of Natural Products on CD-ROM, release 4:2 (1996).** Chapman & Hall, London.
8. **Merck 1989.** *The Merck Index.* 11th edition. Merck, Rahway.
9. **Martindale 1989.** *The Extra Pharmacopoeia.* 29th edition, p. 3913. Pharmaceutical Press, London.

Sansevieria hyacinthoides

Fruits of *Sansevieria hyacinthoides*

Flower cluster of *Sansevieria hyacinthoides*

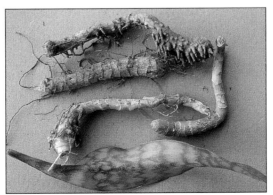

Rhizomes and a leaf of *Sansevieria hyacinthoides*

SCABIOSA COLUMBARIA

Dipsacaceae

> **ibheka (Zulu); makgha (Xhosa); bitterwortel (Afrikaans);
> wild scabious (English)**

BOTANICAL DESCRIPTION. The plant is a perennial herb of up to one metre in height, with annual branches developing from persistent fleshy roots[1]. The thin-textured, slightly hairy leaves form a rosette on the ground and are variable in shape, with characteristically lobed margins. Basal leaves have serrated margins, while those higher up on the stems have deeply lobed margins. Flowers are borne on several multi-branched stalks of up to one metre high. The attractive white flower heads have a distinctive daisy-like shape, resembling those of the family Asteraceae.

PLANT PARTS USED. The leaves or fleshy roots are used.

MEDICINAL USES. The plant is a remedy for colic and heartburn[2,3]. Some other traditional uses have also been recorded[2,3,4,5]. Dried roasted roots are made into a wound-healing ointment, and the powdered roots are also used as a pleasant-smelling baby powder[6].

PREPARATION AND DOSAGE. The roots or leaves are either chewed fresh or taken in dried and powdered form, either directly or as a decoction[2].

ACTIVE INGREDIENTS. Phenolic compounds, chlorogenic acid and ß-methylglucoside have been identified in *Scabiosa* species[7] but there is no certainty about the contribution of these compounds to the activity of the medicine.

PHARMACOLOGICAL EFFECTS. In the absence of published information, it may be speculated that chlorogenic acid is at least partly responsible for the benefits derived from *S. columbaria*. It is interesting to note that phenolic acids (caffeic acid derivatives) are said to be the active ingredients in artichoke (*Cynara scolymus*) – a traditional European choleretic medicine that is recommended for dyspeptic disorders such as indigestion, nausea and bloating[8].

DISTRIBUTION. *S. columbaria* has a wide distribution in southern Africa[1] and is particularly common in the Western Cape and in the grassland areas of the summer rainfall region.

Chlorogenic acid

ß-Methylglucoside

1. **Cannon, M.J. & Cannon, J.F.M. 1983.** Dipsacaceae. *Flora Zambesiaca* 7(1): 77-85. The Crown Agents, London.
2. **Watt, J.M. & Breyer-Brandwijk, M.G. 1962.** *The Medicinal and Poisonous Plants of Southern and Eastern Africa.* 2nd edition. Livingstone, London.
3. **Rood, B. 1994.** *Uit die Veldapteek.* Tafelberg, Cape Town.
4. **Hutchings, A. 1989.** A survey and analysis of traditional medicinal plants as used by the Zulu, Xhosa and Sotho. *Bothalia* 19: 111-123.
5. **Hutchings, A. 1996.** *Zulu Medicinal Plants.* Natal University Press, Pietermaritzburg.
6. **Von Koenen, E. 1996.** *Heil-, Gift- u Essbare Pflanzen in Namibia.* Klauss Hess Verlag, Göttingen.
7. **Dictionary of Natural Products on CD-ROM, release 4:2 (1996).** Chapman & Hall, London.
8. **Bruneton, J. 1995.** *Pharmacognosy, Phytochemistry, Medicinal Plants.* Intercept, Hampshire.

Scabiosa columbaria

Flower heads of *Scabiosa columbaria*

Roots of *Scabiosa columbaria*

Characteristic leaves of *Scabiosa columbaria*

SCADOXUS PUNICEUS

Amaryllidaceae

---

umphompo (Zulu); red paintbrush (English); rooikwas (Afrikaans)

BOTANICAL DESCRIPTION. This distinctive bulbous plant usually grows in shady places[1]. The leaves are erect, long and strap-shaped, with wavy margins and numerous purple spots on the leaf stalk. The attractive orange-red flowers are borne in dense clusters on a long, thick stalk. Leaves are usually formed after the flowering time[1].

PLANT PARTS USED. The bulbs and roots are used.

MEDICINAL USES. The plant is traditionally used to treat coughs and gastro-intestinal problems[2,3,4]. It forms part of a medicine taken regularly during pregnancy to ensure a safe delivery[2,4]. Another species, *S. multiflorus*, is used medicinally in many parts of Africa for wound therapy, colds, asthma and other ailments[5]. Since *Scadoxus* species were previously included in the genus *Haemanthus*[1], most of the early reports go under the latter name. *Haemanthus* is closely related to *Scadoxus* and also contains medicinal plants. An example is *H. coccineus*, widely used as a diuretic and emetic[3] but also a Cape remedy for bruises, sprains, sores, ulcers and asthma[2,4].

PREPARATION AND DOSAGE. For coughs and stomach problems, decoctions are used as emetics. Bulbs of *H. coccineus* (sliced and steeped in vinegar)[6] have been used as a diuretic and the leaves as an antiseptic on sores and ulcers[2,3,4,6].

ACTIVE INGREDIENTS. *Scadoxus* and related plants are rich in isoquinoline alkaloids[7] (so-called Amaryllidaceae alkaloids) of which lycorine is the best known example (see *Clivia miniata*). *S. puniceus* contains haemanthamine and a hydroxylated derivative, haemanthidine[7]. *Haemanthus coccineus* contains coccinine – an alkaloid with a known convulsive action[7].

PHARMACOLOGICAL EFFECTS. Amaryllidaceae alkaloids are highly toxic[8]. Plants containing these alkaloids have limited medicinal value and their indiscriminate use is potentially lethal[8].

DISTRIBUTION. *S. puniceus* has a wide natural distribution in the summer rainfall areas of South Africa[1]. It has become a popular garden plant.

Haemanthamine   Coccinine

---

1. **Friis, I. & Nordal, I. 1976.** Studies on the genus *Haemanthus* (Amaryllidaceae). IV. Division of the genus into *Haemanthus s. str.* and *Scadoxus* with notes on *Haemanthus s. str. Norw. J. Bot.* 23: 63-77.
2. **Watt, J.M. & Breyer-Brandwijk, M.G. 1962.** *The Medicinal and Poisonous Plants of Southern and Eastern Africa.* 2nd edition. Livingstone, London.
3. **Hutchings, A. 1989.** A survey and analysis of traditional medicinal plants as used by the Zulu, Xhosa and Sotho. *Bothalia* 19: 111-123.
4. **Hutchings, A. 1996.** *Zulu Medicinal Plants.* Natal University Press, Pietermaritzburg.
5. **Neuwinger, H.D. 1994.** *Afrikanische Arzneipflanzen und Jagdgifte.* Wissenschaftliche Verlagsgesellschaft, Stuttgart.
6. **Forbes, V.S. (ed.) 1986.** *Carl Peter Thunberg Travels at the Cape of Good Hope 1772-1775.* Van Riebeeck Society, Cape Town.
7. **Dictionary of Natural Products on CD-ROM, release 4:2 (1996).** Chapman & Hall, London.
8. **Bruneton, J. 1995.** *Pharmacognosy, Phytochemistry, Medicinal Plants.* Intercept, Hampshire.

Scadoxus puniceus

Leaves and bulbs of *Scadoxus puniceus*

Bulbs of *Scadoxus puniceus*

SCHOTIA BRACHYPETALA

Fabaceae

---

ihluze (Zulu); mulubi (Venda); umutwa (Tswana); huilboerboon (Afrikaans); weeping boer-bean (English)

BOTANICAL DESCRIPTION. This is a medium-sized to large deciduous tree of up to 16 metres in height, with a wide spreading crown and a rough brown bark. The leaves are divided into four to six pairs of small, glossy green leaflets, each about 30 mm long, with a distinctly asymmetric base. Large clusters of dark red flowers are borne on the old wood of the tree. They produce copious amounts of nectar, which drips from the flowers (hence the common names). The fruits are large woody pods with a characteristic persistent rim, containing large, pale brown seeds[1,2,3].

PLANT PARTS USED. The bark is mainly used, sometimes also the root.

MEDICINAL USES. A decoction of the bark is reported to be taken (presumably as an emetic) to treat heartburn and the effects of too much drinking[4]. Bark mixtures are also used to strengthen the body and for a facial sauna[5]. The bark and root may be used to treat diarrhoea[4,6] or, in Venda, nervous heart conditions[7].

PREPARATION AND DOSAGE. Decoctions of the bark or roots are used, sometimes as an ingredient of other mixtures[3,6].

ACTIVE INGREDIENTS. The chemical compounds of *Schotia* species are poorly known[8]. Polyhydroxystilbenes have been isolated from the heartwood of *S. brachypetala*, of which 3,3',4,5,5'-pentahydroxystilbene is the major compound[9].

PHARMACOLOGICAL EFFECTS. The activity of the medicine may be due to astringent tannins in the bark[10] but no details are available. Many stilbenes have antibiotic properties but the biological activity of the *Schotia* stilbenes appears to be unknown.

DISTRIBUTION. *S. brachypetala* is endemic to the north-eastern parts of southern Africa (Eastern Cape to Zimbabwe)[3,11]. This attractive tree with its glossy foliage and bright red flowers is nowadays a popular ornamental tree in gardens and parks.

3,3',4,5,5'-Pentahydroxystilbene

---

1. **Ross, J.H. 1977.** Subfamily Caesalpinioideae. *Flora of Southern Africa* 16(2). Botanical Research Institute, Pretoria.
2. **Palmer, E. & Pitman, J. 1972.** *Trees of Southern Africa.* Balkema, Cape Town.
3. **Coates Palgrave, K. 1977.** *Trees of Southern Africa.* Struik, Cape Town.
4. **Watt, J.M. & Breyer-Brandwijk, M.G. 1962.** *The Medicinal and Poisonous Plants of Southern and Eastern Africa.* 2nd edition. Livingstone, London.
5. **Pujol, J. 1993.** *Naturafrica – the Herbalist Handbook.* Jean Pujol Natural Healers' Foundation, Durban.
6. **Hutchings, A. 1996.** *Zulu Medicinal Plants.* University of Natal Press, Pietermaritzburg.
7. **Netshiungani, E.N. 1981.** Notes on the uses of indigenous trees in Venda. *Journal of Dendrology* 1: 12-17.
8. **Dictionary of Natural Products on CD-ROM, release 4:2 (1996).** Chapman & Hall, London.
9. **Drewes, S.E. & Fletcher, I.P. 1974.** Polyhydroxystilbenes from the heartwood of *Schotia brachypetala. J. Chem. Soc. Perkin Trans.* I: 961-962.
10. **Bruneton, J. 1995.** *Pharmacognosy, Phytochemistry, Medicinal Plants.* Intercept, Hampshire.
11. **Von Breitenbach, F. 1986.** *National List of Indigenous Trees.* Dendrological Foundation, Pretoria.

Schotia brachypetala

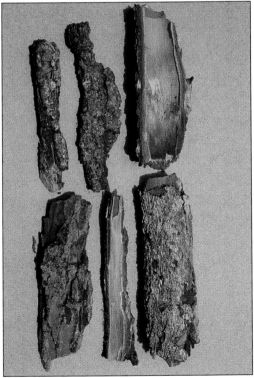

Bark of *Schotia brachypetala*

Leaves and flowers of *Schotia brachypetala*

SCILLA NATALENSIS

Hyacinthaceae

inguduza (Zulu); bloubergleiie, blouslangkop (Afrikaans)

BOTANICAL DESCRIPTION. This bulbous plant has broad, sharply tapering leaves arising from large bulbs of about 100 mm to 150 mm in diameter, which often grow in large groups. The small blue or purplish-blue flowers are borne on long slender stalks of about a metre in height[1]. Species of *Scilla* should not be confused with the true squill, *Urginea maritima* (=*Drimia maritima*), which was previously called *S. maritima*. *S. natalensis* can be distinguished from other South African species by the blue flowers and broad leaves[1].

PLANT PARTS USED. The bulb is used.

MEDICINAL USES. Decoctions are taken as an enema for female infertility and to enhance male potency and libido. Bulbs are also used to treat sprains, fractures, boils and sores[2,3,4]. Their use as purgatives and as an enema for internal tumors has also been recorded[2,3,4].

PREPARATION AND DOSAGE. Decoctions are used externally as ointments for wound-healing[2]. Sometimes the ash from a burnt plant is rubbed into

scarifications[2]. Decoctions have been taken orally as laxatives and administered as enemas, but these practises are potentially dangerous and the plant should only be used for external application[4].

ACTIVE INGREDIENTS. There appears to be no information on the chemical compounds in *S. natalensis*[5]. The plant is said to contain saponins, but no details are given[4]. *Drimia* and *Urginea* species contain heart glycosides of the bufadienolide type, such as scillaren A but the presence of these glycosides in *S. natalensis* still needs to be demonstrated.

PHARMACOLOGICAL EFFECTS. Saponins have a wide range of biological activities[6] but the reported[2,3,4] wound-healing, antiseptic and anti-inflammatory properties are possibly due to the presence of homoiso flavonoids[7].

DISTRIBUTION. *S. natalensis* occurs in the eastern parts of South Africa, from the Eastern Cape Province through KwaZulu-Natal to the Northern Province[1].

1. **Jessop, J.P. 1970.** Studies in the bulbous Liliaceae: 1. *Scilla, Schizocarpus* and *Ledebouria. Jl S. Afr. Bot.* 36: 233-266.
2. **Watt, J.M. & Breyer-Brandwijk, M.G. 1962.** *The Medicinal and Poisonous Plants of Southern and Eastern Africa.* 2nd edition. Livingstone, London.
3. **Hutchings, A. 1989.** A survey and analysis of traditional medicinal plants as used by the Zulu, Xhosa and Sotho. *Bothalia* 19: 111-123.
4. **Hutchings, A. 1996.** *Zulu Medicinal Plants.* Natal University Press, Pietermaritzburg.
5. **Dictionary of Natural Products on CD-ROM, release 4:2 (1996).** Chapman & Hall, London.
6. **Bruneton, J. 1995.** *Pharmacognosy, Phytochemistry, Medicinal Plants.* Intercept, Hampshire.
7. **Mulholland, D.A.,** personal communication

Scilla natalensis

Flowers of *Scilla natalensis*

Bulb of *Scilla natalensis*

SCLEROCARYA BIRREA

Anacardiaceae

umganu (Zulu); morula (Northern Sotho);
marula (English); maroela (Afrikaans)

BOTANICAL DESCRIPTION. The marula is a medium-sized, single-stemmed tree of up to 15 metres in height. The rough bark is flaky, with a mottled appearance due to contrasting grey and pale brown patches. The leaves are divided into 10 or more pairs of leaflets, each about 60 mm long, dark green above, much paler below, with the tip abruptly narrowing to a sharp point. The flowers are borne in small, oblong clusters. Male and female flowers occur separately, usually but not always on separate trees. The flowers are small, with red sepals and yellow petals. Large, rounded, slightly flattened fruits of about 30 mm in diameter are borne in profusion in late summer to mid-winter[1,2]. The fruits are much sought after for their delicious pulp, high vitamin C content and edible nuts. It has become a commercial fruit crop in recent years, the fruit pulp being used to produce a jelly and to flavour liqueur.

PLANT PARTS USED. The bark, roots or leaves are the medicinal products.

MEDICINAL USES. In South Africa, diarrhoea, dysentery and unspecified stomach problems are treated with the bark, which is believed to be of value in combatting fever and in the treatment of malaria[3,4,5]. It is also used as a general tonic[6].

Chewing the fresh leaves and swallowing the astringent juice will help with indigestion. Numerous other traditional uses have been recorded[1,2,3,4,5]. Elsewhere in Africa, the main medicinal use is in the treatment of diabetes[7].

PREPARATION AND DOSAGE. Decoctions of the bark or roots are taken orally or as enemas[3,4,5,6]. Leaf infusions or decoctions are drunk for diabetes[7].

ACTIVE INGREDIENTS. The bark contains procyanidins[8] and the plant is also said to contain gallotannins, flavonoids and catechins[3,7], but few details are available[9]. Procyanidin C_1 has not been found in *Sclerocarya* but is included merely to show a typical procyanidin found in many plant species.

PHARMACOLOGICAL EFFECTS. The bark has an astringent taste and the antidiarrhoeal effects have been experimentally linked to procyanidins[8]. There are claims that the leaves have hypoglycaemic effects[7], but the plant is not listed in a recent comprehensive review of antidiabetic plants[10].

DISTRIBUTION. The tree is widely distributed throughout the African continent. In southern Africa, only the subspecies *caffra* is found[2].

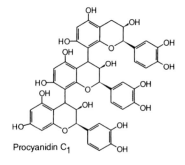

Procyanidin C_1

1. **Palmer, E. & Pitman, J. 1972.** *Trees of Southern Africa.* Balkema, Cape Town.
2. **Coates Palgrave, K. 1977.** *Trees of Southern Africa.* Struik, Cape Town.
3. **Watt, J.M. & Breyer-Brandwijk, M.G. 1962.** *The Medicinal and Poisonous Plants of Southern and Eastern Africa.* 2nd edition. Livingstone, London.
4. **Hutchings, A. 1989.** A survey and analysis of traditional medicinal plants as used by the Zulu, Xhosa and Sotho. *Bothalia* 19: 111-123.
5. **Hutchings, A. 1996.** *Zulu Medicinal Plants.* Natal University Press, Pietermaritzburg.
6. **Pujol, J. 1993.** *Naturafrica – the Herbalist Handbook.* Jean Pujol Natural Healers' Foundation, Durban.
7. **Iwu, M.M. 1993.** *Handbook of African Medicinal Plants.* CRC Press, Boca Raton.
8. **Galvez, J. et al. 1993.** Pharmacological activity of a procyanidin isolated from *Sclerocarya birrea* bark: antidiarrhoeal activity and effects on isolated guinea-pig ileum. *Phytother. Res.* 7: 25-28.
9. **Dictionary of Natural Products on CD-ROM, release 4:2 (1996).** Chapman & Hall, London.
10. **Marles, R.J. & Farnsworth, N.R. 1995.** Antidiabetic plants and their active constituents. *Phytomedicine* 2: 137-189.

Sclerocarya birrea

Flowers of *Sclerocarya birrea*

Leaves and fruits of *Sclerocarya birrea*

Bark of *Sclerocarya birrea*

SECURIDACA LONGIPEDUNCULATA

Polygalaceae

> **mpesu (Venda); violet tree (English); krinkhout (Afrikaans)**

BOTANICAL DESCRIPTION. This is a small, erect tree of up to six metres in height, with a pale grey, smooth bark[1,2]. The oblong, more or less hairless leaves are variable in size and shape, about 30 mm long and crowded towards the stem tips. Clusters of attractive pink to purple flowers are produced in early summer. Each flower is about 10 mm long and is borne on a long, slender stalk. The fruit is a round nut with a single large, curved wing. The plant has a very distinctive appearance and is not likely to be confused with any others.

PLANT PARTS USED. The roots are mainly used, sometimes also the leaves or stem bark.

MEDICINAL USES. In South Africa, the roots are used for coughs and chest complaints, rheumatism, toothache and headache[3]. Externally, it has been applied to wounds and sores and for the relief of rheumatism[3]. This is perhaps one of the most popular of all traditional medicines in Africa and has been used for almost every conceivable ailment[4]. The stem bark is an ingredient of arrow poisons and the plant is known as an ordeal poison[4].

PREPARATION AND DOSAGE. Decoctions are taken for chest complaints, while the roots are chewed to relieve toothache. A hot water poultice of the roots is said to give symptomatic relief of rheumatism, while powdered root or wood scrapings are rubbed into scarifications on the forehead to treat headaches[3].

ACTIVE INGREDIENTS. The volatile oil of the roots contains large amounts of methyl salicylate, better known as wintergreen oil. The plant also produces various sapogenins, including presenegenin, the toxic indole alkaloid securinine and some ergot alkaloids[5].

PHARMACOLOGICAL EFFECTS. The presence of salicylates may partly explain the recorded uses of *S. longipedunculata*. Chemically similar plants (such as queen-of-the-meadow, *Filipendula ulmaria*) are traditionally used in Europe[6] for the symptomatic treatment of minor pain in the joints, fever, headaches and toothache. Methyl salicylate is a toxic counter-irritant[7] which penetrates the skin and underlying tissue to act as an anti-inflammatory. Drugs containing this compound are also ingredients of oral hygiene products[6]. Presenegenin is associated with plant medicines which are traditionally used for the symptomatic treatment of coughs[6] (see notes under *Polygala*).

DISTRIBUTION. The tree is widely distributed in tropical Africa and occurs in the North-West and Northern provinces of South Africa[1,2,8].

Methyl salicylate   Presenegenin   Securinine

1. Palmer, E. & Pitman, J. 1972. *Trees of Southern Africa.* Balkema, Cape Town.
2. Coates Palgrave, K. 1977. *Trees of Southern Africa.* Struik, Cape Town.
3. Watt, J.M. & Breyer-Brandwijk, M.G. 1962. *The Medicinal and Poisonous Plants of Southern and Eastern Africa.* 2nd edition. Livingstone, London.
4. Neuwinger, H.D. 1994. *Afrikanische Arzneipflanzen und Jagdgifte.* Wissenschaftliche Verlagsgesellschaft, Stuttgart.
5. Dictionary of Natural Products on CD-ROM, release 4:2 (1996). Chapman & Hall, London.
6. Bruneton, J. 1995. *Pharmacognosy, Phytochemistry, Medicinal Plants.* Intercept, Hampshire.
7. Merck 1989. *The Merck Index.* 11th edition. Merck, Rahway.
8. Von Breitenbach, F. 1986. *National List of Indigenous Trees.* Dendrological Foundation, Pretoria.

Securidaca longipedunculata

Leaves and flowers of *Securidaca longipedunculata*

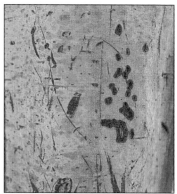

Bark of *Securidaca longipedunculata*

Pieces of root bark of *Securidaca longipedunculata*

SENECIO SERRATULOIDES

Asteraceae

insukumbili (Zulu); two day plant (English)

BOTANICAL DESCRIPTION. The plant is a herbaceous perennial with erect stems of up to a metre in height, sprouting from a woody rootstock[1]. The leaves are about 60 mm long with characteristically serrated margins, making the plant easy to identify. Small yellow flowers are borne in sparse clusters towards the ends of the branches. *S. speciosus* is another example of a commonly used medicinal species. It is a distinctive purple-flowered, sparsely leafed plant which usually grows in damp or marshy places. The leaf stalks are long and flat, and the leaf margins are toothed or lobed[1].

PLANT PARTS USED. The leaves and stems are used, rarely also the roots.

MEDICINAL USES. Leaves are applied externally to cuts, swellings, burns and sores to promote healing[2,3,4]. Infusions are taken in small doses as blood purifiers for skin eruptions or for swollen gums and chest pains[2]. Several other *Senecio* species are used medicinally[2,3,4,5,6]. Leaf and stem decoctions of *S. speciosus*, for example, are either applied to cuts or swellings[3,4,5] or taken orally for pleurisy and chest pains. The dried, powdered leaves are snuffed for treating headaches[6]. This plant is known as "ibohlololo" in Zulu (note that *Aptenia cordifolia* is also called "ibohlololo").

PREPARATION AND DOSAGE. For external use, leaves are applied directly to the skin or in powdered form (sometimes powder from the burnt leaves is used)[2,4,5]. For internal use, weak infusions or decoctions are taken, but this is potentially dangerous, as several *Senecio* species are known to be poisonous.

ACTIVE INGREDIENTS. Nothing appears to be known about the active ingredients of *S. serratuloides* or *S. speciosus*[7]. However, *Senecio* species are well known for the presence of macrocyclic pyrrolizidine alkaloids[7,8]. Typical examples are the toxic senecionine and the non-toxic platyphylline[8,9]. In the non-hepatotoxic alkaloids, the necine base is saturated[8]. These alkaloids are also present in *Crotalaria* species (Fabaceae), some of which are popular traditional medicines.

PHARMACOLOGICAL EFFECTS. The wound-healing properties of *S. serratuloides* may be due to antibiotic effects, but the exact mechanism is not known. The use of *Senecio* species for chest complaints is interesting, as platyphylline is a known antispasmodic and mydriatic and is used as such in several countries[9]. It is important to note that *Senecio* alkaloids are highly toxic liver (and lung) poisons and may cause cell damage or induce hepatic tumours when used on a regular basis[8,9].

DISTRIBUTION. *S. serratuloides* is widely distributed in the summer rainfall area of South Africa[1].

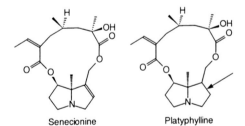

Senecionine   Platyphylline

1. Hilliard, O.M. 1977. *Compositae in Natal.* University of Natal Press, Pietermaritzburg.
2. Watt, J.M. & Breyer-Brandwijk, M.G. 1962. *The Medicinal and Poisonous Plants of Southern and Eastern Africa.* 2nd edition. Livingstone, London.
3. Pujol, J. 1993. *Naturafrica – the Herbalist Handbook.* Jean Pujol Natural Healers' Foundation, Durban.
4. Hutchings, A. 1996. *Zulu Medicinal Plants.* Natal University Press, Pietermaritzburg.
5. Rose, E.F. 1972. *Senecio* species: toxic plants used as food and medicine in the Transkei. *S. Afr. Med. J.* 46: 1039-1043.
6. Hutchings, A. & Van Staden, J. 1994. Plants used for stress-related ailments in traditional Zulu, Xhosa and Sotho medicine. Part 1: Plants used for headaches. *J. Ethnopharmacol.* 43: 89-124.
7. **Dictionary of Natural Products on CD-ROM, release 4:2 (1996).** Chapman & Hall, London.
8. Mattocks, A.R. 1986. *Chemistry and Toxicology of Pyrrolizidine Alkaloids.* Academic Press, London.
9. Bruneton, J. 1995. *Pharmacognosy, Phytochemistry, Medicinal Plants.* Intercept, Hampshire.

Senecio speciosus

Senecio serratuloides

Rhizomes of *Senecio speciosus*

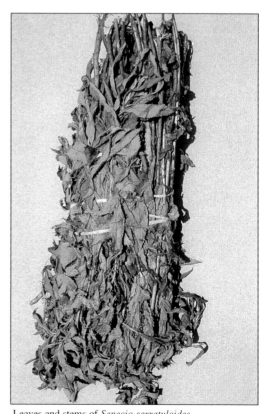

Leaves and stems of *Senecio serratuloides*

SIPHONOCHILUS AETHIOPICUS

Zingiberaceae

isiphephetho, indungulo (Zulu); wild ginger (English)

BOTANICAL DESCRIPTION. Wild ginger is a deciduous plant with large, hairless leaves developing annually from a small, distinctive, cone-shaped rhizome. The spectacular flowers appear at ground level in early summer, from the end of October to early December. They are broadly funnel-shaped, pink and white in colour with a small yellow blotch in the middle[1,2,3]. Most plants are bisexual, and they have much larger flowers than female plants[3]. The small, berry-like fruits are borne below or above the ground. The leaves and rhizomes have a smell similar to that of real ginger, *Zingiber officinale*.

PLANT PARTS USED. The rhizome, which is cone-shaped and narrows to a tapering point, is dug up and sold.

Rhizomes harvested during the growing season will have roots on them and are used as such. Those taken during the dormant period, when the plants are leafless, have no roots on them (see illustration).

MEDICINAL USES. The rhizomes of wild ginger are used for colds (to clear the nasal passages), coughs, influenza and hysteria[4,5,6]. It may also be taken for pain[4,5,6]. Several other traditional and cultural uses have been recorded[2,4,6], including the treatment of asthma and dysmennorhoea.

PREPARATION AND DOSAGE. Rhizomes and roots are chewed fresh.

ACTIVE INGREDIENTS. There is no published information on the chemical compounds of wild ginger[7]. It contains volatile oil with α-terpineol (a natural antiseptic[8]) and various other monoterpenoids, but the main compound is a highly characteristic sesquiterpenoid[9]. The similarity between wild ginger and true ginger appears to be superficial only, as none of the terpenoids of ginger oil are present in the essential oil of *Siphonochilus*[9].

PHARMACOLOGICAL EFFECTS. The monoterpenoids and sesquiterpenoids in the oil are most likely responsible for the reported benefits in colds and influenza. Volatile oils are generally used for their decongestant, antiseptic and diuretic effects[10].

DISTRIBUTION. Wild ginger has a restricted distribution in Mpumalanga and the Northern Province[1] and has become extinct in KwaZulu-Natal[1,3,11] (the map also includes the recorded distribution area in this province). The plant is easily cultivated in the warm parts of South Africa and attempts have been made for the large-scale production of rhizomes through tissue culture, in order to reduce the pressure on wild populations.

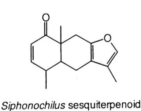

Siphonochilus sesquiterpenoid   α-Terpineol

1. Smith, R.M. Zingiberaceae. *Flora of Southern Africa* 8 (in press).
2. Onderstal, J. 1978. *Kaempferia aethiopica* – wild ginger. *Veld & Flora* 1978: 43-44.
3. Gordon-Gray, K.D. *et al.* 1989. *Siphonochilus aethiopicus* (Zingiberaceae): observations on floral and reproductive biology. *S. Afr. J. Bot.* 55: 281-287.
4. Watt, J.M. & Breyer-Brandwijk, M.G. 1962. *The Medicinal and Poisonous Plants of Southern and Eastern Africa*. 2nd edition. Livingstone, London.
5. Pujol, J. 1993. *Naturafrica – the Herbalist Handbook*. Jean Pujol Natural Healers' Foundation, Durban.
6. Hutchings, A. 1996. *Zulu Medicinal Plants*. Natal University Press, Pietermaritzburg.
7. Dictionary of Natural Products on CD-ROM, release 4:2 (1996). Chapman & Hall, London.
8. Merck 1989. *The Merck Index*. 11th edition. Merck, Rahway.
9. Chemotaxonomy studies currently in progress (Botany Department, Rand Afrikaans University). Structural elucidation of the sesquiterpenoid: Holzapfel, C.W. *et al*. (in preparation).
10. Bruneton, J. 1995. *Pharmacognosy, Phytochemistry, Medicinal Plants*. Intercept, Hampshire.
11. Cunningham, A.B. 1988. *An Investigation of the Herbal Medicine Trade in Natal/KwaZulu*. Investigational report no 29, Institute of Natural Resources, University of Natal.

Female form of *Siphonochilus aethiopicus*, previously known as *S. natalensis*

Normal, bisexual form of *Siphonochilus aethiopicus*

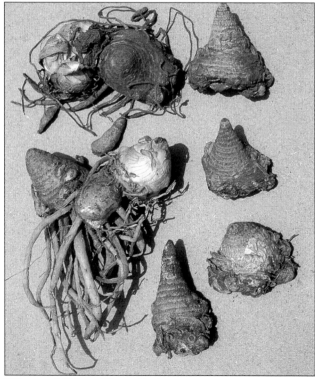

Flower of *Siphonochilus aethiopicus*

Rhizomes of *Siphonochilus aethiopicus*

STANGERIA ERIOPUS

Stangeriaceae

---

imfingo (Zulu); imifingwane (Xhosa); stangeria (Afrikaans, English)

BOTANICAL DESCRIPTION. This cycad is a perennial herb with large fern-like leaves of up to two metres in height, developing from a thick, turnip-shaped, tuberous stem below the ground[1]. Male and female cones appear on separate plants. The male cone is slender, with numerous spirally arranged, overlapping scales. The female cone is broader, with stalked scales bearing large red, fleshy seeds. The plant is so strikingly fern-like that it was originally thought to be a fern rather than a cycad. There is only one genus and one species in the family[1].

PLANT PARTS USED. The tuberous stem, which is white inside, is used; sometimes also the seeds.

The basal part of the stem may in fact originate from the root, so that the distinction between stem and root is lost in the mature plant[1].

MEDICINAL USES. Tubers and seeds are used to induce vomiting when something poisonous has been eaten[2]. The tuber is used for headaches, congestion, high blood pressure and in mixtures as a purgative for flatulence and pain in the bones[3,4,5,6]. Other traditional and magical uses have been recorded[6].

PREPARATION AND DOSAGE. The powdered tuber (or cold water infusions) are taken[6], sometimes mixed with other ingredients. Ash from the burnt tuber is snuffed for headaches[7].

ACTIVE INGREDIENTS. The seeds contain large amounts of macrozamin and small amounts of cycasin[8,9]. These are toxic alkaloids (glycosides of methylazoxymethanol), also known from the seeds of several other cycads[8,9]. In a comparative study, *Stangeria* had the highest alkaloid level of all the cycad genera[9]. Nothing appears to be known about the chemical composition of the tubers[8].

PHARMACOLOGICAL EFFECTS. The toxicity of cycads is due to cycasin and macrozamin, which causes liver damage[10]. Cycasin and methylazoxymethanol are carcinogenic[8,10]. Although typically in the seeds, low levels of these compounds may also occur in the tubers of *Stangeria*, so that their medicinal use is potentially dangerous.

DISTRIBUTION. The plant is unique to South Africa. It occurs along the east coast, from Bathurst in the eastern Cape to Kosi Bay in KwaZulu-Natal[1].

Methylazoxymethanol

Cycasin

Macrozamin

1. Dyer, R.A. 1966. Stangeriaceae. In: *Flora of Southern Africa* 1: 1-3. Botanical Research Institute, Pretoria.
2. Batten, A. & Bokelman, A. 1966. *Wild Flowers of the Eastern Cape*. Books of Africa, Cape Town.
3. Watt, J.M. & Breyer-Brandwijk, M.G. 1962. *The Medicinal and Poisonous Plants of Southern and Eastern Africa*. 2nd edition. Livingstone, London.
4. Pujol, J. 1993. *Naturafrica – the Herbalist Handbook*. Jean Pujol Natural Healers' Foundation, Durban.
5. Hutchings, A. 1996. *Zulu Medicinal Plants*. Natal University Press, Pietermaritzburg.
6. Osborne, R. & Grove, A. 1992. The magical and medicinal usage of *Stangeria eriopus* in Natal. *Cycad Journal* 32: 8-11.
7. Hutchings, A. & Van Staden, J. 1994. Plants used for stress-related ailments in traditional Zulu, Xhosa and Sotho medicine. Part 1: Plants used for headaches. *J. Ethnopharmacol*. 43: 89-124.
8. **Dictionary of Natural Products on CD-ROM, release 4:2 (1996)**. Chapman & Hall, London.
9. Moretti, A. *et al*. 1983. Taxonomic significance of methylazoxymethanol glycosides in the cycads. *Phytochemistry* 22: 115-117.
10. Bruneton, J. 1995. *Pharmacognosy, Phytochemistry, Medicinal Plants*. Intercept, Hampshire.

Stangeria eriopus

Male cone of *Stangeria eriopus*

Female cone of *Stangeria eriopus*, showing the seeds

Tubers of *Stangeria eriopus* as they are sold for medicinal use

STRYCHNOS HENNINGSII

Loganiaceae

> umqalothi (Zulu); umkaloti, umnonono (Xhosa);
> rooibitterbessie (Afrikaans); red bitterberry (English)

BOTANICAL DESCRIPTION. The plant varies in size from a large shrub to a tall tree of more than 15 metres in height. The bark is pale grey and smooth in young trees but becomes darker brown and somewhat flaky in older specimens. The leaves are bright green and glossy, with three main veins arising from the base (a characteristic feature of most *Strychnos* species). Small yellow flowers are produced along the branches in spring and early summer, followed by the bright orange glossy fruits of about 15 mm in diameter[1,2,3].

PLANT PARTS USED. The bark is mainly used, sometimes also the roots or green fruits.

MEDICINAL USES. The bark is used as a treatment for nausea and stomach complaints and has been taken as a bitter tonic[4,5,6]. It is said to be a colic remedy and purgative[4,5] and possibly also of value in rheumatic fever and dysmenorrhoea[4,5,6,7]. The root bark and green fruits of *Strychnos* species are used as a snakebite remedy throughout Southern Africa.

PREPARATION AND DOSAGE. Bark is chewed or cold water extracts of pulverised bark may be taken in small doses[4,6]. Boiled roots have also been used[6].

ACTIVE INGREDIENTS. *Strychnos* species are famous for the presence of strychnine and other indole alkaloids[8]. *S. henningsii* produces numerous alkaloids, structurally closely related to strychnine[8]. An example is henningsiine[8,9].

PHARMACOLOGICAL EFFECTS. Strychnine and related compounds are highly toxic and have been used as rodent, arrow and ordeal poisons[10]. Strychnine tinctures have nevertheless been used as ingredients of invigorating bitter tonics[11,12]. Some *Strychnos* alkaloids (and semisynthetic derivatives thereof) are used in anaesthesiology due to their muscle-relaxing effects[11]. It is likely that the reported beneficial effects of *S. henningsii* bark are due to one or more of its many alkaloids. The presence of strychnine and related compounds in the bark and unripe fruits of *Strychnos* species may account for its use as a snake bite remedy. Strychnine is a powerful central nervous system stimulant which may overcome the respiratory depression that causes death in mamba bites.

DISTRIBUTION. The plant occurs along the east coast of South Africa and northwards into the Kruger National Park[3,13].

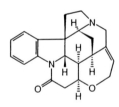

Strychnine

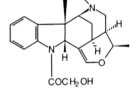

Henningsiine

1. **Palmer, E. & Pitman, J. 1972.** *Trees of Southern Africa.* Balkema, Cape Town.
2. **Coates Palgrave, K. 1977.** *Trees of Southern Africa.* Struik, Cape Town.
3. **Van Wyk, P. 1995.** *Field Guide to the Trees of the Kruger National Park.* Struik, Cape Town.
4. **Watt, J.M. & Breyer-Brandwijk, M.G. 1962.** *The Medicinal and Poisonous Plants of Southern and Eastern Africa.* 2nd edition. Livingstone, London.
5. **Pujol, J. 1993.** *Naturafrica – the Herbalist Handbook.* Jean Pujol Natural Healers' Foundation, Durban.
6. **Hutchings, A. 1996.** *Zulu Medicinal Plants.* Natal University Press, Pietermaritzburg.
7. **Hutchings, A. 1989.** A survey and analysis of traditional medicinal plants as used by the Zulu, Xhosa and Sotho. *Bothalia* 19: 111-123.
8. **Dictionary of Natural Products on CD-ROM, release 4:2 (1996).** Chapman & Hall, London.
9. **Massiot, G. *et al.* 1991.** Alkaloids from *Strychnos henningsii. Phytochemistry* 30: 3449-3456.
10. **Neuwinger, H.D. 1994.** *Afrikanische Arzneipflanzen und Jagdgifte.* Wissenschaftliche Verlagsgesellschaft, Stuttgart.
11. **Bruneton, J. 1995.** *Pharmacognosy, Phytochemistry, Medicinal Plants.* Intercept, Hampshire.
12. **Martindale 1972.** *The Extra Pharmacopoeia.* 26th edition. Pharmaceutical Press, London.
13. **Von Breitenbach, F. 1986.** *National List of Indigenous Trees.* Dendrological Foundation, Pretoria.

Leaves and fruits of *Strychnos henningsii*

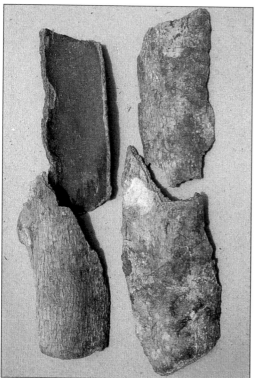

Bark of *Strychnos henningsii*

Flowers of *Strychnos henningsii*

SUTHERLANDIA FRUTESCENS

Fabaceae

kankerbos (Afrikaans); cancer bush (English)

BOTANICAL DESCRIPTION. The cancer bush is an attractive small shrub of up to a metre in height. The leaves are slightly to densely hairy, often giving the plant a silvery appearance. Each leaf is divided into numerous small leaflets. The large red flowers are followed by characteristic bladder-like, papery pods. The six species of *Sutherlandia*[1] are difficult to tell apart and some are likely to be combined[2].

PLANT PARTS USED. The leaves are mainly used, but all above-ground parts are usually included.

MEDICINAL USES. The cancer bush is an old Cape remedy for stomach problems and internal cancers[3,4,5,6]. It is said to be a useful bitter tonic and a good general medicine. According to tradition, the virtues of the plant extend to include remedies for colds, influenza, chicken-pox, diabetes, varicose veins, piles, inflammation, liver problems, backache and rheumatism[3,4,5,6]. The medicinal use probably originated with the Khoi and Nama people, who used decoctions externally to wash wounds and internally for fevers and a variety of other ailments[4,6].

PREPARATION AND DOSAGE. Strong decoctions or alcoholic tinctures are taken, sometimes mixed with other ingredients, such as *Dicoma capensis*. The hairy coastal form of the species, known as *S. frutescens* var. *incana*, is said to be particularly effective against cancer.

ACTIVE INGREDIENTS. *Sutherlandia* seeds contain canavanine, a non-protein α-amino acid[7,8]. The plant is rich in amino acids, but has small amounts of saponins and no alkaloids[2].

PHARMACOLOGICAL EFFECTS. Canavanine has antitumourigenic properties[8] and it is possible that this or some other amino acids are responsible for the reported benefits in treating cancer. It is also possible that the mechanism is one which acts on the immune system but this is pure speculation. There is at present no scientific support for the numerous claims and anecdotes that this traditional medicine can cure cancer.

DISTRIBUTION. The genus is restricted to southern Africa, and occurs in South Africa, Botswana and Namibia. *S. frutescens* is widely distributed and shows remarkable regional variation[2]. Some species have become popular garden plants in many parts of the world[9].

COOH
H_2N—C—H
$CH_2CH_2ONHCNH_2$
‖
NH

Canavanine

1. **Phillips, E.P. & Dyer, R.A. 1934.** The genus *Sutherlandia* R. Br. *Rev. SudAmer. Bot.* 1: 69-80.
2. Biosystematic and chemosystematic studies are currently in progress (Department of Botany, Rand Afrikaans University).
3. **Dykman, E.J. 1891.** *Kook-, Koek- en Resepte Boek.* Paarlse Drukpers Maatskappy, Paarl.
4. **Watt, J.M. & Breyer-Brandwijk, M.G. 1962.** *The Medicinal and Poisonous Plants of Southern and Eastern Africa.* 2nd edition. Livingstone, London.
5. **Cillié, A.M. 1992.** *Kruie op Witblits, Rate, Resepte en Feite.* Unpublished notes, Worcester Museum.
6. **Rood, B. 1994.** *Uit die Veldapteek.* Tafelberg, Cape Town.
7. **Bell, E.A. *et al.* 1978.** Systematic significance of canavanine in the Papilionoideae (Faboideae). *Biochem. Syst. Ecol.* 6: 201-212.
8. **Southon, I.W. 1994.** *Phytochemical Dictionary of the Leguminosae.* Chapman & Hall, London.
9. **Schrire, B.D. & Andrews, S. 1992.** *Sutherlandia*: gansies or balloon peas: part 1. *The Plantsman* 14: 65-69.

Typical form of *Sutherlandia frutescens*

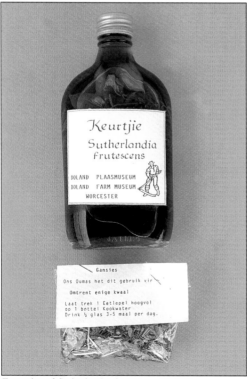

Examples of *Sutherlandia frutescens* products

Flowers and fruits of *Sutherlandia speciosa*

SYNAPTOLEPIS KIRKII

Thymelaeaceae

uvuma-omhlope (Zulu)

BOTANICAL DESCRIPTION. The plant is a multi-branched, scandent shrub with dark brown, almost black stems and bluish-green leaves. Below the ground is a large tuberous root. The leaves have virtually no stalks, are about 25 mm long and are arranged in opposite pairs. Tubular whitish flowers of about 15 mm long are borne in small groups. The fruits are orange and superficially berry-like, but each fruit is actually enclosed within the persistent basal part of the flower, which forms a slightly fleshy covering[1,2].

PLANT PARTS USED. The tuberous root is cut into chunks for sale[2].

The chunks are remarkably pure white in colour ("omhlope" = white) and easy to identify. They have the appearance of pieces of plaster of Paris, with brown fibres embedded in them.

MEDICINAL USES. The main use of the plant is as an emetic[2,3,4]. It is also used to treat epilepsy and constipation[4].

PREPARATION AND DOSAGE. Root decoctions or infusions are used.

ACTIVE INGREDIENTS. An unusual diterpenoid ester known as Synaptolepis factor K_1, has been reported from a *Synaptolepis* species[5,6].

PHARMACOLOGICAL EFFECTS. Nothing appears to be known about the biological activities of the plant or its chemical constituents[6].

DISTRIBUTION. *S. kirkii* is found in the northern parts of KwaZulu-Natal, but it occurs further north into tropical Africa.

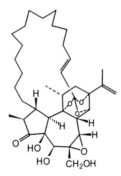

Synaptolepis factor K_1

1. **Wright, C.H. 1915.** Thymelaeaceae. In: Thiselton-Dyer, W.T. (ed.), *Flora Capensis*, Vol 5, part 2. Reeve, London.
2. **Manders, M.** *et al.* **1995.** *Growing and Knowing Muthi Plants.* Institute of Natural Resources, Univerity of Natal, Pietermaritzburg.
3. **Watt, J.M. & Breyer-Brandwijk, M.G. 1962.** *The Medicinal and Poisonous Plants of Southern and Eastern Africa.* 2nd edition. Livingstone, London.
4. **Hutchings, A. 1996.** *Zulu Medicinal Plants.* Natal University Press, Pietermaritzburg.
5. **Dictionary of Natural Products on CD-ROM, release 4:2 (1996).** Chapman & Hall, London.
6. **Zayed, S.** *et al.* **1977.** New highly irritant 1-alkyndaphnane derivatives from several species of Thymelaeaceae. *Tetrahedron Lett.* 39: 3481-3482.

Leaves and flowers of *Synaptolepis kirkii*

Fruits of *Synaptolepis kirkii*

Chunks of the tuber of *Synaptolepis kirkii* as they are sold for medicinal use

SYZYGIUM CORDATUM

Myrtaceae

> umdoni (Xhosa, Zulu); waterbessie (Afrikaans);
> water berry (English); montlho (Northern Sotho)

BOTANICAL DESCRIPTION. The tree is medium-sized and up to 15 metres in height, with a rough, dark brown bark[1,2,3]. The leaves are broad and sometimes almost circular, with a bluish-green colour. They have a distinctive arrangement – in opposite pairs near the ends of the branches, each pair at right angles to the next. Cream-coloured to pinkish flowers with numerous stamens are produced in clusters on the tips of the branches. The egg-shaped, red to dark purple berries are edible but not very tasty.

PLANT PARTS USED. The thick bark, which is fibrous and pinkish-red when fresh, is mainly used, but also the leaves and roots.

MEDICINAL USES. The plant is used to treat respiratory ailments, tuberculosis, stomach complaints and diarrhoea[4,5,6]. It is also commonly used as an emetic[4,5,6]. In central Africa it is known as a remedy for stomach ache and diarrhoea[7].

PREPARATION AND DOSAGE. Decoctions of the bark, leaves and roots are reported to be used.

ACTIVE INGREDIENTS. The wood and bark contain proanthocyanidins, pentacyclic triterpenoids such as arjunolic acid, friedelin and epifriedelinol, steroidal triterpenoids such as ß-sitosterol, as well as gallic acid, ellagic acid and various gallic acid derivatives. Hydrolysis of the bark yielded delphinidin but the proanthocyanidin has not been identified[8].

PHARMACOLOGICAL EFFECTS. The exact pharmacological action of this plant medicine is not known. Its use as an antidiarrhoeal may be explained by the phenolic compounds[9], but there are likely to be other effects. Triterpenoids, for example, show a wide range of activities[9]. It is interesting to note here the use of clove oil (from another *Syzygium, S. aromaticum*) for toothache and mouth infections. The active compound is eugenol, a widely used dental analgesic[10] which appears to be absent from *S. cordatum*.

DISTRIBUTION. *S. cordatum* has a wide distribution in the eastern and north-eastern parts of South Africa[10].

Arjunolic acid   Eugenol

1. **Palmer, E. & Pitman, J. 1972.** *Trees of Southern Africa.* Balkema, Cape Town.
2. **Coates Palgrave, K. 1977.** *Trees of Southern Africa.* Struik, Cape Town.
3. **Van Wyk, P. 1995.** *Field Guide to the Trees of the Kruger National Park.* Struik, Cape Town.
4. **Watt, J.M. & Breyer-Brandwijk, M.G. 1962.** *The Medicinal and Poisonous Plants of Southern and Eastern Africa.* 2nd edition. Livingstone, London.
5. **Hutchings, A. 1989.** A survey and analysis of traditional medicinal plants as used by the Zulu, Xhosa and Sotho. *Bothalia* 19: 111-123.
6. **Hutchings, A. 1996.** *Zulu Medicinal Plants.* Natal University Press, Pietermaritzburg.
7. **Iwu, M.M. 1993.** *Handbook of African Medicinal Plants.* CRC Press, Boca Raton.
8. **Candy, H.A. et al. 1968.** Constituents of *Syzygium cordatum. Phytochemistry* 7: 889-890.
9. **Bruneton, J. 1995.** *Pharmacognosy, Phytochemistry, Medicinal Plants.* Intercept, Hampshire.
10. **Merck 1989.** *The Merck Index.* 11th edition. Merck, Rahway.
11. **Von Breitenbach, F. 1986.** *National List of Indigenous Trees.* Dendrological Foundation, Pretoria.

Syzygium cordatum

Flowers of *Syzygium cordatum*

Fruits of *Syzygium cordatum*

Bark of *Syzygium cordatum*

TARCHONANTHUS CAMPHORATUS

Asteraceae

> mohata (Tswana); mofahlana (Southern Sotho); sefahla (Northern Sotho);
> umgebe (Shona); mathola (Xhosa); igqeba-elimhlophe, siduli-sehlathi (Zulu);
> wildekanferbos, vaalbos (Afrikaans); wild camphor bush (English)

BOTANICAL DESCRIPTION. The plant is a shrub or small tree of rarely more than six metres in height, with a greyish appearance, hence the Afrikaans vernacular name ("vaal" = grey, "bos" = bush). It occurs in a wide range of habitats. The leaves are oblong in shape, with the upper surface dark green and strongly net-veined and the lower surface pale grey and densely velvety. The small, whitish flower heads are followed by small woolly fruits[1,2].

PLANT PARTS USED. The leaves and twigs are used.

MEDICINAL USES. Infusions and tinctures of the leaves and twigs are used for stomach trouble, abdominal pain, headache, toothache, asthma, bronchitis and inflammation[3,4,5]. A hot poultice on the chest is said to give relief from headache, asthma, bronchitis and inflammation. Smoke or fumes from the fresh or dried plant are inhaled for asthma, headache and rheumatism[3,4,5]. There are historic records of the Khoi and San people smoking the dried leaves like tobacco, apparently with a slight narcotic effect[3,6].

PREPARATION AND DOSAGE. Infusions or tinctures are taken orally or the fresh leaves may be chewed. Hot poultices have also been used. The fumes from crushed leaves and branches may be inhaled, as can smoke from the burning fresh leaves or branches[3,4,5].

ACTIVE INGREDIENTS. The volatile oil is highly complex and variable, showing large differences between localities[7]. Despite the camphor-like smell, the plant contains only very small amounts of camphor[7,8]. Material from North Africa yielded α-fenchyl alcohol, 1,8-cineole and α-terpineol as major compounds[8], together with a large number of minor constituents. The plant also contains a flavanone – pinocembrin[9].

PHARMACOLOGICAL EFFECTS. It is possible that flavonoids and ingredients of the volatile oil are responsible for the reported analgesic, diaphoretic, decongestant and antispasmodic effects[10].

DISTRIBUTION. *T. camphoratus* is found in almost any part of South Africa[1,2]. The Vaalbos National Park in the Northern Cape Province is named after it.

α-Fenchol   1,8-Cineole   α-Terpineol   Pinocembrin

1. **Palmer, E. & Pitman, J. 1972.** *Trees of Southern Africa.* Balkema, Cape Town.
2. **Coates Palgrave, K. 1977.** *Trees of Southern Africa.* Struik, Cape Town.
3. **Watt, J.M. & Breyer-Brandwijk, M.G. 1962.** *The Medicinal and Poisonous Plants of Southern and Eastern Africa.* 2nd edition. Livingstone, London.
4. **Hutchings, A. & Van Staden, J. 1994.** Plants used for stress-related ailments in traditional Zulu, Xhosa and Sotho medicine. Part 1: Plants used for headaches. *J. Ethnopharmacol.* 43: 89-124.
5. **Hedberg, I. & Staugård, F. 1989.** *Traditional Medicinal Plants – Traditional Medicine in Botswana.* Ipelegeng, Gabarone.
6. **Watt, J.M. 1967.** African plants potentially useful in mental health. *Lloydia* 30: 1-22.
7. Results of ongoing chemotaxonomic studies (Department of Botany, Rand Afrikaans University).
8. **Mwangi, J.W. et al. 1994.** Volatile constituents of essential oil of *Tarchonanthus camphoratus* L. *J. Essent. Oil Res.* 6: 183-185.
9. **Dictionary of Natural Products on CD-ROM, release 4:2 (1996).** Chapman & Hall, London.
10. **Bruneton, J. 1995.** *Pharmacognosy, Phytochemistry, Medicinal Plants.* Intercept, Hampshire.

Tarchonanthus camphoratus

Flowers of *Tarchonanthus camphoratus*

Leaves and fruits of *Tarchonanthus camphoratus*

TERMINALIA SERICEA

Combretaceae

mogonono (Tswana); moxonono (Northern Sotho); mususu (Shona, Venda); amangwe (Zulu); mangwe (Ndebele); vaalboom (Afrikaans); silver cluster-leaf (English)

BOTANICAL DESCRIPTION. This is a small to medium-sized tree of about five to eight metres in height, with an erect trunk and wide spreading crown[1,2,3]. The bark is grey to pale brown and coarsely fissured. Leaves are characteristically silver-haired and crowded near the branch tips. The flowers are cream-coloured, with an unpleasant smell. The fruits are about 30 mm long, with two broad papery wings surrounding the thickened central part. *Terminalia* species are closely related to *Combretum* species (see below) but the latter have four or more wings on the fruit.

PLANT PARTS USED. The roots are mainly used, sometimes also the stem bark.

MEDICINAL USES. Root decoctions are used as a traditional Tswana remedy for stomach disorders and diarrhoea[2,4,5]. Decoctions and infusions are used as eye lotions and to treat pneumonia[2]. The bark is taken against diabetes[4], and used topically to treat wounds[5,6]. Several species of *Combretum* (for example, *C. kraussii* – Zulu: "umdubu") are also used as antidiarrhoeals, lotions for eye infections and antiseptics on wounds[6,7,8].

PREPARATION AND DOSAGE. Decoctions and infusions are taken orally or applied externally. For diabetes, ground bark is eaten, mixed with mealie meal[4].

ACTIVE INGREDIENTS. Several pentacyclic triterpenoids have been isolated from *Terminalia* species[9], of which sericic acid and an ester thereof, known as sericoside, are the main compounds in roots[10]. *Terminalia* species are known to produce tannins. The fruits of *T. chebula*, for example, are a commercial source of tannins[11]. The activity of *Combretum* species are ascribed mainly to stilbenoids (combretastatins)[9], triterpenoids and saponins[12].

PHARMACOLOGICAL EFFECTS. Triterpenoids and saponins are well known for their antimicrobial and anti-inflammatory activity[11]. The antidiarrhoeal effects may be due to tannins. The powdered dried fruit of *T. chebula*, called "myrobalan" in the British Pharmaceutical Codex, was used as an astringent ointment for the treatment of haemorrhoids[13,14].

DISTRIBUTION. The species is characteristic of sandy savanna areas in the northern parts of South Africa[1,2,3].

Sericic acid

1. **Palmer, E. & Pitman, J. 1972.** *Trees of Southern Africa.* Balkema, Cape Town.
2. **Coates Palgrave, K. 1977.** *Trees of Southern Africa.* Struik, Cape Town.
3. **Van Wyk, P. 1995.** *Field Guide to the Trees of the Kruger National Park.* Struik, Cape Town.
4. **Watt, J.M. & Breyer-Brandwijk, M.G. 1962.** *The Medicinal and Poisonous Plants of Southern and Eastern Africa.* 2nd edition. Livingstone, London.
5. **Hutchings, A. 1996.** *Zulu Medicinal Plants.* Natal University Press, Pietermaritzburg.
6. **Pujol, J. 1990.** *Naturafrica – the Herbalist Handbook.* Jean Pujol Natural Healers' Foundation, Durban.
7. **Iwu, M.M. 1993.** *Handbook of African Medicinal Plants.* CRC Press, Boca Raton.
8. **Breytenbach, J.C. & Malan, S.F. 1989.** Pharmacochemical properties of *Combretum zeyheri. S. Afr. J. Sc.* 85: 372-374.
9. **Dictionary of Natural Products on CD-ROM, release 4:2 (1996).** Chapman & Hall, London.
10. **Bombardelli, E. et al. 1974.** Triterpenoids of *Terminalia sericea. Phytochemistry* 13: 2559-2562.
11. **Bruneton, J. 1995.** *Pharmacognosy, Phytochemistry, Medicinal Plants.* Intercept, Hampshire.
12. **Rogers, C.B. 1996.** Chemistry and biological properties of the African Combretaceae. Lecture presented at the IOCD Symposium, 25 to 28 February 1996, Victoria Falls, Zimbabwe.
13. **Martindale 1972.** *The Extra Pharmacopoeia.* 26th edition. Pharmaceutical Press, London.
14. **British Pharmaceutical Codex 1954.** Pharmaceutical Press, London.

Terminalia sericea

Flowers of *Terminalia sericea*

Fruit of *Terminalia sericea*

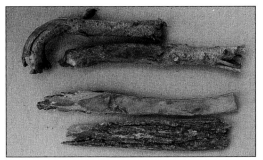
Roots and bark of *Terminalia sericea*

TETRADENIA RIPARIA

Lamiaceae

---

iboza (Zulu); watersalie (Afrikaans); ginger bush (English)

BOTANICAL DESCRIPTION. The plant is a multi-branched shrub or small tree, usually one to three metres in height, but sometimes up to five metres[1]. The leaves and stems are somewhat succulent, with glandular hairs. The large rounded leaves are glandular on both surfaces and the margins have rounded teeth. Male and female flowers are on different plants. The male flower spikes are less densely flowered than the female ones and are usually longer, up to 80 mm long. Female flowers have narrower tubes and they occur in dense spikes of about 20 mm long. Flower colour varies from white to mauve[1].

PLANT PARTS USED. Leaves are used.

MEDICINAL USES. Leaf infusions are mainly used for respiratory ailments (coughs, colds, sore throat)[2,3,4] and for mouth ulcers. Stomach ache, diarrhoea, influenza, fever, malaria and swollen legs have also been treated with this popular remedy[2,3,4,5]. Crushed leaves are inhaled as treatment for headaches[6].

PREPARATION AND DOSAGE. Leaf infusions are mainly used, rarely also decoctions or fumes from the crushed leaf[2,6].

ACTIVE INGREDIENTS. Ibozol, a diterpene diol, and various similar diterpenoids such as 8(14),15-isopimaradiene-7,18-diol, have been isolated from the plant[7,8]. It also contains large amounts of α-pyrones, of which umuravumbolide is the main compound[8,9].

PHARMACOLOGICAL EFFECTS. The diterpenoid diols of *Tetradenia* (particularly the 7,18-diol) have antibiotic and antispasmodic activity[10,11] which may partly explain the traditional use.

DISTRIBUTION. The plant is common in the eastern parts of South Africa[1] and may be found on dry rocky slopes or on stream banks. The distribution extends into Namibia and Angola and northwards through east tropical Africa to Ethiopia[1].

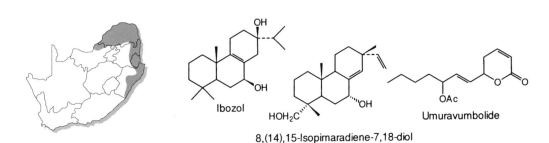

Ibozol   HOH₂C   8,(14),15-Isopimaradiene-7,18-diol   OAc   Umuravumbolide

---

1. **Codd, L.E. 1985.** Lamiaceae. *Flora of Southern Africa* 28(4). Botanical Research Institute, Pretoria.
2. **Watt, J.M. & Breyer-Brandwijk, M.G. 1962.** *The Medicinal and Poisonous Plants of Southern and Eastern Africa*. 2nd edition. Livingstone, London.
3. **Hutchings, A. 1989.** A survey and analysis of traditional medicinal plants as used by the Zulu, Xhosa and Sotho. *Bothalia* 19: 111-123.
4. **Hutchings, A. 1996.** *Zulu Medicinal Plants*. Natal University Press, Pietermaritzburg.
5. **Pujol, J. 1990.** *Naturafrica – the Herbalist Handbook*. Jean Pujol Natural Healers' Foundation, Durban.
6. **Hutchings, A. & Van Staden, J. 1994.** Plants used for stress-related ailments in traditional Zulu, Xhosa and Sotho medicine. Part 1: Plants used for headaches. *J. Ethnopharmacol.* 43: 89-124.
7. **Zelnik, R. et al. 1978.** Ibozol, a new diterpenoid from *Iboza riparia*. *Phytochemistry* 17: 1795-1797.
8. **Dictionary of Natural Products on CD-ROM, release 4:2 (1996).** Chapman & Hall, London.
9. **Van Puyvelde, L. et al. 1979.** New α-pyrones from *Iboza riparia*. *Phytochemistry* 18: 1215-1218.
10. **Van Puyvelde, L. et al. 1986.** Active principles of *Tetradenia riparia*. I. Antimicrobial activity of 8(14),15-sandaracopimaradiene-7,18-diol. *J. Ethnopharmacol.* 17: 269-275.
11. **Van Puyvelde, L. et al. 1987.** Active principles of *Tetradenia riparia*; II. Antispasmodic activity of 8(14),15-sandaracopimaradiene-7α,18-diol. *Planta Med.* 52: 156-158.

Tetradenia riparia

Leaves of *Tetradenia riparia*

Flowers of *Tetradenia riparia*

THESIUM HYSTRIX

Santalaceae

kleinswartstorm (Afrikaans)

BOTANICAL DESCRIPTION. This rigid and seemingly leafless shrublet is a parasite, growing on the roots of other plants[1]. The stems are multi-branched and taper abruptly to form sharp thorns. The minute scale-like leaves are triangular and totally hairless. Inconspicuous whitish flowers occur along the branches, followed by a hard egg-shaped, berry-like fruit of about 4 mm long, which has 10 ribs along the surface[1]. Various species of *Thesium* are used medicinally but they are all very similar and difficult to identify. *T. hystrix* can be distinguished from other thorny species by the spreading branches, scale-like leaves and the total absence of hairs on the twigs[1]. A species provisionally identified as *T. pallidum* is a popular traditional medicine, well known as "umahesaka-obomvu" (Zulu) and usually referred to on the markets as "red maseka"[2,3]. This should not be confused with "umahesaka-omhlophe" ("white maseka"). "White maseka" is a name applied to various different plants, most of them as yet botanically unidentified[3].

PLANT PARTS USED. The dry roots are used.

MEDICINAL USES. The main historical uses of this Griqua and Tswana medicine is as an expectorant for coughs, to treat tuberculosis of the lungs and as a "blood purifier"[4]. Other unidentified species of *Thesium* are used for chest colds[4].

PREPARATION AND DOSAGE. Decoctions of the roots are used.

ACTIVE INGREDIENTS. The chemical compounds of *Thesium* species are poorly known[5] but the roots of *T. hystrix* are said to contain quercitrin[4]. It is interesting that thesinine, a pyrrolizidine alkaloid, has been isolated from *T. minkwitzianum*[5]. Since *Thesium* species are root parasites, it is possible that compounds produced by host plants may be extracted from them.

PHARMACOLOGICAL EFFECTS. The medicinal value of *Thesium* species still needs to be studied. However, it is interesting to note that thesinine is the main alkaloid of borage flowers (*Borago officinalis*), which is still used to treat acute benign bronchial disease[6].

DISTRIBUTION. *T. hystrix* occurs in the dry central interior of South Africa[1].

Quercitrin   Thesinine

1. Hill, A.W. 1915. Santalaceae. In: Thiselton-Dyer, W.T. (ed.), *Flora Capensis*, Vol 5, part 2. Reeve, London.
2. Williams, V.L. 1996. The Witwatersrand muti trade. *Veld & Flora*, March 1996: 12-14.
3. Cunningham, A.B. 1988. *An Investigation of the Herbal Medicine Trade in Natal/Kwazulu*. Investigational report no 29, Institute of Natural Resources, University of Natal.
4. Watt, J.M. & Breyer-Brandwijk, M.G. 1962. *The Medicinal and Poisonous Plants of Southern and Eastern Africa*. 2nd edition. Livingstone, London.
5. Dictionary of Natural Products on CD-ROM, release 4:2 (1996). Chapman & Hall, London.
6. Bruneton, J. 1995. *Pharmacognosy, Phytochemistry, Medicinal Plants*. Intercept, Hampshire.

Thesium hystrix

Flowering branches of *Thesium hystrix*

Roots of "red maseka" (probably *Thesium pallidum*), together with "white maseka" (on the left)

TRICHILIA EMETICA

Meliaceae

> **umkhuhlu (Xhosa, Zulu); Natal mahogany (English);**
> **rooiessenhout (Afrikaans); mmaba (Northern Sotho)**

BOTANICAL DESCRIPTION. This beautiful evergreen tree is about ten metres in height and has a dense, rounded crown and smooth, greyish-brown bark. The large leaves are divided into four or five pairs of leaflets, each about 120 mm long, dark glossy green above, hairy below and tapering towards the base. Yellowish-green flowers are produced in early summer, followed by distinctive round, greenish-brown fruits of about 30 mm in diameter. They split open to reveal the black seeds which are almost completely covered by bright red fleshy arils. A closely related species, *T. dregeana* (forest Natal mahogany, also "umkhuhlu"), is also used medicinally. The latter is a much larger tree and differs in the leaflets (which do not taper strongly towards the base, being almost hairless below) and in the fruits (which lack the narrow neck connecting the fruit with the stalk[1,2,3]).

PLANT PARTS USED. The bark is mainly used, less commonly the roots, leaves or seed oil.

MEDICINAL USES. The plant is a popular remedy for stomach and intestinal complaints[4,5]. Other ailments for which it is used include dysentery, kidney problems, indigestion and parasites[4,5,6]. Root decoctions are used for fever and as purgatives[5,6]. Externally, leaf or fruit poultices are applied to bruises and eczema[4,5,6] and the seed oil for rheumatism. *T. dregeana* is used in much the same way[5,6].

PREPARATION AND DOSAGE. The main method of administration is in the form of an enema. For this purpose, a small square of bark is powdered and mixed with two cups of hot water (or, in the case of *T. dregeana*, one teaspoon of bark in one cup of milk)[5].

ACTIVE INGREDIENTS. The seed oil of *Trichilia* species has been the focus of attention and a large number of limonoids has been isolated from both *T. emetica* and *T. dregeana*[7,8,9,10]. Typical examples are trichilin A and dregeanin. Trichilin A and other "trichilins" were isolated from the root bark of *T. emetica*[8].

PHARMACOLOGICAL EFFECTS. Limonoids of the Meliaceae are well known as insect antifeedants but they also have some antimicrobial and anti-inflammatory activity[11]. However, the exact pharmacological effects of *Trichilia* bark appear to be unknown.

DISTRIBUTION. *T. emetica* occurs from Durban northwards in a narrow zone along the eastern border of South Africa[1,2]. *T. dregeana* has a similar distribution which extends further south into the Eastern Cape. Both species are also found in east tropical Africa.

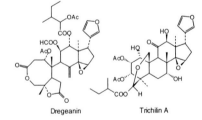

Dregeanin   Trichilin A

1. **Palmer, E. & Pitman, J. 1972.** *Trees of Southern Africa.* Balkema, Cape Town.
2. **Coates Palgrave, K. 1977.** *Trees of Southern Africa.* Struik, Cape Town.
3. **Van Wyk, P. 1995.** *Field Guide to the Trees of the Kruger National Park.* Struik, Cape Town.
4. **Watt, J.M. & Breyer-Brandwijk, M.G. 1962.** *The Medicinal and Poisonous Plants of Southern and Eastern Africa.* 2nd edition. Livingstone, London.
5. **Hutchings, A. 1996.** *Zulu Medicinal Plants.* Natal University Press, Pietermaritzburg.
6. **Pujol, J. 1990.** *Naturafrica – the Herbalist Handbook.* Jean Pujol Natural Healers' Foundation, Durban.
7. **Dictionary of Natural Products on CD-ROM, release 4:2 (1996).** Chapman & Hall, London.
8. **Nakatani, M. et al. 1981.** Isolation and structures of trichilins, antifeedants against the southern army worm. *J. Am. Chem. Soc.* 103: 1228-1230.
9. **Taylor, D.A.H. 1984.** The chemistry of the limonoids from Meliaceae. In: Herz, W. et al. (eds), *Progress in the Chemistry of Organic Natural Products* 45, pp. 2-92. Springer-Verlag, New York.
10. **Mulholland, D.A. & Taylor, D.A.H. 1980.** Limonoids from the seed of the Natal mahogany, *Trichilia dregeana. Phytochemistry* 19: 2421-2425.
11. **Bruneton, J. 1995.** *Pharmacognosy, Phytochemistry, Medicinal Plants.* Intercept, Hampshire.

Leaves and fruits of *Trichilia dregeana*

Flowers of *Trichilia emetica*

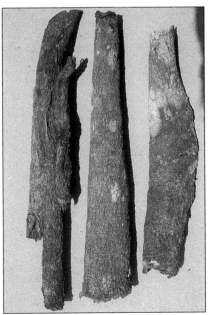

Bark of *Trichilia emetica*

Fruits of *Trichilia emetica*

TULBAGHIA VIOLACEA

Alliaceae

wild garlic (English); wilde knoffel (Afrikaans); isihaqa (Zulu)

BOTANICAL DESCRIPTION. The wild garlic is a bulbous plant with long, narrow, hairless leaves arising from several white, fleshy bases. All parts of the plant have a strong smell of garlic when damaged. The attractive mauve or pale purple flowers occur in groups of about ten or more at the tip of a slender stalk[1]. Two species are commonly cultivated in gardens in South Africa, namely *T. violacea* and *T. simmleri* (see below).

PLANT PARTS USED. Bulbs and leaves are used.

MEDICINAL USES. Wild garlic is traditionally used for fever and colds, but also for asthma and tuberculosis[2,3]. Decoctions are administered as enemas for stomach problems[4]. The leaves are used to treat cancer of the oesophagus. Another species, *T. alliacea*, was an early Cape remedy for fever[5] and is also used as a purgative and for fits, rheumatism and paralysis[2,4]. *T. simmleri* is often used as a substitute for *T. violacea*.

PREPARATION AND DOSAGE. The freshly harvested bulbs are boiled in water and the decoctions either taken orally or as an enema. The leaves may be eaten as vegetables[1].

ACTIVE INGREDIENTS. The true garlic, *Allium sativum*, has been used for centuries for its antiseptic properties. The characteristic smell is due to a complex process in which sulphur-containing compounds are broken down enzymatically when the plant is damaged[6]. The main sulphur-containing substance in the intact plant is alliin. The garlic-like smell of wild garlic is most likely due to the same or similar sulphur compounds[7].

PHARMACOLOGICAL EFFECTS. Wild garlic may prove to have the same or similar antibacterial and antifungal activities as has been scientifically verified for real garlic[6,8]. The latter also decreases blood cholesterol and has antihypertensive and antiplatelet effects[6,8,9].

DISTRIBUTION. *T. violacea* occurs in the Eastern Cape and also in southern KwaZulu-Natal[1]. Records from further north need verification as these may represent cultivated plants or garden escapes.

Alliin

1. **Burbidge, R.B. 1978.** A revision of the genus *Tulbaghia* (Liliaceae). *Notes RBG Edinb.* 36: 77-103.
2. **Watt, J.M. & Breyer-Brandwijk, M.G. 1962.** *The Medicinal and Poisonous Plants of Southern and Eastern Africa.* 2nd edition. Livingstone, London.
3. **Cillié, A.M. 1992.** *Kruie op Witblits, Rate, Resepte en Feite.* Unpublished notes, Worcester Museum.
4. **Hutchings, A. 1996.** *Zulu Medicinal Plants.* Natal University Press, Pietermaritzburg.
5. **Forbes, V.S. (ed.) 1986.** *Carl Peter Thunberg Travels at the Cape of Good Hope 1772-1775.* Van Riebeeck Society, Cape Town.
6. **Bruneton, J. 1995.** *Pharmacognosy, Phytochemistry, Medicinal Plants.* Intercept, Hampshire.
7. **Burton, J.S. 1990.** A Chemical Investigation of *Tulbaghia violacea.* Unpublished M.Sc. thesis, Department of Chemistry, Rhodes University.
8. **Martindale 1993.** *The Extra Pharmacopoeia.* 30th edition. Pharmaceutical Press, London.
9. **Reuter, H.D. 1995.** *Allium sativum* and *Allium ursinum*: Part 2. Pharmacology and medical application. *Phytomedicine* 2: 73-91.

Tulbaghia violacea

Flowers of *Tulbaghia alliacea*

Flower clusters of *Tulbaghia violacea*

Flowers of *Tulbaghia simmleri*

Flower of *Tulbaghia violacea*

TYPHA CAPENSIS

Typhaceae

---

ibhuma (Zulu); bulrush (English); papkuil (Afrikaans)

BOTANICAL DESCRIPTION. This is a robust, perennial, reed-like plant of up to three metres in height. The plant has thick, fleshy, creeping rhizomes with erect stems and long, strap-shaped, hairless leaves. The characteristic flower stalk has minute male flowers towards the tip and equally minute female flowers tightly packed into a thick brown mass just below the male part. The male flowers soon fall off, leaving the characteristic bulrush "flower", which is actually the fruiting part of the plant[1].

PLANT PARTS USED. The thick, fleshy rhizomes, which have a spongy texture, are harvested.

MEDICINAL USES. A decoction of the rhizomes is used for venereal diseases or during pregnancy to ensure an easy delivery[2,3], and for dysmennorhoea, diarrhoea, dysentery and to enhance male potency and libido. It is also taken to treat unspecified problems related to the genitals, to promote fertility in women, and to improve circulation (it is said to open the veins and increase blood circulation)[4]. Decoctions are taken orally or applied externally to promote the expulsion of the placenta[2,3]. It is said to strengthen uterine contractions[2].

PREPARATION AND DOSAGE. The rhizomes are cut into pieces and boiled in water for a few minutes. One or two cups of this preparation are taken daily for a week[4].

ACTIVE INGREDIENTS. Nothing appears to be known about the chemical constituents of *T. capensis*[5]. However, several compounds have been isolated from the closely related *T. latifolia* (*T. capensis* was until recently considered to be a subspecies of the latter[1]). Several flavonoids and other phenolic compounds have been found[5], but of particular interest are various triterpenoids with a steroidal skeleton, such as typhasterol.

PHARMACOLOGICAL EFFECTS. No published information could be found on the biological activities of *Typha* species. However, in view of the traditional uses of *T. capensis*, the presence of typhasterol and other steroid-like constituents seems very interesting. These belong to the class of steroids known as ecdysteroids, whose pharmacological and biological activities are currently receiving attention[6]. There are indications that this group of phytosteroids can be metabolised in the mammalian body to either androgen or estrogen-like substances[7].

DISTRIBUTION. The plant is exceptionally common in South Africa and is usually found in wet or seasonally wet places[1].

Typhasterol

1. **Anderson, J.G. 1966.** Typhaceae. In: *Flora of Southern Africa* 1: 53-56. Botanical Research Institute, Pretoria.
2. **Watt, J.M. & Breyer-Brandwijk, M.G. 1962.** *The Medicinal and Poisonous Plants of Southern and Eastern Africa.* 2nd edition. Livingstone, London.
3. **Hutchings, A. 1996.** *Zulu Medicinal Plants.* Natal University Press, Pietermaritzburg.
4. **Pujol, J. 1990.** *Naturafrica – the Herbalist Handbook.* Jean Pujol Natural Healers' Foundation, Durban.
5. **Dictionary of Natural Products on CD-ROM, release 4:2 (1996).** Chapman & Hall, London.
6. **Bruneton, J. 1995.** *Pharmacognosy, Phytochemistry, Medicinal Plants.* Intercept, Hampshire.
7. **Sandermann, H. 1994.** Higher plant metabolism of xenobiotics: the "green liver" concept. *Pharmacogenetics* 4: 225-241.

Typha capensis

Flowering and fruiting stalks of *Typha capensis*

Rhizomes of *Typha capensis* as they are sold for
medicinal use

VALERIANA CAPENSIS

Valerianaceae

Cape valerian (English); wildebalderjan (Afrikaans)

BOTANICAL DESCRIPTION. This plant is a robust, perennial herb with erect, hollow, grooved stems developing from numerous long, thin rhizomes which grow along the ground. The leaves are very variable in size and shape[1,2]. They are unequally divided, with a large leaflet at the top and several pairs of smaller leaflets lower down. The topmost leaflet is 50 mm to 100 mm long and 10 to 50 mm wide. Erect spreading clusters of inconspicuous flowers are borne on the branch ends. The flowers vary in colour and may be white, pink, lilac or mauve[1]. This species is closely related to the real valerian, *V. officinalis*, a well known European phytomedicine. The terminal (topmost) leaflet in the latter is always smaller than those lower down, not larger as in *V. capensis*[1].

PLANT PARTS USED. The rhizomes, which are long thin creeping underground stems, together with the fleshy roots, are dug up and used.

MEDICINAL USES. The plant is an early Cape remedy for nervous disorders, hysteria and epilepsy[3,4,5]. Some other uses have also been recorded[3,4]. In the Cape, for example, it is mixed with *Ballota africana* and *Stachys thunbergii* (both "kattekruie" in Afrikaans) in a medicine to treat asthma, bronchitis, heart trouble, hysteria and insomnia[3].

PREPARATION AND DOSAGE. Dried roots or root extracts are used in the same way as real valerian.

ACTIVE INGREDIENTS. *Valeriana* species contain a wide range of sesquiterpenoids and iridoids, the latter usually referred to as the valepotriates[6,7]. The sesquiterpenoids include valerenic acid and valeranone, while the iridoids form complex mixtures, with valtrate as the main compound[6,7]. Since *V. capensis* is very closely related to *V. officinalis*[1], it is likely to have a similar chemical composition.

PHARMACOLOGICAL EFFECTS. There is much uncertainty about the exact effects of the terpenoids and valepotriates on the central nervous system[7], but extracts of *V. officinalis* have GABA-A activity, which may well be the basis for the sedative effects[8]. The sesquiterpenoids are sedatives, while spasmolytic activity has been attributed to both the terpenoid and valepotriate fractions[7]. Valerian is traditionally used to treat insomnia and other symptoms of neurotonic disorders[7].

DISTRIBUTION. *V. capensis* is widely distributed in South Africa and further north into tropical Africa[1]. In addition to the typical form of the plant, two high altitude forms of the species have been described as distinct varieties[2].

Valerenic acid   Valeranone   Valtrate

1. **Meyer, F.G. 1958.** The genus *Valeriana* in east tropical Africa and South Africa. *J. Linn. Soc., Bot.* 55: 761-771.
2. **Burtt, B.L. 1986.** Valerianaceae. *Notes RBG Edinb.* 43: 402-405.
3. **Watt, J.M. & Breyer-Brandwijk, M.G. 1962.** *The Medicinal and Poisonous Plants of Southern and Eastern Africa.* 2nd edition. Livingstone, London.
4. **Smith, C.A. 1966.** *Common Names of South African Plants. Memoirs of the Botanical Survey of South Africa* 35.
5. **Watt, J.M. 1967.** African plants potentially useful in mental health. *Lloydia* 30: 1-22.
6. **Dictionary of Natural Products on CD-ROM, release 4:2 (1996).** Chapman & Hall, London.
7. **Bruneton, J. 1995.** *Pharmacognosy, Phytochemistry, Medicinal Plants.* Intercept, Hampshire.
8. **Bernasconi, T.M.P.** *et al.* **1993.** *In vitro* study on the interaction of extracts and pure compounds from *Valeriana officinalis* roots with GABA, benzodiazepine and barbiturate receptors in rat brain. *Fitoterapia* volume LXIV, No 4, 1993.

Valeriana capensis

Stem and flower cluster of *Valeriana capensis*

Leaf and flowers of *Valeriana capensis*

Dried roots of *Valeriana officinalis*

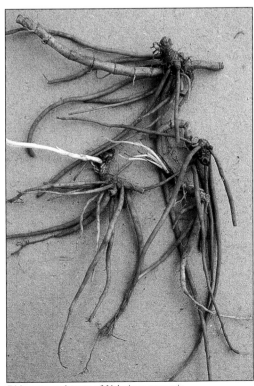

Rhizomes and roots of *Valeriana capensis*

VERNONIA OLIGOCEPHALA

Asteraceae

> groenamara (Afrikaans); mofolotsane (Southern Sotho);
> sefafatse (Tswana); ihlambihloshane (Zulu)

BOTANICAL DESCRIPTION. The plant is a herbaceous perennial with erect, flowering branches developing from a woody rootstock. The leaves are elliptic in shape, usually not more than twice as long as broad, with a sharp point and a very short stalk. They are dark green and almost hairless on the upper side but densely hairy and silvery below. This marked difference between the upper and lower surfaces is a useful feature, together with leaf shape, to distinguish the plant from its close relatives (see below)[1]. The bright violet flower heads are about 10 mm in diameter and are borne in large groups towards the branch tips. Several other species are also regularly used as medicine. Among the best known ones are *V. adoensis* (Zulu: "inyathelo"), *V. natalensis* (also "ihlambihloshane" in Zulu) and *V. neocorymbosa* (Zulu: "umhlunguhlungu").

PLANT PARTS USED. Leaves and twigs are used, rarely the roots.

MEDICINAL USES. Infusions are taken as stomach bitters to treat abdominal pain and colic[2,3,4]. Other ailments treated include rheumatism, dysentery and diabetes[2,3,4]. The roots have been used to treat ulcerative colitis[2].

PREPARATION AND DOSAGE. Infusions are made of the leaves, which are extremely bitter (hence the Afrikaans common name, which suggests a similarity with real amara, *Quassia amara*).

ACTIVE INGREDIENTS. A large number of different sesquiterpenoid lactones have been isolated from *Vernonia* species[5], including germacranolides and glaucolides[6]. A typical example is glaucolide A.

PHARMACOLOGICAL EFFECTS. Sesquiterpenoid lactones are responsible for the bitter taste of *Vernonia* species. Plants containing these compounds (see also *Cnicus*) are traditionally used as stomachics and tonics and externally to treat wounds and ulcers. Apart from known antibacterial and antifungal activity[7], there is nothing to prove that the activity of the medicine is due to these lactones.

DISTRIBUTION. The plant is widespread in the grassland regions of South Africa. It may be confused with *V. natalensis*, which has much the same distribution and flowers at the same time. In the latter, however, the leaves are narrower and similar on both sides[1].

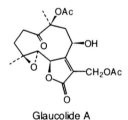

Glaucolide A

1. **Hilliard, O.M. 1977.** *Compositae in Natal.* University of Natal Press, Pietermaritzburg.
2. **Watt, J.M. & Breyer-Brandwijk, M.G. 1962.** *The Medicinal and Poisonous Plants of Southern and Eastern Africa.* 2nd edition. Livingstone, London.
3. **Pujol, J. 1990.** *Naturafrica – the Herbalist Handbook.* Jean Pujol Natural Healers' Foundation, Durban.
4. **Hutchings, A. 1996.** *Zulu Medicinal Plants.* Natal University Press, Pietermaritzburg.
5. **Dictionary of Natural Products on CD-ROM, release 4:2 (1996).** Chapman & Hall, London.
6. **Bohlman, F. *et al.* 1984.** Further glaucolides from South African *Vernonia* species. *Phytochemistry* 23: 1795-1798.
7. **Bruneton, J. 1995.** *Pharmacognosy, Phytochemistry, Medicinal Plants.* Intercept, Hampshire.

Vernonia oligocephala

Leaves and flower heads of *Vernonia oligocephala*

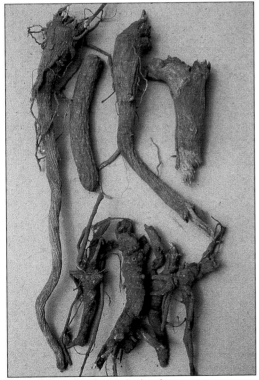

Roots of *Vernonia adoensis* (top) and
V. neocorymbosa (bottom)

Leaves of *Vernonia oligocephala*

VISCUM CAPENSE

Viscaceae

---

lidjiestee, voëlent (Afrikaans); Cape mistletoe (English)

BOTANICAL DESCRIPTION. This parasite grows on other shrubs and trees. The stems are yellowish-green and seemingly leafless, as the leaves are minute and scale-like. The stems are characteristically divided into short sections (Afrikaans: "lidjies" = joints). Minute white flowers are followed by small, white, translucent berries of about 4 mm in diameter[1,2].

PLANT PARTS USED. The whole plant is harvested, sometimes also the fruits.

MEDICINAL USES. This is an early Cape remedy for diarrhoea, which was taken as a herbal tea or tea substitute[3]. It is also a traditional Cape medicine for asthma, bronchitis and excessive or irregular menstruation[4,5]. Infusions of the fruits were used to stop bleeding and to remove warts[4,5].

PREPARATION AND DOSAGE. Infusions were taken as tea or applied externally.

ACTIVE INGREDIENTS. Various tannins and phenolic compounds are known from *Viscum* species, although nothing appears to be known about *V. capense*[6]. High levels of flavonoids, of which viscumside A is an example[6], are present in different *Viscum* species. Complex viscotoxins and lectins are known from *V. album*.

PHARMACOLOGICAL EFFECTS. The antidiarrhoeal effects may be ascribed to astringent phenolics and tannins, several of which are known from other species of *Viscum*[6]. The activity of the medicine may also be partly due to the presence of high levels of flavonoids. Much attention has recently been given to the cytotoxicity of *V. album*, a traditional European medicine[7,8]. A preparation of this plant is sold as an antitumour agent[7]. The cytotoxicity of *V. album* is due to various viscotoxins (complex molecules with 46 amino acids) and lectins (such as viscumin, which is similar to ricin in its mode of action)[9].

DISTRIBUTION. *V. capense* is widely distributed in South Africa, but is particularly common in the Western and Eastern Cape[1,2].

Viscumside A

1. Wiens, D. & Tölken, H.R. 1979. Viscaceae. *Flora of Southern Africa* 10(1): 43-59. Botanical Research Institute, Pretoria.
2. Visser, J. 1981. *South African Parasitic Flowering Plants.* Juta, Cape Town.
3. Forbes, V.S. (ed.) 1986. *Carl Peter Thunberg Travels at the Cape of Good Hope 1772-1775.* Van Riebeeck Society, Cape Town.
4. Watt, J.M. & Breyer-Brandwijk, M.G. 1962. *The Medicinal and Poisonous Plants of Southern and Eastern Africa.* 2nd edition. Livingstone, London.
5. Laidler, P.W. 1926. The magic medicine of the hottentots. *S. Afr. J. Sci.* 25: 433-447.
6. Dictionary of Natural Products on CD-ROM, release 4:2 (1996). Chapman & Hall, London.
7. Bruneton, J. 1995. *Pharmacognosy, Phytochemistry, Medicinal Plants.* Intercept, Hampshire.
8. Grieve, M. 1967. *A Modern Herbal.* Hafner, London.
9. Coghlan, A. 1995. Mistletoe's kiss of death revealed. *New Scientist*, 4 November 1995, p. 21.

Flowering stems of *Viscum capense*

Viscum capense growing on its host plant

Harvested stems of *Viscum capense*

Fruits of *Viscum capense*

WARBURGIA SALUTARIS

Canellaceae

> mulanga, manaka (Venda); shibaha (Tsonga); isibhaha (Zulu);
> pepper-bark tree (English); peperbasboom (Afrikaans)

BOTANICAL DESCRIPTION. The pepper-bark is a medium-sized tree of about ten metres in height, with a rough, mottled bark which is reddish on the inner side. The leaves are oblong, about 60 mm long, glossy green above and paler below. Small, greenish-yellow flowers are produced between the leaves on the stem, followed by round, green fruits with several flat seeds inside[1,2,3].

PLANT PARTS USED. The bark or root bark, which has a strong peppery taste, is used.

MEDICINAL USES. This is a popular and widely used remedy for coughs, colds and chest complaints[4,5,6,7]. It is particularly sought after for a serious cough productive of purulent sputum. The numerous other ailments for which it is used include influenza, rheumatism, malaria, venereal diseases, headache, toothache[4,5,6,7] and gastric ulcers.

PREPARATION AND DOSAGE. Cold water infusions of the powdered bark are taken orally as expectorants, or it is smoked as a cough and cold remedy.

ACTIVE INGREDIENTS. The bark contains numerous drimane sesquiterpenoids such as warburganal and polygodial. It is also said to contain mannitol[4].

PHARMACOLOGICAL EFFECTS. The activity of *Warburgia* bark seems to be due to the drimanes, which are biologically active, potent insect antifeedants[8] and which also show antibacterial and anti-ulcer activity. Mannitol is used medicinally (for dyspepsia and as a diuretic) and also in human nutrition and as a sweetener for diabetics[8,9]. Plants from this family were used as a mild aromatic bitter. A mixture of the powdered bark of *Canella alba* with aloes has been used as an emmenagogue[10].

DISTRIBUTION. The tree is known only from a few localities in the north-eastern parts of South Africa and has been heavily exploited for its bark. Many plants are being propagated from cuttings in an attempt to reduce pressure on the natural populations[11].

Warburganal   Mannitol

1. **Codd, L.E. 1976.** Canellaceae. *Flora of Southern Africa* 22: 39-41.
2. **Coates Palgrave, K. 1977.** *Trees of Southern Africa.* Struik, Cape Town.
3. **Van Wyk, P. 1995.** *Field Guide to the Trees of the Kruger National Park.* Struik, Cape Town.
4. **Watt, J.M. & Breyer-Brandwijk, M.G. 1962.** *The Medicinal and Poisonous Plants of Southern and Eastern Africa.* 2nd edition. Livingstone, London.
5. **Pujol, J. 1990.** *Naturafrica – the Herbalist Handbook.* Jean Pujol Natural Healers' Foundation, Durban.
6. **Hutchings, A. & Van Staden, J. 1994.** Plants used for stress-related ailments in traditional Zulu, Xhosa and Sotho medicine. Part 1: Plants used for headaches. *J. Ethnopharmacol.* 43: 89-124.
7. **Hutchings, A. 1996.** *Zulu Medicinal Plants.* Natal University Press, Pietermaritzburg.
8. **Bruneton, J. 1995.** *Pharmacognosy, Phytochemistry, Medicinal Plants.* Intercept, Hampshire.
9. **Dictionary of Natural Products on CD-ROM, release 4:2 (1996).** Chapman & Hall, London.
10. **Martindale 1972.** *The Extra Pharmacopoeia.* 26th edition. Pharmaceutical Press, London.
11. **Esterhuyse, C.J. 1996.** *Trees of the Year 1996. Warburgia salutaris, Kiggelaria africana.* Department of Water Affairs and Forestry, Pretoria.

Warburgia salutaris

Fruit of *Warburgia salutaris*

Flowers of *Warburgia salutaris*

Bark of *Warburgia salutaris*

WITHANIA SOMNIFERA

Solanaceae

---

ubuvimbha (Zulu); ubuvuma (Xhosa); bofepha (Sotho); geneesblaarbossie (Afrikaans); winter cherry (English)

BOTANICAL DESCRIPTION. This is an erect, perennial shrublet with densely velvety stems and leaves. The leaves are oblong, pale green and covered with short, dense hairs, particularly when young. Small white or yellowish flowers are produced in short clusters, followed by small, round, orange-red berries of about 8 mm in diameter. The berries are completely enclosed in brown papery and bladdery structures (these are remains from the sepals)[1].

PLANT PARTS USED. The leaves or root bark are mainly used.

MEDICINAL USES. Leaf poultices are widely used in South Africa for wound healing. It is applied externally to treat open cuts, wounds, abscesses, inflammation, haemorrhoids, rheumatism and syphilis[2,3,4,5,6]. Root infusions are taken for asthma and tinctures as tonics[2,5]. In Ayuvedic medicine, the plant is considered to be sedative and hypnotic[7,8], as well as adaptogenic. In India, the plant is known as "ashwaganda" and is regarded as an Indian ginseng.

PREPARATION AND DOSAGE. A paste of leaves is applied, or ointments are made with fat or oil[2,3]. For internal use, decoctions, infusions or tinctures of the whole plant, leaves or roots are taken.

ACTIVE INGREDIENTS. The plant is chemically very complex and more than 80 compounds are known from it[9]. Of pharmaceutical interest are numerous steroids with an ergostane skeleton, the so-called withanolides[8,9]. Withaferin A is a well-known example[9,10]. Also present are alkaloids such as withasomnine[8].

PHARMACOLOGICAL EFFECTS. The activity of withanolides and other compounds have been the subject of numerous studies, particularly the antibiotic and anti-inflammatory effects. Sedative and hypnotic effects have been ascribed to the alkaloids but there are doubts about the narcotic properties[6].

DISTRIBUTION. *W. somnifera* has a wide distribution in Africa, Southern Europe and Asia. It is considered to be indigenous to South Africa and has become a weed of disturbed places[1].

Withaferin A   Withasomnine

1. **Henderson, M. & Anderson, J.G. 1966.** *Common Weeds in South Africa. Memoirs of the Botanical Survey of South Africa* 37.
2. **Watt, J.M. & Breyer-Brandwijk, M.G. 1962.** *The Medicinal and Poisonous Plants of Southern and Eastern Africa.* 2nd edition. Livingstone, London.
3. **Pujol, J. 1990.** *Naturafrica – the Herbalist Handbook.* Jean Pujol Natural Healers' Foundation, Durban.
4. **Hutchings, A. & Van Staden, J. 1994.** Plants used for stress-related ailments in traditional Zulu, Xhosa and Sotho medicine. Part 1: Plants used for headaches. *J. Ethnopharmacol.* 43: 89-124.
5. **Hutchings, A. 1996.** *Zulu Medicinal Plants.* Natal University Press, Pietermaritzburg.
6. **Iwu, M.M. 1993.** *Handbook of African Medicinal Plants.* CRC Press, Boca Raton.
7. **Watt, J.M. 1967.** African plants potentially useful in mental health. *Lloydia* 30: 1-22.
8. **Bruneton, J. 1995.** *Pharmacognosy, Phytochemistry, Medicinal Plants.* Intercept, Hampshire.
9. **Dictionary of Natural Products on CD-ROM, release 4:2 (1996).** Chapman & Hall, London.
10. **Merck 1989.** *The Merck Index.* 11th edition. Merck, Rahway.

Withania somnifera

Foliage of *Withania somnifera*

Fruits of *Withania somnifera*, showing the green or papery calyx with the bright red berry inside

Flower of *Withania somnifera*

XEROPHYTA RETINERVIS

Velloziaceae

**isiphemba, isiqumama (Zulu); monkey's tail (English);
bobbejaanstert (Afrikaans)**

BOTANICAL DESCRIPTION. This peculiar plant has thick, erect stems covered with the matted black, charred remains of leaf bases. Long, strap-shaped leaves occur in tufts at the tip of the stem. The attractive flowers are borne in groups on long, slender stalks. They are usually mauve or pale blue – rarely white. The plant survives annual veldfires through the protective coat of fibrous leaf bases which persist on the stem[1].

PLANT PARTS USED. The roots, whole plant or stem bark are used[2,3,4].

MEDICINAL USES. The dried roots of *Xerophyta* species are smoked for asthma relief or smoke from the whole plant is used to stop nose bleeding[2,3,4]. The stem bark of *X. spekei* is used for general aches of the body, as an anti-inflammatory and for postpartum haemorrhage[4].

PREPARATION AND DOSAGE. The roots are reported to be smoked but few details are known about the methods of administration[2,3,4].

ACTIVE INGREDIENTS. The chemical compounds in *Xerophyta* are poorly known[5] but biflavonoids have been reported[6]. The main compound is amentoflavone, a dimer known from ginkgo extract (*Ginkgo biloba*)[7]. Also noteworthy is a series of diterpenoids known as cleistanthatetraenes and cleistanthatetranols, isolated from various species of the closely related genus *Vellozia*[8].

PHARMACOLOGICAL EFFECTS. *Xerophyta* has not been studied but it is possible that the flavonoids are responsible for the reported activities. Flavonoids are known to reduce capillary fragility and can also be antispasmodic and anti-allergic[7].

DISTRIBUTION. The plant is widely distributed in the grassland areas of South Africa[1] and is usually found in rocky areas.

Amentoflavone

1. **Smith, L.B. & Ayensu, E.S. 1974.** Classification of the Old World *Velloziaceae. Kew Bull.* 29: 181-205.
2. **Watt, J.M. & Breyer-Brandwijk, M.G. 1962.** *The Medicinal and Poisonous Plants of Southern and Eastern Africa.* 2nd edition. Livingstone, London.
3. **Hutchings, A. 1996.** *Zulu Medicinal Plants.* Natal University Press, Pietermaritzburg.
4. **Iwu, M.M. 1993.** *Handbook of African Medicinal Plants.* CRC Press, Boca Raton.
5. **Dictionary of Natural Products on CD-ROM, release 4:2 (1996).** Chapman & Hall, London.
6. **Williams, C.A. & Harborne, J.B. 1988.** Distribution and evolution of flavonoids in the monocotyledons. Chapter 15 in Harborne, J.B. (ed.), *The Flavonoids - Advances in Research Since 1980.* Chapman & Hall, London.
7. **Bruneton, J. 1995.** *Pharmacognosy, Phytochemistry, Medicinal Plants.* Intercept, Hampshire.
8. **Pinto, A.C. *et al.* 1992.** Diterpenoids from *Vellozia declinans. Phytochemistry* 31: 4241-4243, and references cited therein.

Flowering stem of *Xerophyta retinervis*

Xerophyta retinervis

Flower of *Xerophyta retinervis*

XYSMALOBIUM UNDULATUM

Asclepiadaceae

> uzara (German, English); ishongwe (Zulu); bitterwortel (Afrikaans)

BOTANICAL DESCRIPTION. This important medicinal plant is a perennial herb of up to about a metre in height, with robust, erect, flowering stems developing from a branched fleshy root system. The characteristic large leaves are arranged in opposite pairs and exude a milky latex when broken. Rounded clusters of small, yellowish-brown, bell-shaped flowers are borne along the stems, followed by large, hairy capsules which contain numerous fluffy seeds. The plant is similar to *Asclepias fruticosa* but it is much more robust with larger leaves and flowers. Other members of the family with medicinal value include *Pachycarpus* species and *A. crispa* (also known as "bitterwortel" and used in much the same way)[1].

PLANT PARTS USED. The roots are harvested. They are pale brown outside and white inside and have a peculiar sweet, somewhat nauseating smell.

MEDICINAL USES. This is one of the most important and widely used medicinal plants of South Africa. It has been used since early times as a remedy for diarrhoea and colic[1]. Known by the trade name "uzara" (and various others), the powdered root or root extracts were extensively marketed by the pharmaceutical industry[2]. Its main use was as an antidiarrhoeal and to treat afterbirth cramps. Numerous traditional uses have been recorded[2,3,4,5], mainly to treat diarrhoea, dysentery and stomach cramps, but also for headache, oedema (as a diuretic[1]), indigestion and dysmennorhoea. Externally, the powdered root is a popular remedy for sores and wounds[2,3,4].

PREPARATION AND DOSAGE. For the traditional use, half a cup of powdered root is boiled in one litre of water. Half a cup of this intensely bitter infusion is taken twice daily[3]. The powdered root is snuffed for headache or it is directly applied to wounds and abscesses[2,3,4].

ACTIVE INGREDIENTS. Roots contain several cardiac glycosides, of which uzarin is the best known compound[6]. The aglycone is known as uzarigenin. The low toxicity of Asclepiadaceae constituents compared with other cardiac glycosides may be linked to their unusual *trans-trans-cis* configuration[7,8].

PHARMACOLOGICAL EFFECTS. Uzarin is a known antidiarrhoeal[8].

DISTRIBUTION. *X. undulatum* is widely distributed in the grassland regions of South Africa and it is often found in seasonally wet places.

Uzarin

1. **Forbes, V.S. (ed.) 1986.** *Carl Peter Thunberg Travels at the Cape of Good Hope 1772-1775.* Van Riebeeck Society, Cape Town.
2. **Watt, J.M. & Breyer-Brandwijk, M.G. 1962.** *The Medicinal and Poisonous Plants of Southern and Eastern Africa.* 2nd edition. Livingstone, London.
3. **Pujol, J. 1990.** *Naturafrica – the Herbalist Handbook.* Jean Pujol Natural Healers' Foundation, Durban.
4. **Hutchings, A. & Van Staden, J. 1994.** Plants used for stress-related ailments in traditional Zulu, Xhosa and Sotho medicine. Part 1: Plants used for headaches. *J. Ethnopharmacol.* 43: 89-124.
5. **Hutchings, A. 1996.** *Zulu Medicinal Plants.* Natal University Press, Pietermaritzburg.
6. **Dictionary of Natural Products on CD-ROM, release 4:2 (1996).** Chapman & Hall, London.
7. **Bruneton, J. 1995.** *Pharmacognosy, Phytochemistry, Medicinal Plants.* Intercept, Hampshire.
8. **Merck 1989.** *The Merck Index.* 11th edition. Merck, Rahway.

Xysmalobium undulatum

Leaves and flower clusters of *Xysmalobium undulatum*

Flowers of *Xysmalobium undulatum*

Sliced and dried roots of *Xysmalobium undulatum*

Roots of *Xysmalobium undulatum* as sold on muti markets

ZANTEDESCHIA AETHIOPICA

Araceae

> **arum lily (English); aronskelk, varklelie, varkblom (Afrikaans)**

BOTANICAL DESCRIPTION. The common arum lily is a robust, evergreen herb of up to about a metre in height, with large, fleshy leaves developing from a tuberous rhizome. The leaves are dark glossy green and hairless, with a thick, spongy stalk. The minute yellow or cream-coloured flowers are borne in a dense group on a finger-like column (so-called spadix), surrounded by a large, white, leaflike structure (the spathe). A dense mass of small, fleshy, berry-like fruits develop at the base of the spadix. *Z. aethiopica* is the only evergreen species in South Africa - it does not die back annually and is therefore easy to distinguish from other species[1]. The rhizomes are dug up and eaten by pigs, hence the Afrikaans common names ("vark" = pig)[2].

PLANT PARTS USED. The leaves are mainly used, rarely the rhizomes.

MEDICINAL USES. Leaves have been widely used in South Africa to treat wounds, sores and boils[3,4]. It was also applied to parts affected by rheumatism and gout[3]. Boiled rhizomes were sometimes mixed with honey or syrup and taken for bronchitis, asthma, heartburn and rheumatism or gargled for a sore throat[4].

PREPARATION AND DOSAGE. The fresh leaf is warmed before application to the affected area[3,4]. Plant parts should not be eaten fresh as it results in swelling of the tongue and throat, due to needle-shaped calcium oxalate crystals, causing mechanical irritation.

ACTIVE INGREDIENTS. No pharmacologically interesting compounds are known from *Zantedeschia* species[5].

PHARMACOLOGICAL EFFECTS. The wound-healing results obtained are probably due to a protective and moisturising effect rather than to any chemical substances.

DISTRIBUTION. The genus *Zantedeschia* is restricted to the African continent and is found mainly in southern Africa[1]. *Z. aethiopica* is exceptionally common and occurs over a large part of South Africa, where it grows only in wet or seasonally wet places.

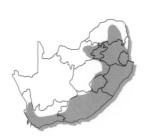

1. **Letty, C. 1973.** The genus *Zantedeschia. Bothalia* 11: 5-26.
2. **Smith, C.A. 1966.** *Common Names of South African Plants. Memoirs of the Botanical Survey of South Africa* 35.
3. **Watt, J.M. & Breyer-Brandwijk, M.G. 1962.** *The Medicinal and Poisonous Plants of Southern and Eastern Africa.* 2nd edition. Livingstone, London.
4. **Rood, B. 1994.** *Uit die Veldapteek.* Tafelberg, Cape Town.
5. **Dictionary of Natural Products on CD-ROM, release 4:2 (1996).** Chapman & Hall, London.

Zantedeschia aethiopica

"Flower" (spadix and spathe) of *Zantedeschia aethiopica*

Characteristic leaf of *Zantedeschia aethiopica*

ZANTHOXYLUM CAPENSE

Rutaceae

> umnungamabele (Zulu); umlungumabele (Xhosa); monokwane (Sotho);
> small knobwood (English); kleinperdepram (Afrikaans)

BOTANICAL DESCRIPTION. This is usually a small, multi-branched tree of about five metres in height, but may reach ten metres under favourable conditions[1,2,3]. The presence of thick thorns on the grey bark is a characteristic feature of the tree and the common names all refer to these breast-like structures. Scattered, sharp thorns may be present on the stems. The leaves are divided into several pairs of leaflets, each about 20 mm in length, with translucent dots (oil glands) along the edges. The flowers are greenish-white and inconspicuous. Small orange-brown fruits of about 5 mm in diameter, resembling minute oranges, are produced in clusters. They split open when ripe, showing the shiny black seeds inside.

PLANT PARTS USED. Root, bark, leaves and fruit are used.

MEDICINAL USES. Early records[4] show that this traditional medicine was widely used, mainly for flatulent colic[4], stomach ache and fever[5,6] and also for toothache and as a mouthwash[5,6,7]. It is an old remedy for epilepsy[8] and numerous other ailments[5,6].

PREPARATION AND DOSAGE. Infusions or decoctions of the fruits or leaves are used as a carminative and to treat fever. One teaspoon of fruits or crushed leaves is taken in one cup of water[7]. Root or bark decoctions are used as mouthwashes[4,5,6].

ACTIVE INGREDIENTS. No detailed study of *Z. capense* seems to have been made and the plant is chemically poorly known[9]. However, a large number of *Zanthoxylum* species have been studied and most of them contain biologically active benzophenanthridine alkaloids[9]. Of particular significance is sanguinarine and related alkaloids, which are likely to be present also in *Z. capense*.

PHARMACOLOGICAL EFFECTS. Sanguinarine has antiplaque and anti-inflammatory activity and is commercially used in toothpastes and oral rinses[9,10]. It binds selectively to the dental plaque and almost completely inhibits bacterial growth, even at low concentrations[11].

DISTRIBUTION. *Z. capense* is widely distributed in the eastern and northern parts of South Africa[1,2,3].

Sanguinarine

1. Palmer, E. & Pitman, J. 1972. *Trees of Southern Africa*. Balkema, Cape Town.
2. Coates Palgrave, K. 1977. *Trees of Southern Africa*. Struik, Cape Town.
3. Van Wyk, P. 1995. *Field Guide to the Trees of the Kruger National Park*. Struik, Cape Town.
4. Forbes, V.S. (ed.) 1986. *Carl Peter Thunberg Travels at the Cape of Good Hope 1772-1775*. Van Riebeeck Society, Cape Town.
5. Watt, J.M. & Breyer-Brandwijk, M.G. 1962. *The Medicinal and Poisonous Plants of Southern and Eastern Africa*. 2nd edition. Livingstone, London.
6. Hutchings, A. 1996. *Zulu Medicinal Plants*. Natal University Press, Pietermaritzburg.
7. Pujol, J. 1990. *Naturafrica – the Herbalist Handbook*. Jean Pujol Natural Healers' Foundation, Durban.
8. Watt, J.M. 1967. African plants potentially useful in mental health. *Lloydia* 30: 1-22.
9. Dictionary of Natural Products on CD-ROM, release 4:2 (1996). Chapman & Hall, London.
10. Merck 1989. *The Merck Index*. 11th edition. Merck, Rahway.
11. Bruneton, J. 1995. *Pharmacognosy, Phytochemistry, Medicinal Plants*. Intercept, Hampshire.

Zanthoxylum capense

Branch of *Zanthoxylum capense* showing the characteristic thorns

Fruits of *Zanthoxylum capense*

Flowers of *Zanthoxylum capense*

ZINGIBER OFFICINALE

Zingiberaceae

> **ginger (English); gemmer (Afrikaans)**

BOTANICAL DESCRIPTION. Ginger is an herbaceous perennial of about a metre in height, with large leaves developing from a branched rhizome[1,2]. The rather inconspicuous flowers occur in a dense spike consisting of several overlapping scales on an elongated stalk. Each flower has three yellowish-orange petals with an additional purplish, lip-like structure[2]. Ginger is cultivated vegetatively only[2], because the plants are sterile.

PLANT PARTS USED. The fresh (or dried) rhizomes, which are greyish-brown with a wrinkled surface and pale yellow inside, are grown commercially.

MEDICINAL USES. The dried rhizomes or extracts thereof are important ingredients of several traditional South African medicines, mainly used as stomachics and tonics to treat indigestion, flatulence and nausea. These include "Lewensessens" and "Jamaica Ginger". Ginger has also been used in African folk medicine[3,4]. For example, an alcoholic tincture (Afrikaans: "gemmerbrandewyn") is an old Cape remedy for colds and influenza[5].

PREPARATION AND DOSAGE. Five to 10 drops of Jamaica Ginger are added to a glass of water.

ACTIVE INGREDIENTS. The rhizomes of ginger are chemically highly complex and contain a wide range of compounds[6]. The volatile oil is characterised by the presence of monoterpenoids (for example, camphene, ß-phellandrene, neral and geranial) and sesquiterpenoids (mainly α-zingiberene and *ar*-curcumene)[7]. The pungent taste is due to a series of compounds known as the gingerols[6,7,8]. An example is [6]-gingerol, a known cholagogue[9].

PHARMACOLOGICAL EFFECTS. Ginger is traditionally used for functional dyspepsia[9] and the activity is due mostly to [6]-gingerol and [8]-gingerol, as well as α-zingiberene[9]. The latter has anti-ulcer effects[9]. Recent studies have shown the inhibition of prostaglandin biosynthesis[10] and also an anti-5-hydroxytryptamine effect[11]. Some clinical studies have shown ginger to be effective in controlling postoperative nausea and travel sickness[12,13].

DISTRIBUTION. Wild forms of ginger have not been found in nature[1]. Ginger probably originated in north-eastern India, where it shows maximum variability[1]. The plant is commercially cultivated as an annual crop in the warm, subtropical parts of South Africa.

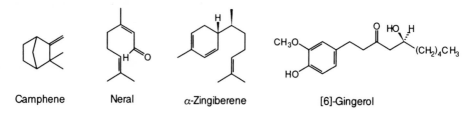

Camphene   Neral   α-Zingiberene   [6]-Gingerol

1. **Nayar, N.M. & Ravindran 1995.** Herb spices. In: Smartt, J. & Simmonds, N.W. (eds), *Evolution of Crop Plants*, pp. 491-494. Longman Scientific, Essex.
2. **Borget, M. 1993.** *Spice plants*. Macmillan, London.
3. **Watt, J.M. & Breyer-Brandwijk, M.G. 1962.** *The Medicinal and Poisonous Plants of Southern and Eastern Africa*. 2nd edition. Livingstone, London.
4. **Iwu, M.M. 1993.** *Handbook of African Medicinal Plants*. CRC Press, Boca Raton.
5. **Cillié, A.M. 1992.** *Kruie op Witblits, Rate, Resepte en Feite*. Unpublished notes, Worcester Museum.
6. **Dictionary of Natural Products on CD-ROM, release 4:2 (1996).** Chapman & Hall, London.
7. **Van Beek, T.A. 1991.** Special methods for the essential oil of ginger. In: Linskens, H.F. & Jackson, J.F. (eds), *Essential oils and waxes*, pp. 79-97. Springer-Verlag, Berlin.
8. **Wagner, H. & Bladt, S. 1996.** *Plant Drug Analysis, a Thin Layer Chromatographic Atlas*. 2nd edition. Springer-Verlag, Berlin.
9. **Bruneton, J. 1995.** *Pharmacognosy, Phytochemistry, Medicinal Plants*. Intercept, Hampshire.
10. **Kiuchi, F. et al. 1992.** Inhibition of prostaglandin and leukotriene biosynthesis. *Chem. Pharm. Bull.* 40: 387-391.
11. **Huang Q. et al. 1991.** Anti-5-hydroxytryptamine effect of galanolactone from ginger. *Chem. Pharm. Bull.* 39: 397-399.
12. **Grontved, A. et al. 1988.** Ginger root against seasickness. A controlled trial on the open sea. *Acta Otolaryngol. (Stockh.)* 105: 45-49.
13. **Phillips, S. et al. 1993.** *Zingiber officinale* (Ginger) – an antiemetic for day case surgery. *Anaesthesia* 48: 715-717.

Zingiber officinale

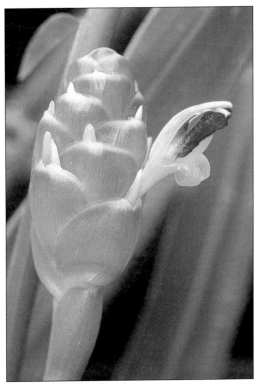

Flower of *Zingiber officinale*

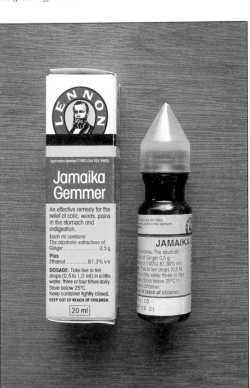

Example of a traditional medicinal product from *Zingiber officinale*

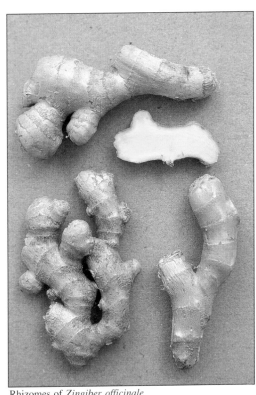

Rhizomes of *Zingiber officinale*

ZIZIPHUS MUCRONATA

Rhamnaceae

---

mokgalo (North Sotho, Tswana); umphafa (Xhosa, Zulu); umlahlankosi (Zulu); buffalo-thorn (English); blinkblaar-wag-'n-bietjie (Afrikaans)

BOTANICAL DESCRIPTION. This widely used medicinal plant is a small to medium-sized tree, mostly about five metres in height but sometimes up to ten metres or more[1,2,3]. It has a wide, spreading crown and rough, greyish-brown bark. Sharp thorns are usually present on the twigs. They are paired – the one straight, the other curved. The leaves are bright green and shiny above, slightly paler beneath, with three main veins arising from the base and with the margins toothed in the upper half. Small yellowish-green flowers are borne in clusters above each leaf. The fruits are small, rounded berries of about 10 mm in diameter, which become reddish-brown when mature.

PLANT PARTS USED. The roots, bark or leaves are used separately or in combination.

MEDICINAL USES. Warm bark infusions (sometimes with roots or leaves added) are used as expectorants (also as emetics) in cough and chest problems, while root infusions are popular as a remedy for diarrhoea and dysentery[4,5,6,7]. Decoctions of roots and leaves (or chewed leaves[6]) are applied externally to boils, sores and glandular swellings, not only to promote healing but also for pain relief[4,5,7].

PREPARATION AND DOSAGE. Warm infusions of roots, bark or leaves are taken orally as tea or decoctions are used topically to treat painful sores, boils and swellings.

ACTIVE INGREDIENTS. Several alkaloids, commonly referred to as peptide alkaloids, are known from *Ziziphus* species[8]. About 12 structurally related alkaloids from this class have been isolated from the roots, stem bark and leaves of *Z. mucronata*[9]. Mucronine D is a typical example.

PHARMACOLOGICAL EFFECTS. The strong sedative effects of *Z. vulgaris* and *Z. jujuba* (the sources of two Chinese phytomedicines) are due to the presence of frangufoline (also known as sanjoinine A)[8,10]. This alkaloid is structurally closely related to some of the alkaloids extracted from *Z. mucronata*.

DISTRIBUTION. The buffalo thorn is one of the most widely distributed of all South African trees[1,2].

Mucronine D

Sanjoinine A
(Frangufoline)

1. **Palmer, E. & Pitman, J. 1972.** *Trees of Southern Africa*. Balkema, Cape Town.
2. **Coates Palgrave, K. 1977.** *Trees of Southern Africa*. Struik, Cape Town.
3. **Van Wyk, P. 1995.** *Field Guide to the Trees of the Kruger National Park*. Struik, Cape Town.
4. **Watt, J.M. & Breyer-Brandwijk, M.G. 1962.** *The Medicinal and Poisonous Plants of Southern and Eastern Africa*. 2nd edition. Livingstone, London.
5. **Rood, B. 1994.** *Uit die Veldapteek*. Tafelberg, Cape Town.
6. **Makgakga, C. 1995.** Useful plants of the Northern Province: a preliminary list of North Sotho plant names and their uses. *Plantlife* 13: 27-29.
7. **Hutchings, A. 1996.** *Zulu Medicinal Plants*. Natal University Press, Pietermaritzburg.
8. **Dictionary of Natural Products on CD-ROM, release 4:2 (1996).** Chapman & Hall, London.
9. **Tschesche, R. et al. 1974.** Peptide alkaloids from *Ziziphus mucronata*. *Phytochemistry* 13: 2328.
10. **Bruneton, J. 1995.** *Pharmacognosy, Phytochemistry, Medicinal Plants*. Intercept, Hampshire.

Ziziphus mucronata

Characteristic thorns of *Ziziphus mucronata*

Flowers of *Ziziphus mucronata*

Bark and leaves of *Ziziphus mucronata*

GLOSSARY OF MEDICAL TERMS

adaptogenic: a medication used to increase resistance and resilience to stress.

adenoma: a benign tumour usually derived from glandular epithelial cells.

analeptic: a medication used as a central nervous system stimulant.

analgesic: a medication that reduces or eliminates pain.

anorexia: absence of appetite.

antenatal: during pregnancy; literally 'before birth'.

anthelmintic: an agent that destroys or causes the expulsion of parasitic intestinal worms.

antibacterial: a substance that kills bacteria or inhibits their growth.

anti-inflammatory: a substance that reduces swelling and inflammation.

antimicrobial: a substance capable of destroying or inhibiting the growth of micro-organisms.

antipruritic: a substance preventing or alleviating itching.

antipyretic: a substance that reduces fever.

antispasmodic: a substance relieving or preventing spasms, especially of smooth muscles.

antitumour: anti-cancer; counteracting or preventing the formation of malignant tumours.

antitussive: a substance relieving or suppressing coughing.

apoplexy: see stroke.

appendicitis: inflammation of the appendix.

arrhythmia: variation from the normal rhythm of the heartbeat.

ascites: the accummulation of serous fluid in the abdominal cavity.

astringent: a substance that causes contraction of body tissue and blood vessels.

bronchitis: inflammation of the bronchial mucous membrane.

catarrh (somewhat outdated): inflammation of a mucous membrane, usually of the head and neck, with copious discharge or secretions.

carminative: a substance that relieves flatulence.

cestodes: the true tapeworms, belonging to the subclass Cestoda.

cholagogue: a substance which increases the flow of bile by stimulating the evacuation of the gall bladder.

choleretic: a substance which stimulates the liver to secrete more bile.

clinical study: a scientific study of the efficacy of a drug in humans.

conjuctivitis (see also opthalmia): inflammation of the conjunctiva of the eye – commonly called 'pink-eye'.

counter-irritant: a mildly irritating substance usually applied to the skin over the site of pain to decrease the sensation of pain.

decongestant: a medication that breaks up congestion, especially of the sinuses.

demulcent: a soothing mucilaginous or oily medicine, usually applied topically.

depressant: a substance tending to slow vital physiological activities.

dermatitis: inflammation of the skin – there are numerous possible causes.

diaphoretic: a substance producing or increasing perspiration.

diarrhoea: abnormally frequent evacuation of watery stools.

diuretic: a substance that increases the discharge of urine.

dropsy (no longer in scientific use): see oedema.

dysentery: diarrhoea associated with blood, puss or mucous in the stool, indicating a bacterial or parasitic infection.

dysmennorhoea: painful menstruation.

dyspepsia: indigestion; **dyspeptic:** adj. n.

eczema: a skin inflammation marked by redness, itching and lesions.

emetic: a substance that causes vomiting.

emmenagogue: a substance that promotes menstruation.

emollient: an agent that softens and soothes, especially the skin.

epigastrium: the upper and middle region of the abdomen. **epigastric:** adj.

epilepsy: any of various neurological disorders marked by loss of consciousness or convulsive seizures.

expectorant: a substance promoting secretion or expulsion of mucous from the respiratory system.

febrifuge: a medication that reduces a fever.

fibrositis: inflammation of fibrous tissue, usually of the locomotor system.

flatulence: excessive formation of gasses in the stomach or intestine.

GABA-A receptor: a neuroreceptor of the main inhibitory system of the central nervous system.

gout: inflammation of the smaller joints.

haemoptysis: spitting of blood, or blood-stained sputum.

haemorrhoids: dilated anal veins which may cause discomfort and bleeding.

haemostat: an agent used to stop bleeding; **haemostatic:** adj.

hallucination: a false or distorted perception of objects or events.

hepatitis: inflammation of the liver.
Hodgkins lymphoma: see lymphoma.
hypertensive: abnormally high (arterial) blood pressure.
hyperthermia: greatly increased body temperature.
hypoglycaemic: an agent that lowers blood glucose levels.
hypotension: abnormally low arterial blood pressure; **hypotensive:** an agent that lowers arterial blood pressure.
immunoregulatory: a substance that influences the immune system, usually by stimulating it when it is depressed.
inhalant: a substance that is taken into the body by inhaling it through the nose or trachea.
in vitro: scientific tests in the laboratory, often in test-tubes or petri-dishes.
in vivo: scientific tests done on an experimental animal.
intra-ocular: within the eye ball.
jaundice: yellowness of the skin, scleras, and mucous membranes due to excessive blood levels of bilirubin – a common cause is viral hepatitis.
laxative: a substance stimulating evacuation of the bowels.
lumbago: a painful condition of the lower back.
lymphoma: a malignancy of lymphoid tissue (Hodgkins and non-Hodgkins are two types of lymphoma distinguishable on biopsy).
MAO inhibition: significant inhibition of the enzyme mono-amine oxidase which results in anti-depressant activity.
micturition: urination.
mineralocorticoid: any group of corticosteroids involved in the regulation of water and electrolyte balance.
mydriatic: a substance causing dilation of the pupils.
neuralgia: episodes of pain occurring along the course of one or more nerves.
neurotonic: having a tonic effect on the nerves.
obesity: excessive accumulation of body fat.
oedema: swollen state of tissue caused by accumulation of fluid between cells.
oesophagus: the passage for food running from the throat to the stomach.
ophthalmia: inflammation of the eye – term sometimes used instead of conjunctivitis.
ordeal poison: usually a poison administered as a trial, the belief being that the guilty succumb, while the innocent survive.
parturition: the act of giving birth; childbirth.
peptic ulcer: an ulcer of the stomach or duodenum.
photosensitisation: extreme sensitivity of the skin to sunlight, caused by chemical substances such as furanocoumarins.
piles: see haemorrhoids.
pleurisy: inflammation of the pleura – the lining of the lungs and thoracic cavity.
post partem: after birth.
pruritis: violent itching of the skin.
psoriasis: a chronic hereditary skin disease.
purgative: a substance that causes evacuation of the bowels.
purulent sputum: sputum containing pus.
rheumatism: disease marked by inflammation and pain in the joints, muscles or fibrous tissue.
rubefacient: a substance that irritates the skin, causing redness.
scabies: contagious skin disease due to the mite *Sarcoptes scabiei.*
scrofula: a form of tuberculosis affecting the lymph nodes.
sedative: having a soothing, calming, or tranquillising effect.
sinusitis: inflammation of a sinus, especially in the nasal region.
spasmolytic: an agent that causes the arrest of spasm.
stomachic: stimulating digestion in the stomach.
stroke: sudden impairment of neurological function, usually due to cerebral haemorrhage or blood clot.
styptic: an agent that arrests bleeding, usually due to its astringent quality.
thrush: a fungal infection of the oral or vaginal mucous membranes caused by *Candida albicans.*
tonsillitis: inflammation of the tonsils, usually due to viral or bacterial infection.
topical: agent applied directly to a localised area.
ulcerative colitis: chronic ulceration of the colon.
uterotonic: a substance that increases the tone of uterine muscle.
varicose veins: usually dilated, tortuous superficial veins.
vasoconstrictor: a substance that causes constriction of the blood vessels.
venotonic: agent that tonifies the veins.
vermifuge: see anthelmintic.
visceral spasm: spasm of the smooth muscle of the gastro-intestinal tract.

PLANTS LISTED ACCORDING TO AILMENTS

Recorded traditional uses are listed below, but the list is by no means comprehensive. In many instances, the scientific rationale behind the remedies are poorly known and the authors do not necessarily agree with or support all the claims that have been made. Some plants are toxic or may cause severe allergic reactions. Do not attempt self-diagnosis and self-treatment without consulting a qualified health practitioner (See IMPORTANT WARNING on page 4).

INDIGESTION, HEARTBURN, NAUSEA, COLIC

Acorus calamus
Agathosma betulina
Aloe ferox
Artemisia afra
Aspalathus linearis
Cichorium intybus
Cissampelos capensis
Cnicus benedictus
Cyclopia intermedia
Elytropappus rhinocerotis
Embelia ruminata
Foeniculum vulgare
Gethyllis spp.
Glycyrrhiza glabra
Harpagophytum procumbens
Lippia javanica
Pentanisia prunelloides
Scabiosa columbaria
Schotia brachypetala
Sclerocarya birrea
Strychnos henningsii
Sutherlandia frutescens
Vernonia oligocephala
Viscum capense
Withania somnifera
Zanthoxylum capense
Zingiber officinale

CONSTIPATION

Acorus calamus
Agathosma betulina
Aloe ferox
Aster bakeranus
Cassine transvaalensis
Cichorium intybus
Curtisia dentata
Dicoma capensis
Foeniculum vulgare
Gethyllis spp.
Glycyrrhiza glabra
Heteromorpha arborescens
Jatropha curcas
Pittosporum viridiflorum
Ricinus communis
Synaptolepis kirkii
Tarchonanthus camphoratus
Zanthoxylum capense
Zingiber officinale

DIARRHOEA AND DYSENTERY

Acacia karroo
Acorus calamus
Cassine transvaalensis
Cissampelos capensis
Curtisia dentata
Dicoma capensis
Dombeya rotundifolia
Elephantorrhiza elephantina
Elytropappus rhinocerotis
Geranium incanum
Hypericum perforatum
Kigelia africana
Lannea edulis
Pelargonium luridum
Psidium guajava
Punica granatum
Rhus undulata
Schotia brachypetala
Sclerocarya birrea
Syzygium cordatum
Terminalia sericea
Viscum capense
Xysmalobium undulatum
Ziziphus mucronata

WORMS, INCLUDING PINWORM, ROUNDWORM AND TAPEWORM

Aster bakeranus
Cotyledon orbiculata
Embelia ruminata
Punica granatum
Rumex lanceolatus
Sansevieria hyacinthoides

COUGH, BRONCHITIS, ASTHMA

Agathosma betulina
Alepidea amatymbica
Ballota africana
Cannabis sativa
Catha edulis
Croton gratissimus
Datura stramonium
Drimia robusta
Glycyrrhiza glabra
Leonotis leonurus
Lippia javanica
Mentha longifolia
Myrothamnus flabellifolius
Osmitopsis asteriscoides
Pellaea calomelanos

Protea repens
Prunus africana
Rapanea melanophloeos
Scadoxus puniceus
Securidaca longipedunculata
Siphonochilus aethiopicus
Tarchonanthus camphoratus
Tetradenia riparia
Thesium hystrix
Tulbaghia violacea
Viscum capense
Warburgia salutaris
Withania somnifera
Xerophyta retinervis
Ziziphus mucronata

FEVERS, COLDS, INFLUENZA

Adansonia digitata
Agathosma betulina
Alepidea amatymbica
Artemisia afra
Ballota africana
Cinnamomum camphora
Croton gratissimus
Dicoma capensis
Dodonaea angustifolia
Helichrysum spp.
Heteropyxis natalensis
Lippia javanica
Mentha longifolia
Myrothamnus flabellifolius
Osmitopsis asteriscoides
Rauvolfia caffra
Rhus undulata
Salix mucronata
Siphonochilus aethiopicus
Tarchonanthus camphoratus
Tetradenia riparia
Tulbaghia violacea
Zanthoxylum capense
Zingiber officinale

HEADACHE

Acokanthera oppositifolia
Artemisia afra
Asclepias fruticosa
Aster bakeranus
Erythrophleum lasianthum
Ocotea bullata
Plumbago auriculata
Ptaeroxylon obliquum
Securidaca longipedunculata

Tarchonanthus camphoratus
Tetradenia riparia

INSOMNIA, ANXIETY, HYSTERIA, CONVULSIONS, EPILEPSY
Arctopus echinatus
Ballota africana
Bersama lucens
Boophane disticha
Cannabis sativa
Catha edulis
Datura stramonium
Dioscorea dregeana
Hypericum perforatum
Rauvolfia caffra
Ruta graveolens
Synaptolepis kirkii
Valeriana capensis
Withania somnifera

HIGH BLOOD PRESSURE
Dicoma capensis
Olea europaea

DIABETES
Artemisia afra
Catharanthus roseus
Cnicus benedictus
Psidium guajava
Terminalia sericea

STERILITY, INFERTILITY, IMPOTENCE
Bersama lucens
Rhoicissus tridentata
Scilla natalensis
Typha capensis

MENSTRUAL DISORDERS, ANTENATAL AND POSTNATAL DISORDERS
Agapanthus africanus
Arctopus echinatus
Bersama lucens
Clivia miniata
Eucomis autumnalis
Geranium incanum
Gunnera perpensa
Harpagophytum procumbens
Pentanisia prunelloides
Rhoicissus tridentata
Scadoxus puniceus
Typha capensis
Viscum capense
Xysmalobium undulatum

PROSTATE PROBLEMS, BENIGN PROSTATIC HYPERTROPHY
Hypoxis hemerocallidea
Prunus africana

URINARY TRACT INFECTIONS, KIDNEY AND BLADDER HEALTH
Agathosma betulina
Arctopus echinatus
Drimia robusta
Foeniculum vulgare
Hypericum perforatum
Hypoxis hemerocallidea
Olea europaea
Peucedanum galbanum
Rhoicissus tridentata
Tetradenia riparia
Xysmalobium undulatum

HAEMORRHOIDS
Chironia baccifera
Dicoma capensis
Dombeya rotundifolia
Sansevieria hyacinthoides

RHEUMATISM, ARTHRITIS, GOUT
Aloe ferox
Capparis tomentosa
Catharanthus roseus
Cnicus benedictus
Datura stramonium
Dodonaea angustifolia
Erythrina lysistemon
Eucomis autumnalis
Harpagophytum procumbens
Hypericum perforatum
Kigelia africana
Knowltonia vesicatoria
Pentanisia prunelloides
Ruta graveolens
Salix mucronata
Securidaca longipedunculata
Withania somnifera

TOOTHACHE, EARACHE, SORE GUMS, ORAL THRUSH
Acacia karroo
Berula erecta
Carpobrotus edulis
Cotyledon orbiculata
Datura stramonium
Dodonaea angustifolia
Ruta graveolens
Sansevieria hyacinthoides
Securidaca longipedunculata
Tetradenia riparia
Zanthoxylum capense

WOUNDS, BOILS, SORES, RASHES, BURNS
Agathosma betulina
Aloe spp.
Boophane disticha
Bulbine latifolia
Carpobrotus edulis

Centella asiatica
Chironia baccifera
Cinnamomum camphora
Cissampelos capensis
Cnicus benedictus
Cotyledon orbiculata
Datura stramonium
Dioscorea dregeana
Dodonaea angustifolia
Elephantorrhiza elephantina
Erythrina lysistemon
Glycyrrhiza glabra
Harpagophytum procumbens
Harpephyllum caffrum
Helichrysum spp.
Hypericum perforatum
Jatropha curcas
Kigelia africana
Lannea edulis
Leonotis leonurus
Lobostemon fruticosus
Melianthus comosus
Myrothamnus flabellifolius
Osmitopsis asteriscoides
Ricinus communis
Rumex lanceolatus
Scabiosa columbaria
Haemanthus coccinea
Scilla natalensis
Senecio serratuloides
Terminalia sericea
Withania somnifera
Xysmalobium undulatum
Zantedeschia aethiopica
Ziziphus mucronata

CONJUNCTIVITIS
Aloe ferox
Terminalia sericea

SNAKEBITE
Acokanthera oppositifolia
Leonotis leonurus
Melianthus comosus
Strychnos henningsii

BLEEDING (HAEMOSTATICS)
Heteropyxis natalensis
Rumex lanceolatus
Viscum capense
Xerophyta retinervis

CANCER
Catharanthus roseus
Centella asiatica
Cnicus benedictus
Dicoma capensis
Elytropappus rhinocerotis
Hypoxis hemerocallidea
Sutherlandia frutescens
Tulbaghia violacea

INDEX